Also by Douglas Fairbairn

A Man's World
The Voice of Charlie Pont
A Gazelle on the Lawn
Shoot
Street 8

DOWN AND OUT

IN

CAMBRIDGE

Douglas Fairbairn

Coward, McCann & Geoghegan
New York

Library of Congress Cataloging in Publication Data

Fairbairn, Douglas, date.
  Down and out in Cambridge.

  I. Title.
PS3556.A362D6   813'.54   81-7782
ISBN 0-698-11089-7   AACR2

Printed in the United States of America

Part One

❧

NEUROTIC SYMPTOMS

IN A REMINISCENCE about the *Harvard Lampoon,* John Updike wrote: "I first saw and scented the inside of the Lampoon building as a freshman, in 1950. That rank deep smell of old magazines subaqueously stored in the basement, the unexpectedly domestic Dutch tiles, the frightened cluster of candidates with their wet umbrellas and galoshes (there is a definite humidity about my early recollections), have stayed with me, as a benevolent and exciting confusion at the gates of Paradise. This was in the presidency of the remarkable draughtsman and actor, Fred Gwynne. But my real contacts on the editorial board were Doug Bunce, Mike Arlen and Charlie Osborne. Bunce, a romantic figure, lived in the building, maintained oblique relations with the college, and cared greatly for the magazine."

I remember very well that rainy night in 1950. I was the Bunce. The Doug Bunce. Actually, I was christened Douglas Behl, but when I was about two my mother, whose maiden name was Jean Fairbairn, divorced Martin E. Behl, and a few years later married a man by the name of Wesley Hibbard Bunce. Before they got married, he made it clear to her that he really wasn't interested in adopting her children legally, and he never did, but, anyway, my sister and my brother and I suddenly found ourselves being called Sally Bunce and Marcus Bunce and Douglas

9

Bunce, whether we liked it or not. Of course I didn't care much one way or another at the time, but in 1955 I had my name changed from Behl to Fairbairn.

A ROMANTIC FIGURE? When I read that I wondered if Updike was just being generous, in retrospect, or had he, too, like all the others, really been taken in by my act?

My act, which was telling everybody I knew in Cambridge that I was working on a novel that a big New York publisher was dying to get its hands on, was bullshit. There *was* a novel—the one I had begun down in Miami three years before, in the summer of 1947, and had sent the first hundred pages of to a big New York publisher, who had returned it along with a miraculous letter from an editor saying that my manuscript had had several readings in the house and they really liked it very much so far and were anxious to see it again as soon as it was finished.

Everybody saw that first letter. I carried it around with me all the time and produced it at the slightest provocation. But no one ever saw the last letter from the same editor, the one saying that she was very sorry but whatever quality there had been about my writing that had captivated them all so much in the first draft was utterly lost now, and *please* don't send us this material again.

That first letter was my whole identity. My friends believed in it and had made me into a romantic figure in their imaginations just on the strength of it: Doug Bunce, the starving artist, maybe a *genius,* who lived in the Lampoon, where no one except Elmer Green, the janitor, had ever lived before, and was working on a novel that was probably going to be one of the most fantastic bestsellers of all time.

However, I never thought of myself as a romantic figure. I never thought of myself as anything but a grubby, stinking, quivering, semi-hysterical, chain-smoking, yellow-fingered little fraud who lived in the Lampoon for one reason and one reason alone, because there was nowhere else for me to go.

I wore the cast-off clothes the other members of the magazine left lying around and subsisted on the loose change I fished out of the cracks between the cushions of sofas, plus the occasional two bucks for a subscription to the magazine that came in the mail from someone who was innocent enough to send cash instead of a check, and five or ten dollars once in a while from the cash box in the Business Office when I really had to have it and was pretty sure I could get away with it cleanly, and slept high up at the top of the building in the Ibis Room, on a sofa that was thick with the rubbed-in ashes of millions and millions of cigarets and cigars going all the way back to Robert Benchley, under a pile of old costumes left over from past *Lampoon* stunts, mostly Inverness capes and top hats, both of which, weirdly enough, had always been very popular.

Usually, some of the younger members would come stomping up the winding tower steps to the Ibis Room early in the morning on their way to the Yard for their first lectures of the day and catch me still in bed, so to speak. They would be all rosy-cheeked and jolly from steamy showers and great big breakfasts in their House dining halls, and would want to wake me up to talk about the next issue of the magazine or final clubs or something, and I would have to pretend I didn't mind at all, even though I was just like anyone else who's scared, meaning, basically, you just want to stay in bed all day with the covers over your head.

But I couldn't let them see I was scared, or how much I hated living that way, because then my presence in the building would certainly have made everyone embarrassed and uncomfortable, and after that there would simply have been no way I could have gone on living there.

So I crawled out partway from under the Inverness capes and top hats, waved to everybody, grabbed a cigaret from someone, lit up and joined in the conversation as if I were loving every minute of it.

The Ibis Room wasn't so much a room as a sort of gallery that overlooked the Great Hall of the *Lampoon*. It had a stone floor and leaded glass windows and looked like a place where monks would have sat around illuminating manuscripts in the Middle Ages. Everything in the room was always covered with a nice film of soot, which filtered through the many cracks in the leaded glass windows, along with the blast-furnace winds of summer and the icy breezes of winter.

Once, one of my early morning visitors looked around him at the scene in the Ibis Room, my dirty clothes in heaps in the corners, my pants and jackets hanging from the fixtures, ties and socks and shirt cardboards scattered around everywhere, and said, "You know, only a *goat* could live here." And it got a big laugh, and caught on, and after that, sooner or later, somebody would always look around the room and say, "You know, only a *goat* could live here," and it always got a laugh. Even the thirty-sixth time. And the *thirty-seventh* time.

Finally, a very good friend of mine on the *Lampoon* said to me one day, *absolutely* not in a mean way, but only as if he had given it a hell of a lot of thought and decided that for my own sake it simply was time I knew the truth: "Douglas, I'm going to tell you why girls don't want to go out with you. Okay? Because you always *smell* so terrible."

Well, I already *knew* that, for God's sake! And I was trying my best, wasn't I? But there were no showers or bathtubs or anything like that in the Lampoon—just a little stall where there was a toilet ("Crane Winton With Jet") that had an overhead water tank with a chain you pulled, and next to that another little stall with a rust-stained washbasin in it. Of course there was never any hot water in the building so shaving was always excruciating, and in winter sheer murder.

I was twenty-four. That was the worst part of all, because when you're twenty-four, people who are eighteen or nineteen, or even twenty, which was what most of the other members of the Lampoon were, seem very, very young.

I had first come to Cambridge as a Harvard freshman in the fall of 1946, and had had my "connections" severed the next spring, exactly two weeks before my final exams, which meant that I got no credit for the whole year. I kept thinking it was like a death wish. When I went for my last-chance interview with the Dean I cried and quivered and told him how fucked-up my family was and what it was going to do to my mother, but the Dean said I should have thought of all that before I got drunk and started throwing all those empty quart beer bottles into Mt. Auburn Street from the window of my room on the fourth floor of Claverly Hall, and then threatened to beat up the Proctor who came and asked me to surrender my Bursar's Card, and I knew the game was over.

So I went back home to Miami in disgrace, faced the really pitiful disappointment of my mother and the total silent treatment of Wesley Hibbard Bunce, worked on a line gang for a subcontractor of Florida Power & Light for two years, and at last was permitted to return to Harvard in the fall of 1949.

My present, "oblique" relationship with Harvard was that I owed so much money from unpaid term bills that I had been told I couldn't register for another term until all the bills were paid. The bills were unpaid because I hadn't been able to save very much from my two years with Midland Constructors—not at $1.25 an hour when we weren't out on strike, which seemed practically all the time. Also, University Hall knew I was living in the Lampoon and didn't like it. There was a hard and fast rule against undergraduates' living in a Harvard College building after they had ceased to be undergraduates. But the feeling around the Lampoon was that the powers that be were uncertain about how to get me out of there, and beyond that whether or not it was a good idea to open up that can of worms anyway since I was a romantic figure and, historically, making martyrs out of romantic figures has not always been the best p.r. in the world. So from University Hall there had emanated no edicts, bulls, ultimatums or pronunciamentos yet, but of course I couldn't be sure how long that would last.

When I was alone in the building late at night, after all the others had gone back to their dormitories, I wandered from room to room, upstairs and then back downstairs, smoking myself dizzy, feeling crazy, even surrealistic, and completely detached from everyday life, trying to think what to do, how to get out of there, of a way to save myself.

But it always came back to the same thing, that the only chance I really had was to rewrite my famous novel for the eighth or ninth or twenty-third time, whichever it was by then, and just hope to Christ that this time some publisher would at least like it well enough to give me even a small advance on it.

The Lampoon was not a good place to be alone when you weren't feeling too well mentally. All the effects that were meant to have been lighthearted and amusing only looked grim. Sometimes the air seemed so dense I could barely breathe it, and I would think I heard voices from the past and smelled cigar smoke from fifty years ago, and I was afraid of all the dark corners, and the drafts that seemed to come from nowhere, and the lights and shadows skimming high up along the walls.

GROUND WAS BROKEN for the Lampoon building in May 1909 and work was completed in February 1910, and what they had when they were finished was a small-scale reconstruction of a sixteenth-century Amsterdam town house, made of "bench brick" accented with glazed colored tile, trimmed with Indiana limestone and roofed with "Ludovici" tile.

This was thirty-four years after the magazine was actually started up. In the words of one of the Founders: "While Professor Norton was lecturing upon the Fine Arts in Holden Chapel, one day in January 1876, Ralph Curtis snapped at me a little three-cornered note—'Come to Sherwood's room after lecture. We are to start a College *Punch.*'"

The *Lampoon*'s first off-campus quarters was a room on Brattle Street, provided by that "munificent keeper of the purse strings, William Randolph Hearst, '86." Soon the *Lampoon* moved to 77 Mt. Auburn Street, then to 3 Linden Street and finally to 8 Holyoke Street where it remained until the new building was completed.

The new building stood on a triangular spit of land where Mt. Auburn Street divided and became Bow Street on one side of the building and continued on as Upper Mt. Auburn Street on the other all the way to Central Square. The business entrance was at 44 Bow Street. The formal entrance was in a tower that looked out on Mt. Auburn Street and was approached by a flight of granite steps that led up to a heavy wooden door painted in the *Lampoon*'s colors, purple and golden yellow, combined with the crimson of Harvard. Over the formal entrance hung a fifteenth-century Spanish lantern, and the roof of the tower was capped by a copper finial which terminated in a copper reproduction of an ibis, the symbol of the *Lampoon*.

After the building was finished many of the members went to Europe on their summer vacations and began sending back piles of antiquities from all over the continent to furnish the building. Almost everything they bought was massive or grotesque or bewildering, from the colossal Elizabethan limestone mantelpiece in the Great Hall to the seven thousand blue- and raspberry-colored seventeenth-century Delft tiles that were used to cover most of the walls in the lower floor of the building.

Since the building had been designed as a long, narrow triangle to conform to the land it stood on, the overall effect in its interior was of strange perspectives, angles and planes, which in a subtle way made much worse my feelings of general disorientation.

EVENTUALLY, when I had put it off as long as I could, I made a fire in the President's Room, a very small room at the foot of the tower stairs that was full of nostalgia in the form of rows of framed covers by *Lampoon* greats from over the years, all kinds of eccentric bric-a-brac, plus a complete bound set of *Punch,* a complete bound set of the *Lampoon* and a complete set of Common Books, which were the thick ledgers where the members of the Lampoon drew dirty pictures and wrote notes and complaints and insults, and made threats, and made up, and sulked, and were bitter, and funny, and hurt, and obscene, and sometimes very sweet.

After I made the fire I settled down on the sofa, of course first having checked it out quickly for change, drew the wobbly bench on which a very old Remington office standard typewriter was insecurely balanced in close to me, and started writing. Outside, Cambridge quieted down and I heard fewer and fewer cars and footsteps going past the windows. When I had worked for a while and nothing much had come of it, meaning that I had written page one over ten or fifteen times and it still didn't sound like anything, I went and prowled around the building some more, and then came back to the President's Room and read old Common Books for a while. By then the steam heat would have gone off in the building and my fire would have burned down to embers, so what was there left for me to do but go up to the Ibis Room and crawl under the cloaks and the top hats, with my clothes on, and go to sleep wishing that when I woke up tomorrow morning I would somehow be able to write the way I had written at first, or just wouldn't wake up at all.

 za

ST. MARK'S SCHOOL. Southborough, Massachusetts. MDCCLXV. *Age Quod Agis.*

This was the High Church Episcopalian boarding school that the fathers in J. P. Marquand's novels were always sending their sons away to—and where, as a matter of fact, he sent his *own* son away to.

The only reason I, a kid from the steaming tropical pavements of Miami and the definitely non-ivy-covered halls of Miami Senior High, got into St. Mark's was that it was "the war years" and they had been forced to let down their standards temporarily in order to fill out the enrollment. Normally, a fairly large percentage of the two hundred or so boys who attended St. Mark's were the sons of fathers who had gone there, and a lot of them had even been registered in the school at birth. But during the war, in the words of the official centennial history of St. Mark's (published in 1967): "The quality of replacements for both faculty and student body was distinctly limited, and it would be necessary for Brewster (the Headmaster) to accept forty-seven new boys—an all-time record—to arrive even at the figure of 181 for September, 1943."

There were six "forms" at St. Mark's, corresponding to the last six grades in a public school. Before the war most boys had entered the school in the first, second or third form—rarely the fourth, almost never the fifth or sixth. The idea being that a boy who came in later than the third form could never really have been considered to have had a true St. Mark's education.

I entered the fifth form in September 1943, along with four other ex-high-school boys. None of us was of the traditional St. Mark's mainstream, and we were all equally out of our element in a form that, with one or two exceptions, had been together since September 1940.

There were several things we were required to get through our heads immediately.

First, the words to all six verses of "Sun of my Soul," the school hymn.

Second, never cheer against an opposing team, only *for* your own team.

Third, the enemy was Groton School, and winning The Groton Game was worth dying for.

Fourth, not just the translation from the Latin but the real meaning of the school motto *Age Quod Agis,* which turned out to be, "No matter what you do, do it well."

Fifth, social contacts between forms were thought *not* to be a good idea. Your friendships were to be made within your own form.

Last, the sixth form ran the school. The sixth form was boss. The sixth form had immense power, prestige, privileges and leverage. So try to stick around, because when you get into the sixth form *you* will be boss and have immense power, prestige, privileges and leverage.

One of the first things I noticed about St. Mark's was that many of the boys had famous names, like Roosevelt, Pulitzer, Widener, Armour and Lowell and Saltonstall—and it always turned out that they were the *real* Roosevelts, Pulitzers, Wideners, Armours and Lowells and Saltonstalls.

Also, I noticed that the school was divided into two basic cliques: those boys who were in the New York Social Register and those who were in the Boston Social Register. The Boston boys were vaguely contemptuous of the New York boys, whom they seemed to think perhaps a little too slick for their own good, and the New York boys looked down their noses at the Boston boys, whom they seemed to think were very small-town.

Generally, you could tell the Boston boys from the New York boys because the Boston boys' gray flannel suits were usually baggy and their shirt collars slightly frayed, while the New York boys' gray flannel suits were usually a little less baggy and their shirt collars a little less frayed.

Having to wear a jacket and tie at all times was a pretty exotic concept for an ex-Miami-High boy who had never had to dress up like that for anything except parties and going to the Friday night ballroom dancing classes down on West Flagler Street. My mother had bought me several "outfits" that she thought would be appropriate for St. Mark's. The trouble was that she had never been anywhere near the place and so had had no way of knowing that to St. Mark's boys the only "outfits" that were really appropriate were their eternal gray flannel suits or else khaki-colored chino pants worn with the jackets from their eternal gray flannel suits. Nor could she have known that the necktie was almost always the St. Mark's School string tie, either in its basic pattern of a single white stripe on a dark blue field for the school at large, or in one of its four variations of stripe spacings for those heroic boys who had been awarded a letter in one of the four major sports, football, baseball, hockey and crew.

Of all my outfits my mother's top favorite was an "ensemble" that was built around what we in Miami called a "loafer jacket"—a sort of boxy, unstructured garment with bone buttons and big patch pockets that came in only one color, a light tan, or "camel," as my mother preferred. Loafer jackets were the very height of fashion at Miami Senior High. To the girls you might as well not have existed if you didn't have one to wear to parties and the dance classes and football games.

To go with the loafer jacket my mother had bought me a pair of chocolate-brown pants, a tan or "camel" shirt, a chocolate-brown tie and chocolate-brown penny loafers. "A symphony in brown," she had said when I had tried the outfit on for her. "You'll be the hit of the whole school."

I, never having been anywhere near the place either, had to take her word for it, but when I wore the ensemble for the first time my classmates almost choked to death trying to keep from laughing, so I never wore it again, or a couple of the others that also stopped traffic when I put them on, and when I went home at Christmas I told my mother I didn't want anything for Christmas but a bunch of chinos and a gray flannel suit so I could just look like everybody else.

I found the sophistication of the boys at St. Mark's astonishing. My roommate, Campbell Gosse, had already been to Europe *twice!*—and his mother invested in Broadway shows, so he talked about the New York theater scene as if he owned it, and his father had a seat on the New York Stock Exchange so he talked about that as if he owned it, too. On vacations he spent a lot of time passing fake IDs on Fifty-second Street so he could listen to jazz, and he could rattle off names like Zutty Singleton, Billy Eckstein ("Mr. B." to him), Wingy Manone, Wild Bill Davidson,

Fletcher Henderson, Lionel Hampton, Teddy Wilson and Coleman Hawkins with enormous familiarity. His family lived in Tuxedo Park (a great St. Mark's stronghold) in the summer and in a five-story brownstone on East Sixty-eighth Street the rest of the time. Like most of the other New York boys he subscribed to *The New York Times* and read it from front to back at breakfast just like a little stockbroker. It was the most impressive thing I had ever seen in my life.

Southborough was a town that as far as I could tell had a total population of about a hundred and fifty, and that was counting dogs and cats. St. Mark's stood at the top of a long slope around a half mile from the town, a handsome Tudor facade looking out across Belmont Field, where The Groton Games were played.

I used to sneak off into the trees at the far side of Belmont Field sometimes in the afternoon and look back at St. Mark's from a distance. I was more or less terrified of the whole school and everybody in it, but at the same time I had an intense desire to be accepted. The problem was that the best way to get yourself accepted was to be very good at some sport, preferably football, though baseball or hockey would do. (Crew was thought of simply as a dumb way for jerks who were too uncoordinated to hack anything else to kill time in the spring.) I knew from the start I wasn't going to gain acceptance as an athlete. I had never been much good at contact sports, partly because I was small, partly because I was easily intimidated by anyone who was even slightly bigger than I was, but mostly because I had a way of suddenly going to pieces in "pressure situations."

At Miami High at least they had left you alone if you didn't want to try out for a team. Maybe you had to do a half hour of calisthenics every morning, but their attitude was that they didn't want you cluttering up "the program" unless you really had something to contribute.

Therefore I was shocked to find that at St. Mark's everybody had to play football, and not just touch football or anything like that. For the first time in my life I had to put on a football uniform, helmet, shoulder pads, kidney pads, everything, and go out there in the rain and the mud and try to help my team move the ball from one end of the field to the other. And it didn't make the least bit of difference if you weren't any good. You played anyway. Nobody got to stand and watch from the sidelines at St. Mark's, and you played the good old-fashioned way, both offense and defense.

It didn't take me long to grasp the fact that one of the surest ways *not* to gain acceptance at St. Mark's was to become known as a "grind." Boys who were known as "grinds" were never popular and spent most of their time in deep isolation, even from each other. One "grind" in my form became so lonely that he finally made friends with a couple of big gray rabbits one of the masters kept in back of his house, and they said he took them out of their cage in the afternoons and the three of them would go off into the woods together, the boy leading the way, his two pals hopping along after him, with the boy talking to them a mile a minute on his favorite subject, which happened to have been binomial theorems.

Ultimately, I became very popular in my form, partly because I was considered rather exotic. It seemed impossible for the other boys to accept that anyone could actually "come from" someplace like Miami, Florida, and allowances were made for me as if I were some sort of noble savage. It never did any good for me to try to explain to them that Miami was not *Miami Beach,* that it was just a sleepy Southern town at the mouth of a minor river, where there were very few tourists, because there were very few tourist *attractions,* and that it bore no resemblance whatsoever to the flashy resort across Biscayne Bay. To them, Miami and Miami Beach were synonymous and that was all there was to it, and as far as they were concerned it was simply a hell of a crazy place to "come from," and anyone who "came from" there clearly had to be given the benefit of the doubt in practically every situation.

Even the masters were deferential to me—as if they couldn't conceive of anyone who had come from a high school in Miami as being the equal in education to a boy who had gone to St. Mark's for three or four years. Of course, they were right. Miami High was not on a level with St. Mark's, where the classes were small enough so that the masters were able to take a personal interest in their pupils—and where, in fact, several of the masters had been at the school long enough to have taught not only the older brothers but the fathers of the boys who sat before them.

I was fairly good at history and languages, but I had trouble with physics, math and chemistry, because they all involved numbers, and I had, even back then, what they call nowadays "mathematical anxiety"— which doesn't mean that if you try to add 59 and 86 you get 157, but that if you try to add 59 and 86 you get hysterical.

Amazing concessions were made. For instance, when I was in the fifth form, it was soon discovered that I couldn't handle trigonometry, which was the fifth form math, so they let me take plane geometry with the fourth form, which I also couldn't handle. And when I was in the sixth form and certainly couldn't handle calculus, I was made to sit there in the classroom anyway with everything passing straight over my head, and the master just looked at me despairingly when I never got a single problem right on any of the tests.

I had entered St. Mark's as an "accelerator," which was the term they used during the Second World War to describe boys who had to accelerate their schooling so that they could graduate before they turned eighteen and have their diplomas in hand when they were called up by the draft, and therefore would be eligible to apply for Officers Training School.

I had to go to summer school between my fifth and sixth form years, went home briefly, and then returned to school as a sixth former, with all the power, prestige, privileges and leverage that pertained thereto, as promised. Sixth formers could stroll around on the sixth form quadrangle, and sixth formers had a special path leading into the village of Southborough that only sixth formers could use. Sixth formers could smoke in the headmaster's study in the evenings, and wear sixth form blazers, and had a beautiful room called the Sixth Form Room, with a fireplace and leather chairs and couches, where no one could enter but sixth formers— not even masters, unless, of course, they had gone to St. Mark's. And the sixth formers supervised all the work programs that were carried out by the lower forms—sweeping the dorms and the hallways, waiting on tables, etc.—but never had to do any of that grubby stuff anymore themselves, and generally lorded it over everybody.

I liked being in the sixth form, and had a marvelous time all that fall. Unfortunately, too good a time, as it turned out, because when we accelerators took our final exams in February 1945, I failed physics, math and chemistry. For the other accelerators there was a ceremony in the School Room at which diplomas were handed out by the headmaster, while I sat there like an idiot, not knowing what was going to happen to me next. The fact was, the school didn't know what to do with me. Nothing like this had ever happened before at St. Mark's. For about a week I just hung around, waiting for a decision. At last, it was decided that I would be required to stay on at Southborough for two weeks of intensive tutoring, and then take make-up exams. But obviously there was nothing that two weeks of tutoring could do for me that half a year of regular classes hadn't been able to do, so I failed all three exams again.

More consternation, but the war was still on, and they must have thought I might be soon dead anyway, so they passed me, and I got my diploma all alone in an intensely awkward ceremony that the headmaster told me bitterly afterward was without precedent in the entire almost-one-

21

hundred-year history of St. Mark's School, and I was sent home to Miami
in disgrace.

≈

My mother, "Missy," was a small, cheerful woman who came originally
from Huntsville, Ontario, where her father was in the lumber business. In
the United States she became a model, and an actress, and met "Wes" in
New York, when she had a part in a soap opera at NBC. After she
divorced Martin E. Behl (I have never known what the "E" stood for), he
went away and was never seen again or heard from by any of us. Missy
avoided talking about him to Sally and Marcus and me, and carefully
clipped his face out of all the snapshots in which he appeared, so we never
knew what he looked like, either. As a matter of fact, the only occasion
on which she ever said anything to me about him was the day before I left
for St. Mark's. I was standing around watching her pack my stuff, and out
of a clear sky she said, "Dougie, I'll tell you this much about your father.
He wasn't much good, but he could be very nice when he wanted to, and
sometimes I miss him." That was it. But I never cared much anyway. How
could you care about someone who never even sent you a birthday card,
or called you up maybe once a year to ask how you were doing in school?

Wes was a very handsome man. I guess, at least partly because of that,
one time when he was riding in a Pullman car going from New York to
Boston, the woman sitting across from him fell in love with him at first
sight. It turned out that this woman, Nell Foster, was very rich, which
must have appealed to Wes a lot, because although he was just some sort
of a traveling salesman at the time, he had expensive tastes. And it
probably didn't bother him at all that she was about ten years older than
him. They got married, and she bought him big cars and beautiful clothes,
and gave him lots of money to spend, and took him on a couple of Grand
Tours of Europe that were really and truly *Grand.* They were married
about three years—until the day her heart, which had never been very
strong anyway, stopped, while they were watching a race at Aqueduct in
which a horse she had bought for him broke down and had to be
destroyed. And it turned out that in her will she had left him everything.

Years later, Wes's brother Ralph told me that Wes's sudden wealth was
divided by the terms of the will into two categories of assets, which Wes
described as the "touchable" and the "untouchable." The "untouchable"

asset was thirty-three-and-a-third percent ownership of a steel mill in Conshohocken, Pa. The "touchable" assets meant all the stocks and bonds, jewelry, and miscellaneous holdings, like six apartment houses and a fifteen-story office building in Pittsburgh, that Wes was allowed to "administer"—meaning, of course, "sell off"—on his own, without having to ask one soul's permission. He began selling immediately after Nell's death, taking big losses just to keep himself going in the style to which he had by then become accustomed, and to underwrite all the crackpot friends with crackpot schemes who led him by the nose from one financial disaster to the next as easy as a stroll in the park.

The binge lasted about a year and a half, and then Wes had to come back down to earth very abruptly, because he finally had nothing left but the "untouchable," which was tied up in a trust that was absolutely unbreakable without the unanimous approval of the board of directors, who, not surprisingly, hated Wes's guts right down to the last man. Still, he wasn't so badly off. He got a regular income through the trust of somewhere around thirty thousand dollars a year, plus substantial dividends that were always disbursed very conveniently just before Christmas, and all of this continued right on through the darkest years of the Depression.

Ralph told me that for a long time after the joyride was over, Wes used to do nothing but hang around the clothing store that Ralph owned in Montclair and play enormously complicated practical jokes on the salesmen, and, indeed, one of the things Sally and Marc and I had to get used to about Wes from the very beginning was that he had a sort of joke-shop sense of humor.

For instance, his pride and joy for years was a shiny, metallic, ochre-colored, absolutely believable joke-shop pile of dog turds that he carried around with him all the time, planting it wherever he knew it would get a big reaction—from libraries to famous restaurants to museums, to the spot right next to the potato salad at the picnic spread. But I know the happiest moments of his life came when he set that glistening pile of shit in the middle of the living room rug of some house where he particularly disliked the family mutt, and then had the immense satisfaction of watching the red-faced master or mistress kick the little perisher's ass all around their backyard.

We also had to get used to the tremendous contradictions in his personality. He could be warm, kind, considerate, even sentimental, but he had a hair-trigger temper that, if you happened to say the wrong thing at the wrong time, could turn him in an instant from his usual smoky, detached, totally loose self into a snarling, frightening monster with a tongue that lashed out at you with stunning fierceness, and icy blue eyes that looked as if all they really wanted was to see you dead. And the trouble was that you never knew what it was that you had said wrong this time—just that somehow you had touched a nerve, and God save you if you ever did it again.

Just a few more quick things about Wes.

He always washed out his own handkerchiefs, which were of the finest linen, and bore his monogram, WHB, and while they were still soaking wet plastered them to the tile wall in the bathroom. When they dried he peeled them off the wall and carefully folded them. He said this was a little trick he had learned "on the road."

He also always washed out his own socks.

He claimed to have been the creator of the Packard Motor Company's slogan: "Ask The Man Who Owns One," and was furious that Packard had not only never paid him for it, but wouldn't even give him credit for having thought it up.

He also claimed to have been the first person ever to have had a car radio installed in a car in the state of New Jersey.

Most people liked him immediately. They thought he was funny, charming, a fabulous storyteller, and a marvelous host.

He drank a lot, and would drink almost anything, but he very seldom got drunk.

He loved nothing in the world more than hearing someone make the same grammatical mistake over and over again, or hearing someone use the same dumb cliché over and over again, or hearing someone mispronounce the same word over and over again.

He had no religion, and he had no politics.

He seldom used dirty words, and never told what he called "off-color" stories.

He loved to tell stories about his boyhood summers spent in Quonochontaug, Rhode Island, where his family had had a house on the beach.

He never used shaving cream to shave with, just plain hand soap.

In 1944–45 he was the head of the gasoline rationing section of the OPA for south Florida, where he was so popular that after the war he was asked to run for state senator, by both the Democrats and the Republicans. He was flattered by the thought, but, having no politics, he refused both parties and returned to what he had been doing before, in other words, nothing.

He loved to tell stories about all the excursions, or *fahrts*, he took when he was in Germany, on one of the Grand Tours. There were two-day *fahrts* here and three-day *fahrts* there, but he always said that although he enjoyed every one of the *fahrts* immensely, he found the seven-day *Rheinfahrt* by far the most satisfying *fahrt* of all.

RIGHT AFTER they got married, Missy and Wes put Sally and Marcus and me into a sort of Oliver Twist "home" for children in Verona, New Jersey, called "Maridor," which was a place where children from broken homes could be warehoused indefinitely. Then they went to Europe.

ꝫ

MARIDOR was a great big dark-brown three-story house that stood near the foot of a fairly steep hill. Across the street was a beautiful park with a lake and a boathouse where you could rent rowboats and buy sassafras pop. Out in back of the house was a barn and a small corral for two horses named Magic and Black Beauty, and a large garden where they grew tomatoes, lettuce, potatoes, radishes, carrots, green beans, yellow squash, onions, strawberries and rhubarb.

Maridor was actually way ahead of its time. It was a commune long before most people had ever even heard of the word. There was a constant population of around twenty-five kids, ranging in age from thirteen on down to three or four, and there was no free ride for anyone except the very littlest kids. Everybody else had to work. The girls did most of the cooking and the serving of the meals and the washing up, and they took care of the little kids, gave them their baths and everything. The boys mucked out the stables and groomed and fed the horses, and it was their responsibility to keep all the floors in the house scrubbed and swept so clean you could eat off them. Both boys and girls worked in the garden in the summer, and they both had to make their own beds every morning and change their own sheets twice a week.

The interesting thing was that none of them ever complained. These were not the children of even middle-class parents. Some of the mothers were waitresses. One of the fathers was an iceman. Another sold vacuum cleaners door to door. Therefore they couldn't afford to pay much to keep their children in Maridor, so the children had to pitch in and help pay their way, and they all seemed to understand that perfectly, and went about their tasks really very cheerfully, and did an amazingly good job, everything considered.

Perhaps one of the things that kept the Maridor kids from feeling sorry for themselves was the fact that right next door there was a large orphanage, which was separated from Maridor by a very high and forbidding chain-link fence that completely enclosed the orphanage's grounds and was put there to keep the little wretches from running away. All day long the orphans would hang by their fingers along the fence gazing silently at the Maridor kids, and the Maridor kids seemed to realize that maybe their lives were pretty hard, but at least on Sundays their moms might come to see them.

I KNOW Missy must have warned "Auntie" and "Jimmy," the two middle-aged women who ran Maridor, about me when she made the arrangements for leaving Marc and Sally and me there just before she and Wes left for Europe. She had to have. She was a very honest person and would never have done anything like that to anyone without giving them fair warning.

But I imagine Auntie and Jimmy, little knowing, just smiled and said, "Listen, Mrs. Bunce, we want you to rest assured that we have dealt very effectively with this problem in the past, so don't worry your head about it for a minute. Go to Europe, have a wonderful time, and just leave this to us."

So Missy closed the deal, if not in good conscience, at least feeling that she had given them their chance.

The "problem" was that I pissed my bed, and I don't mean occasionally, or now and then, or even pretty regularly. I mean every fucking night of my life, in *torrents*.

It didn't take long for it to dawn on Auntie and Jimmy that they had made a terrible mistake, but of course by then it was too late. Wes and Missy were somewhere in Europe, and they were just plain stuck with me.

This was in 1932, when I was six, Sally was seven and Marc was five.

At first they let me sleep in a big cozy dormitory on the second floor along with Marc and about a dozen other little boys. Every night I tried to stay awake, the purpose being to try to delay the inevitable as long as possible. Usually I would succeed in staying awake for quite a while after the other boys had gone to sleep, but eventually I just couldn't keep my eyes open any longer, and a few hours later I would be awake again, lying in a puddle of fresh warm piss. However, that warmth only lasted a few minutes and then I was lying there in cold wet pajamas between cold wet sheets.

Since I usually had to lie in my piss for the rest of the night after I let go, I learned to stay flat on my back and not move, because your body heat keeps the urine right under you fairly warm, but the slightest movement sends you out into the cold and cheerless swamp that surrounds you, and also the steam wafts up from under the covers and sickens you.

But the worst part was that, especially in winter, the cheeks of my ass got severely chapped from constantly soaking in my own brine, and once this began it got worse and worse until that very tender skin, which felt to the touch like a coating of dried egg white, slowly cracked and peeled away and got raw and burned like fire every time I pissed myself from then on.

When you've been a bed-wetter for a long time the aggressive stench of piss becomes so familiar that you come to believe it never really leaves you, and even after a shower you're positive you can still smell it clinging to you.

And when you've been a bed-wetter for a long time you're afraid to go near anyone or let anyone come near you. You feel yourself to be disgusting. You cannot possibly develop any self-confidence even though you may be naturally bright or talented in some way.

In any sort of confrontation, even with kids who are not as strong or as smart as you are, you always back down. You can't seem to join in horseplay, or have any sort of easy relationships. Every phase of every relationship is painful. You pander to people you have contempt for. You let yourself be victimized, and pretend you don't mind at all, or maybe even like it. You can't really concentrate on games or schoolwork because the only thing you have room for in your consciousness is your bed-wetting.

I prayed to God every night to let me stop wetting my bed. If I could have missed just one night I would have been the happiest boy in the world. That was what I thought about when I was trying to stay awake, how it would feel to wake up just one morning and feel like anyone else, dry and warm and sweet-smelling.

Soon the complaints from the boys in the dormitory became so persistent that Auntie and Jimmy moved me out of there and set up a cot for me in the music room down on the first floor, where the girls practiced their piano. But I stank up that room too and there were wails from the girls, who said they simply could *not* practice "To Springtime" in a room that smelled so awful. So Auntie and Jimmy moved my cot out on the front porch, where it was cold as hell and rain came in on you. But at least the kids couldn't complain about me when I was out there.

It was at about this time that Auntie and Jimmy got very frustrated and bitter, and decided they were going to have to start doing something about me. Auntie took me into her office one day and said she wanted me to tell her why I wet my bed every night, and she didn't want to hear anything but the truth.

I said I didn't know why.

She said, "I know why. Because your mother let you get away with it from the beginning, without ever punishing you for it." She said that from then on every time I wet my bed she was going to whip me, much as she hated to have to do it. That was the first part of the punishment. The second part was that I was going to eat salt every night before I went to bed.

So I went into her office every morning and dropped my pants and leaned over a chair and got six strokes across the back of the legs with a blackboard pointer. Then every night just before bedtime they gathered all the kids in the kitchen and I stood on a chair in front of them and ate a slice of bread and butter that Jimmy had covered with a layer of salt.

At this point even Marcus and Sally began avoiding me, and I honestly didn't blame them a bit.

When Auntie saw that the whipping and the salt weren't doing any good, Auntie began to hate me. I could see it in her eyes when I went into her office, and I could feel it in the way she whipped me harder and harder until sometimes it actually drew a little blood, and in the names she called me under her breath.

The whippings and the salt went on for about a month, and then Auntie said that she had given up on me and wasn't going to try to "help" me any more, but I was going to have to go on sleeping on the porch as long as I stayed at Maridor because she refused to have her whole house smelling like a barn.

I didn't really mind sleeping on the porch, except that it made me more and more isolated from the other kids, and I became more and more of a curiosity.

For instance, I remember one Sunday when I was sitting on a bench outside Auntie's office working on a drawing. I liked to copy comic strip characters out of the funnies. Dick Tracy and Abby & Slats were my favorites. Across the hall, in the living room, several of the kids and their mothers were visiting with each other. Sunday was the only officially sanctioned visiting day at Maridor, and it was almost always the moms who came. You seldom saw any of the dads around the place.

This Sunday I was just drawing away, minding my own business, when I happened to look up and saw one of the little boys standing with his mother in the doorway of the living room smiling at me. I smiled back. Then the boy took his mother by the hand and began leading her toward me, both of them still smiling. He was rather a nice boy, about a year younger than me, and not one of those who liked to tease me about my bed-wetting. In fact, he was quite fascinated by my drawings and I had given him one once, and he had really appreciated it.

So I thought he was going to introduce me to his mother as the boy who could draw so well and ask me to show her the picture I was working on right then, and I think that that was what she expected too, because she approached me exuding amused anticipation.

Instead, the boy said, "Mommy, this is Dougie Bunce. He's the one I told you about who wets his bed every single night."

The woman looked startled, and put her hands up to her face as her cheeks suddenly got very red. She stood there gazing at me helplessly, wanting desperately to say something but truly embarrassed beyond words, and then she turned and hurried back into the living room and out of my line of vision, pulling her little boy behind her.

≥

WHEN WES and Missy got back from Europe we all went to live in the very large and impressive house Wes had bought for his mother in Montclair, and he announced that he was going to deal with the question of my bed-wetting "personally."

He took me into the study and told me that since nothing else seemed to work he was going to take me to Dr. Fahva, who was just going to cut off my "dingus" and sew it up, and in that way put an end to my bed-wetting once and for all. He promised me it wouldn't hurt a bit. He said he had called Dr. Fahva to tell him we would be there on Wednesday, and Dr.

Fahva had assured him that he would have his cleaver very sharp and the whole thing would be over before I even knew it.

Then Wes led me over to the desk, and holding my imaginary "dingus" between the thumb and first finger of his left hand, demonstrated to me very precisely how Dr. Fahva was going to lay it out on the operating table. Then he raised his right hand and brought the edge of it down on the imaginary "dingus" on the imaginary operating table in one quick, clean chopping motion.

"And that," he said, "is what you call cutting off the problem at the source."

When I asked my mother if she was going to let Dr. Fahva do that to me, she got very upset and wouldn't even look at me and said, "Well, *something* has to be done about this."

I thought and dreamed of nothing but Dr. Fahva all that week. In my dreams I could see his cleaver gleaming in the bright light of his operating room and I could see it fall on my "dingus," and I could see my amputated "dingus" there looking like a little finger on the operating table. And then I could see myself with a dimple like a belly-button down there where my "dingus" had been.

On Wednesday, when we got to Dr. Fahva's office a nurse took me and put me into a little room all by myself. The room was very bright and cold and absolutely soundproof, and there were no pictures on the walls, and silver surgical instruments were visible everywhere, on tabletops and sticking out of half-opened drawers and in glass-enclosed cases. After I had been in the room sitting on a little round stool for about ten minutes I felt as if the blood had all left my face, and my whole face got numb and felt cold. I went over to a washbasin and tried to be sick but nothing came up and I was just left with the taste of bile in the back of my throat.

About half an hour later Wes and Missy came and got me and took me back out to the car. Going back to the house Wes said, "Dr. Fahva decided not to do it today. Said he just wasn't in the right mood for this kind of an operation. But next Wednesday definitely."

I didn't exactly know how it was supposed to work, but I believed Wes when he said the operation would solve my problem once and for all. I thought maybe they were going to give me another little hole somewhere else, that you perhaps could plug up somehow at night before you went to bed and then open up again in the morning. I was dimly aware of what it would mean to have my penis cut off, that it would make me a freak, almost a girl, but the truth was that deep down in my heart I really wanted it, because I wouldn't have cared what they did to me if it would have ended the humiliation of my bed-wetting.

We kept going to Dr. Fahva's office every Wednesday afternoon for six weeks, and it was always the same. I sat in the little room and waited and then we went back home with nothing having happened—but next Wednesday *definitely*.

Then, without any explanation, we didn't go to Dr. Fahva's anymore.

It wasn't until years later that I found out Dr. Fahva was a chiropractor who was treating Missy those Wednesday afternoons for lower back pain.

Anyhow, I kept on wetting my bed until I was fourteen, and then all of a sudden it just stopped.

❧

WHEN I GOT HOME from St. Mark's Wes wouldn't speak to me except to keep saying what a "hell of a note" it was that he had gone to all the trouble of getting me into St. Mark's and spending money he couldn't afford to keep me there, just so I could come home with this "phony diploma."

Missy tried to smooth things over by reminding him that he wouldn't have to spend any more money on my education from now on because I was about to be drafted into the army and when I got out I would go to college on the GI Bill.

Sure enough, pretty soon the notice ("Greetings from the President . . .") arrived in the mail, telling me to report to Camp Blanding for my preinduction physical. That made Wes feel a lot better, and he began regaling me with cheerful stories about when he was over there in 1918 and his company took seventy percent casualties in the Argonne offensive.

The morning I left for Blanding Missy cried because the war still wasn't completely over and I guess she thought I might soon be dead.

But I could have told her I would never pass the physical.

It took a full day on the army bus to reach Blanding, way up in the northern part of Florida. All the way the other draftees horsed around cheerfully and sang:

> The chicken in the army
> They say is mighty fine.
> It gets up on the table

And starts in marking time.
Oh, I don't want no more of army life!
Gee, Ma, I wanna go!
Oh, Ma, I wanna go!
Hey, Ma, I wanna go!
HOME!

We slept that night in a barracks that took me back to Camp Cloudmont in Tennessee when I was thirteen, and the next day we spent eating army chow, smoking our heads off on tax-free PX cigarets and watching some Luftwaffe prisoners dig a ditch in the rain.

The third day we took our physicals. The minute we got in line my heart started going very fast, just as I knew it would, and I started quivering all over, just as I knew I would. There was nothing in the world that made me more nervous than being closely looked at.

The doctor who took my blood pressure and pulse gave me a funny look but didn't say anything, just wrote it down, shaking his head. From there on it got worse and worse. I was trembling so badly by the time I got to the station where you had your eyes tested that I couldn't hold up the little card over one eye the way you were supposed to do, and the examining doctor couldn't believe it and went and got several of his colleagues and they all came and looked at me with amazement, and finally the examining doctor wrote something in his chart and waved me on, saying, "What did you think we were going to do, execute you if you flunked the eye test?"

The last stop was the little room where you had to stand stark naked in front of a psychiatrist for your "mental evaluation." I was completely demoralized when I arrived there and could barely speak to answer his questions, none of which I could really see the purpose of, so I would try to guess what he was getting at before I answered him, and that made him do funny things with his mouth and tap his pencil impatiently. The worst part came when I happened to look down and saw that my dick had shrunk to the size of a gherkin and was vibrating like a watch spring. The psychiatrist saw it too, and was fascinated. "Hey, listen, take it easy, will you?" he said.

Then he wrote something on a card and handed it to me and told me to give it to the major at the end of the line, and as I was going out he said, "Good luck, okay?"

On my way down to the end of the line I looked at what he had written on the card. It said he recommended that I be rejected because I had displayed "severe neurotic symptoms," and so I was classified 4-F and went back to Miami in disgrace.

At home there was shock and bewilderment. Wes wanted to know what could possibly be wrong with me that I couldn't pass a lousy little army physical. At first I wasn't able to tell him. Then I told him. Missy was there too. He looked at her with his mouth wide open and she looked at him with mouth wide open, and then they both looked at me with their mouths wide open.

"Neurotic symptoms?" they said, together.

They wanted me to tell them I was kidding. I *had* to be kidding. Nobody got rejected for "neurotic symptoms" back then. You could have "weak eyes" or a perforated eardrum or flat feet, but "neurotic symptoms" meant you were crazy, and to be considered crazy you really had to be *crazy* back then. "Neurotic symptoms" wasn't anywhere near good enough. You had to really show them something, like wearing dresses or blowing away your entire family with a double-barreled shotgun.

"Neurotic symptoms?" Wes said, starting to get sore, "Jesus *Christ,* what's *that* supposed to mean?"

Wes and Missy were basically very happy-go-lucky people. They really didn't want to know the truth about this thing, but they realized, sinkingly, they couldn't avoid it.

"Tell me what happened up there," Wes said.

"I just got scared, that's all," I said.

"Scared?" he said. "What was there to be scared about? I've been through those physicals a million times. There's nothing to be scared of. What happens? You go along the line. They take your pulse and your blood pressure, right? You spread your cheeks, right? They check your eyes and your ears. That's it. So how could you get scared?"

"I'm just scared of everything," I said.

"Scared of *everything?*" He was really getting sore now.

"Practically everything," I said.

He gazed at me, not only sore but also suspicious as hell. "You know what I think?" he said, turning to Missy. "I think what we have on our hands here is what we used to call a malingerer. I think he went there and put on some kind of a *show.* Scared of everything, my ass. The only thing he's scared of is having to get up at five o'clock in the morning and twenty-mile hikes in full field pack."

Missy didn't know what to say. She saw my GI Bill going out the window.

Wes saw more room and board and tuition money going out the window, if by some miracle I got into Harvard, for which I had taken the College Boards at St. Mark's, with my "phony diploma."

He said, "Okay, mister, we're not going to say anymore about this, but when they call you up for your next physical I want you to pass, and no ifs ands or buts about it, understand?"

The notice for my next physical came six months later, but by then the war was over and they were having the "I Wanna Go Home!" riots out in the Pacific and nobody cared so much about the draft anymore. In fact I didn't even have to go to Blanding this time, but just hopped a Miami Beach bus and went over the MacArthur Causeway and had my physical all alone in a doctor's office on Lincoln Road.

"I don't understand this," the doctor said. "There's nothing wrong with you physically. What are you so *nervous* for?"

"I don't know," I said.

"Do you think you could make it through basic without jumping out of your skin?"

"I don't think so," I said.

"Listen, the war's over," he said. "The only way you could get killed is if you slipped on a banana peel. You sure you don't want to try it? You'll get the GI Bill, you know."

I realized he was leaving it entirely up to me and I was really torn, because in the meantime a letter had come from Harvard saying I had been accepted for the coming fall term, which was a miracle considering that in the math section of the College Boards I hadn't even wasted time reading over the questions but had simply filled in the "C" column straight down the line figuring that the worst I could do that way was probably something like thirty-three-and-a-third percent correct. Anyway, it was "the immediate postwar period" and all the colleges were having enrollment problems while they waited for the great waves of returning servicemen that were soon going to overwhelm them.

Taking everything into consideration, it seemed to me that I should go to Harvard while the going was good, because there was no telling if I would ever make it there again after my time was up in the army.

"I'd rather not," I said.

The doctor shrugged. "Okay," he said. "I'll reject you for the neurotic symptoms again." He paused, gazing at me exactly the way the doctor at

Blanding had. "I really wish I could think of something to tell you," he said. "But what is there? Take a lot of cold showers . . . ?"

When I got home, Wes said he had only one question for me.

"Is the 'neurotic symptoms' just a cute way of saying you're a pansy?" he said. "Because if you're a goddam pansy I can tell you right now you're all through around here as far as I'm concerned."

I said no it didn't mean that, and then Missy told me to leave him alone with her for a while, which I did, and when I saw her again she said she had persuaded Wes to send me to Cambridge for one term and what she wanted me to do was to work very hard and see if I couldn't get some kind of a scholarship to carry me along the rest of the way.

I promised them both I would make them proud of me this time, and that made them feel better and in September they saw me off on the train.

ə.

BUT IT DIDN'T WORK out in Cambridge. I felt completely lost there from the beginning and it got worse as it went along. Actually, this was the first time I had ever been strictly on my own, and of course Harvard's attitude was that they had taken you in on the assumption that you were grown-up now so you had better act like it, because otherwise you wouldn't be around long. Nobody made you get up at a certain time or go to bed at a certain time, or eat at a certain time. Nothing like that. You didn't have to study if you didn't feel like it. You didn't even have to go to your lectures if you didn't feel like it.

I made it through the fall, but in the spring when a lot of my friends from St. Mark's got out of the service and entered Harvard it was parties all the time. During the week it was sitting around Jim Cronin's or the Rathskeller drinking beer until closing time or else getting drunk on the hard stuff in somebody's room. On the weekends it was coming out parties at The Country Club or the Ritz Carlton or the Longwood Cricket Club. Obviously all my aristocratic friends were invited to these things, but I went along with them and they would sneak me in, through a window or a back door, or by creating some kind of a distraction at the front door so I could slip in while everybody was looking the other way.

One of the things I noticed about myself immediately when I began drinking seriously was that champagne, scotch, even beer, seemed to hit me much harder and faster than anyone else, and it always brought out the very worst in me. In other words, first I got loud-mouthed and crazy, and then I got sick all over the place.

All of this led up to the fine night in May when I threw the twenty-seven quart beer bottles from my fourth-floor window down into Mt. Auburn Street, the refusing to surrender my Bursar's Card to the Proctor when he demanded it, my severed connections, and my going back to Miami in disgrace.

When I came into the house Wes told me he just wanted me to know that we were all through from this moment on as far as he was concerned, and after that he refused to speak to me, or even look straight at me.

Missy burst into tears every time she looked at me for the first couple of days, but then I told her that the Freshman Dean said the only way I could get back into Harvard was to get a hard job and stick with it for at least a year, so she made a phone call to someone she knew who got me the job with Midland Constructors, because she was absolutely determined that I would go back to Harvard. At $1.25 an hour she figured that I would have about two thousand dollars if I put every dime in the bank, and she was going to make sure I put every dime in the bank.

For about four months everything went along as well as could be expected, considering that Wes was relentless with his silent treatment. Missy got up at the crack of dawn every morning and made my lunches for me to take on the truck, and I was really sort of enjoying my job, even though it was very hard work.

But then Missy started having her "spells." I only saw one. We were all sitting out on the front lawn one Saturday morning when suddenly she let out a yelp and I turned and saw that it looked as if she had on a rubber mask and someone had grabbed it and yanked it down to the left. She put her hands over her face and ran into the house, and when we ran in after her we found her crouched in a corner in the kitchen.

That was the second time it had happened. The first time she and Wes had persuaded themselves that it was just some sort of an exaggerated muscular twitch that probably would never come again.

But it came again, three or four times. And when she finally let Wes take her to see a doctor about it, he said she would have to be put into the hospital right away for an encephalogram, and when he saw the result of the encephalogram he told us she would have to be operated on immediately because there was a tumor in there about the size of an orange.

She went into the operating room scared to death, and never came out of it. I mean, in place of the youthful, innocent woman who loved driving very fast, who had been a friend of Amelia Earhart, who always thought she was beautiful although she never really was, they brought into her bedroom a great big bald hideously ugly baby all hooked up with bottles and tubes and needles that never did anything but lie there and shit and drool and let out bloodcurdling screams.

At first the surgeon said he was pretty sure he had gotten all of it, but then later he said it was just a question of time, but it would probably be a long time.

That was when I began my novel.

₨

MY NOVEL was called "Welcome Stamp Collectors." It was about a young couple who, in the early thirties, buy a small abandoned hotel on a remote island on the Gulf coast of Florida, hoping to bring it back to life by attracting convention business. What they find out much too late is that the reason the hotel failed to begin with was that the people in the nearby town, Punta Rassa, who of course represent the only available labor pool, are intensely hostile to strangers, and did their best to make sure the hotel would fail, even though it gave employment to many of them. Therefore, when the young couple finally get the hotel fixed up and then are actually successful in booking a convention of stamp collectors from Chicago, their real troubles start, because the townspeople are determined to see that the hotel will fail all over again.

The story was a little grim, but the young couple gradually developed a sort of gallant, slap-happy Big Depression sense of humor about what was happening to them, and I intended that to be the thing that would save them in the end.

I didn't have a typewriter so I rented one downtown for fifteen dollars a month and started punching the words out as fast as I could go two-fingered. I tried to work at night, after supper, but I usually couldn't get too much done because I was dead tired from digging seven-foot holes in the coral rock out west of Miami, where Midland Constructors was building a new high-tension line for Florida Power & Light. The heat was terrific and the glare of the sun on the white coral rock was blinding and when I got off the truck late in the afternoon I felt dazed. But I wrote practically all day on weekends, and the writing went painfully but quite steadily once I got going.

Crescent Beach, the setting of "Welcome Stamp Collectors," was really Fort Myers Beach, the town on Estero Island where we had lived when we had first come down to Florida from New Jersey, in 1934. The first European explorers to visit Estero Island were members of the Ponce de León expedition in 1513. In 1528 Alverez Panfilio de Navaraez and Cabeza de Vaca passed by, and on May 25, 1539, Hernando de Soto's expedition sighted the island. In 1564 Pedro Menéndez de Avilés sent his longboats through the pass at the south end of the island to visit Caaluus, the cacique of the Calusa Indians who had settled in the area. The Spanish couldn't seem to get Caaluus's name right. They insisted on calling him Carlos, and even named the channel at the south end of Estero Island Big Carlos Pass in his honor. Later, Avilés married one of Caaluus's daughters and built a fort, San Anton, a few hundred yards east of Estero Island in Estero Bay.

It wasn't until 1877 that the first white settlers came to the island. The first town was called Crescent Beach, but it was renamed Bayview because it turned out there was an existing Crescent Beach, near Jacksonville. In the thirties Bayview was renamed Fort Myers' Beach, because some of the residents of Fort Myers had built cottages there, but finally that became just plain Fort Myers Beach.

About the only thing that ever happened to Fort Myers Beach that even came close to putting it on the map was when Cyrus Teed, who called himself Koresh and was the founder of Koreshan Unity, came down from Elmira, New York, in 1915 along with a group of his followers and bought some land on Estero Island. Koresh's concept of the world was unique in that he believed the world was a huge ball and that everyone lived on the inside surface. When he died he was buried in a bathtub near the shore at the south end of the island and his followers built a tomb over the bathtub, which regrettably was destroyed in the hurricane of 1921.

We hadn't started out to go there. But, actually, we hadn't started out to go anywhere in Florida in particular. Just Florida. One dark winter morning we all piled into Wes's big black Packard and headed south in a snowstorm, Wes, Missy and Sally up front, Marcus and I in the rumbleseat. When the snow and the cold got too much for us, Marcus and I pulled down the lid of the rumbleseat and went to sleep on the floorboards.

It took us about a week to reach Florida, sleeping in rooming houses and "tourist courts" along the way. The road maps weren't very good in those days and we got lost a couple of times, and several times got stuck in the mud when we had to take detours. When we finally crossed over the Georgia line into Florida we all got out of the car and cheered, and a little farther along the road there was a "Welcome Station" where a girl gave us each a Dixie cup full of "fresh-squeezed Florida orange juice."

A couple of days later we ended up on Fort Myers Beach, as if we had been drawn there.

To get to Fort Myers Beach you went through Fort Myers, a dusty cowtown on the Caloosahatchee River, and drove southwest along an avenue bordered by royal palms past THE WINTER HOME OF THOMAS A. EDISON, then through open country and farmland, and finally by a narrow tar road over a couple of wooden bridges into deep mangrove where fiddler crabs ran in waves across the sand, and the smell of salt kept getting stronger, and you went over one more bridge, over Mantanzas Pass, and you were in Fort Myers Beach.

When we crossed over the last bridge we kept on going to the other side of Estero Island, a few hundred yards, and there in front of us was the Gulf of Mexico.

It really was like coming to the end of the world.

We got out of the car and stood looking around us, and we kids were bitterly disappointed. Wes had said we were going to live on the ocean. This was an ocean? We had all been to Asbury Park and knew what a real ocean looked like. Where were the crowds, the crashing waves, the hot dog stands, the noise, the excitement? We gazed at the flat surface of the Gulf, with its ripples instead of combers, its golden sandbars, its serenity, its pale green water. The beach was totally deserted except for a bunch of brown pelicans bobbing placidly on the ripples.

WHEN WE GOT THERE the town of Fort Myers Beach consisted of a combination gas station and general store, a "juke joint," and a very small hotel called the Gulf Shore Inn. There were only a few houses on the island and most of them were clustered at the north end near the Mantanzas Pass bridge. The total population could not have been more than a hundred. Everyone drove on the beach itself, which was a glorious curve of smooth, hard-packed pure white sand where there was room for four lanes of traffic on a normal tide. The island was about five miles long but only a couple of hundred yards across at its widest point. In the distance to the north you could see Sanibel Island, which at that time was accessible only by boat.

Wes had told us when we left New Jersey that we were going to find a place to live in Florida where we would be able to catch fish off our own back porch, get our vegetables fresh out of the fields and take our eggs right out of the hen's *tokus,* and that was just about how it turned out.

He rented a weatherbeaten old house that, like almost all the houses on the island, stood on ten-foot pilings as a precaution against hurricanes. In 1922 the town had decided to put in a public water system, but in 1934 there were still only a few houses hooked up to it as most of the settlers had their own "flowing wells," which exuded strong odors of hydrogen sulphide and made everything smell like rotten eggs. There were telephones at the hotel and the gas station and the juke joint but none of the houses had lines of their own. As for electricity, again only the gas station and the hotel and the juke joint were on the line, and the rest of the residents lived by the dim glow of smoky kerosene lamps.

I would say we were all very happy there. We lived, as they say, "in our bathing suits," and although all of our days were pretty much the same I don't think we were ever bored. It didn't take long for us to get used to the kerosene lamps and the foul-smelling water, hot weather in the dead of winter, hordes of mosquitoes and gnats that swarmed out of the mangroves and chased you into the house the minute the sun went down, and the "ocean" that was like an enormous bathtub, and the monotony and isolation of life on an island.

All day we swam and fished and collected shells and dove for sand dollars, and watched pelicans skimming past very low over the water in their perfect formations or folding their wings dropping like bombs down into the water after mullet. Two or three times a day we saw a school of porpoises surprise a shark that had made the big mistake of coming into the shallow water over the sandbars and start going around him in ever tightening circles until he caught on to what had happened and began jumping frantically, trying to get out of the trap. But then it would be too late and the powerful tails of the porpoises would lash the shark until he was either dead or somehow escaped.

The people who lived on the island seldom went down to the south end. If anyone had asked them why they didn't go there, they would have said that's easy, because there's nothing there. That was the truth. There was absolutely nothing there but the wind in the pine trees, the sun, the empty horizon and the dazzling curve of the white beach.

When you were there you always felt as if you were intruding, that you should speak softly, that every time you put your foot down you were standing on a spot where no man had ever stood before. At least not any white man.

There were never any planes in the sky. No boats went past. All you ever heard was the whistling of the sandpipers running along the beach and gulls in the air and the waves hissing in and hissing out, and inevitably you were drawn to the very end of the island, where the beach dropped off sharply into Big Carlos Pass and deep and dark and profoundly menacing currents raced by, and where they said gigantic hammerhead sharks lurked. When we went down there we always somehow ended up standing in a row, all of us from Wes on down, gazing into the writhing, swift-running depths, trying to see the hammerhead sharks and imagining what they would do to us if they ever got hold of us.

SOON THE ISLAND became our whole world. What happened on the island was interesting and important, but everything that was happening off the island seemed to be happening to people who lived in a different world. Even Fort Myers, which was only about twenty miles away, seemed very remote to us. When we all piled into Wes's Packard about once a week and drove over to Fort Myers to do our shopping, we thought of it almost as a trip to a foreign country. After all, the people we saw on the streets over there were people who got up early every morning and went to work, who were trying to survive in the middle years of the greatest Depression in history and who existed within the context of the NRA, the CCC and the WPA. Of course Fort Myers wasn't anything like Newark where we had seen the long gray lines of men waiting in the snow and the rain to reach the soup kitchens, but still the town was going through very hard times.

I remember one morning in Fort Myers when we were driving with the top down past the docks and saw a gang of men laying down railroad track in the scorching heat, and Wes stopped the Packard across the street and sat there with the engine idling as he gazed at the men. We kids all gazed at them too, not knowing why, or what we were supposed to be thinking, but confident that Wes was going to tell us his thoughts when he had formed them properly.

Finally he said, "You know, they do that for a dollar a day."

We all stared at him, not knowing what he meant. Was that good or bad? Was that a lot of money for work like that or not a lot of money for work like that? Did he expect us to say something? Were we to feel bad about it or good about it?

We kept on sitting there in the blinding sunlight for a minute or two more. Then we drove on and I think the feeling we kids had was that he really hadn't said that to us at all, but to himself.

On the island at least nobody had to worry about where the next meal was coming from. In the first place, there was so much fish around that if you couldn't go to the Mantanzas Pass bridge or the pier up at the north end of the island and in an hour or two bring in enough fat sheepheads or snappers or whiting or mullet to feed a family of six there really had to be something wrong with you. And all around us on the mainland were fields and fields of collard greens and cucumbers and corn and tomatoes and watermelon and everything else, that you could buy dirt cheap at the little stands they all had out by the road, and where you could also get your eggs that actually were right out of the hen's *tokus*.

The population of the island was about equally divided between retired people who had come down mostly from New York and New Jersey, and who of course could live very comfortably on their pension checks in a place where you seldom wore anything but shorts and bathing suits and never had to buy coal and were probably spending around five dollars a week for food, and the local people who ran the juke joint and the general store and worked in the fish canning plant that was right there by the Mantanzas Pass bridge, and also hired out as fishing guides.

Generally speaking everybody got along just fine, and no wonder because we had what amounted to an almost Utopian society. The local people needed the money from the pension checks and the retirees needed all the services they got from the local people, and everybody knew where everybody stood and appreciated and valued each other.

Wes was the only man on the island who came close to being rich, but no one resented that because he was much liked both by the Northerners and the locals. They all considered him a prince of a guy, and of course they liked Missy too. So they fitted right into the life on the island from the beginning, and I'm sure this was the happiest time of their whole lives.

Well, how could it have been any better? They were in love, had a very good time together, there was lots of money, they were still young, both around thirty-five, and the skies, literally, were not cloudy all day.

Wes wasn't that crazy about children, but he did sort of like the idea of having a bunch of kids to boss around. He always got us out of bed very early and took us swimming with him before breakfast. He led the way out into the Gulf and we all followed him, from one sandbar to the next, going down into the troughs where the water might be up to our armpits and then up onto a sandbar where it was only a few inches deep and made you look from a distance as if you were walking on water.

Schools of minnows being chased by fierce jacks with a blood lust would shimmer all around us for an instant, tickling our legs, and then flash away in zigzag ripples.

The sand on the bottom was absolutely clean and warm and yellow and it was marvelous to dig your toes into it and feel the firm ridges under the soles of your feet. All of a sudden you saw a big cloud of sand billow up and a skate that had been frightened out of hiding by our approach took off on a straight line so fast you would barely catch a glimpse of him before he disappeared.

Wes was a powerful swimmer and he went alone out into the deep water beyond all the sandbars and swam back and forth for about half an hour, while Marc and Sally and I splashed each other and skipped sand dollars across the surface of the Gulf, which most mornings was dead smooth all the way to the horizon.

After our swim, Wes made us breakfast. He liked to cook and really took it hard if we all didn't stuff ourselves to the eyes on the tons of eggs and bacon and enormous stacks of pancakes he kept loading up on our plates.

He had been a miler and a football player at Cornell. In fact, one of the things he was proudest of was that he had been on the 1919 Cornell team that had played against the Rutgers team that Paul Robeson had been on. Anyway, after breakfast he took his football out on the beach and boomed high spiraling punts back and forth. In the afternoons he and Missy either worked on their tans or lay out in the sun broiling in cocoons of thick blankets sweating buckets in what they called their "reducing program," which, to be less poetic about it, mostly was intended to purge the booze from their systems so they could go at it again the next night. They drank a lot, like everybody else on the island, and, for that matter, like everybody else in the whole country, ever since the Volstead Act had been repealed. But one of the funny things about it was the enormous amount of nostalgia for Prohibition. It seemed as if down in their hearts everybody truly missed their "bootleggers" and their "speakeasies," because when the grownups got together that was practically all you heard them talk about. What fond stories they had to tell about the nights they had been in speakeasies that had been raided and everybody had gone to the can, and all the wonderful times they had paid a small fortune for a case of "genuine scotch whiskey" only to discover it was tea, or water when it was supposed to have been London Dry Gin. And tears would come into their eyes when they told about the times when they may have been a little late with a payment to their bootlegger and he told them they either had his money there by twelve o'clock the next day or he would send a guy around to break their thumbs.

At night Wes and Missy had people over for a party or went to a party at someone else's house, or they went out fishing for tarpon. They had their own boat and their own personal guide, a medium sinister young man named Pernell. They would leave soon after sunset and stay out in the Gulf until two or three o'clock in the morning, and come home all lit up and wake us kids to tell about the huge fish they had caught, or the colossal one that got away, and then a few hours later Wes would be dragging us out of bed to go swimming with him.

When Wes or Missy caught a really big tarpon they always wrote their "W" or "M" in red nail polish on one of the fish's big silvery scales along with the date and tacked it to the dining room wall, under a snapshot of them with Pernell, grinning the way nobody ever grins except in pictures with a fishing guide.

❧

SO THAT WAS what it was like on Fort Myers Beach until the morning in February 1934 when we heard that John Dillinger and Homer Van Meter had checked into the Gulf Shore Inn the night before. Everybody was talking about it but nobody seemed to know what to do about it, because it really was difficult to know what to do in a situation like that. In the first place Dillinger was practically a national folk hero because every time he knocked over a bank all "the little guys" felt he had struck a blow for them against the flint-hearts who had foreclosed on their mortgage. Never mind that he happened to be one of the most cold-blooded killers of all time, with sixteen dead men to his credit. Nobody wanted to talk about that, only how great it was to think of the bankers squirming over all the hundreds of thousands of dollars Dillinger had taken from them.

In the second place, there was no such thing as a policeman on the island. (What possible use would we have had for one?)

Which brings up the third thing. Of course somebody could have called the Lee County sheriff's office and told them to send over a couple of thousand deputies to shoot it out with Dillinger and Van Meter (and that was about how many everybody thought it would really take to bring them down), but it was just that nobody seemed to be the one to make the call. In fact, according to Wes, who was keeping in very close touch with the situation, there was a feeling on the island that the person who called in the cops on Dillinger would be making himself very unpopular.

The rest of that day went by with everybody just waiting to see what would happen. The only thing we heard all morning was that Dillinger and Van Meter had eaten breakfast in the kitchen with their guns on the table. Later we heard that they had gone out on the beach and stood out there for a little while, and had asked somebody what kind of fish they caught around here and then had told Gino Mascagni, the owner-manager of the Gulf Shore Inn, that they wanted a boat to go out for tarpon on Thursday night, so fix it up. This was on a Tuesday.

Gino Mascagni, a middle-aged guy with some health problems, mostly arthritis, had come down to Fort Myers Beach from Camden, New Jersey, in 1928 with his wife Angela, because Angela's father had told them about this little hotel on the beach where he and his wife had stayed the last time they came to Florida, which they had heard was up for sale, and which they would probably get for a song. Gino had made a small killing in the stock market with White Sewing Machine and was looking for two things to do with the money: get away from those awful winters in New Jersey and invest in something that would give him an income for the rest of his life.

He and Angela took one look at the Gulf Shore Inn and saw the possibilities and bought it on the spot with cash money.

When they took over the Gulf Shore Inn it didn't have a restaurant, so the guests always had to eat their meals at the juke joint where the specialty of the day *every day* was fried mullet with collard greens, blackeyed peas and cornbread that weighed six pounds per square inch and even the coffee tasted like deep-fried mullet.

Gino and Angela didn't really know much about running a hotel, but they did know how to run a restaurant, because that was what they had been doing back in Camden for ten years, where their restaurant was supposed to have had the reputation of being one of the best Italian restaurants in the entire state of New Jersey.

They decided to start giving their guests breakfast, mostly out of plain compassion for their stomachs. They cooked the food on the little stove in the manager's apartment and served it on six tables they set up in the lobby. The breakfasts were so good that the guests started clamoring for lunch and dinner too, and pretty soon Gino and Angela had to put over a dozen tables in the lobby and hire a couple of local girls as waitresses, to handle the business not only from the hotel guests but also people from the island and even from the mainland. And in the summer of 1929 they made the big step and knocked out the six rooms at the north end of the hotel and built a glassed-in dining room with a great view of the Gulf that they called Angela's Kitchen, where the specialty of the day was always something called Spaghetti alla Papalina or Lobster Fra Diavolo, for about eighty-five cents.

Even in 1930, when the Depression really began setting in and not so many people could afford to come down to Fort Myers Beach anymore, the restaurant continued to do a lot of business, with people coming from as far away as Naples and Punta Gorda to the south and maybe Venice to the north.

GINO DROVE down to our house that afternoon to talk to Wes. He liked Wes and really trusted his judgment in things. In fact at one time he and Wes had been seriously talking about going into a partnership that would have involved Wes financing what would have amounted to a whole string of Angela's Kitchens, one in Fort Myers and another in Venice and a third in Punta Gorda, but then Angela had gotten sick and Gino had had qualms and the project had been put on the back burner. Still, Gino and Wes were close and so Gino naturally wanted to talk to Wes. He looked sick.

He said the few guests he had in the hotel had cleared out and probably never would come back, and all the help had refused to come to work except Albert, his dishwasher.

We all stood around in the kitchen while Wes gave Gino a couple of slugs of scotch to calm him down.

"You're sure it's them?" Wes said.

Gino nodded. "It's them. I recognized them the minute they came through the door last night."

"And you've actually talked to Dillinger?" Wes said, fascinated, and clearly envious.

"No, Van Meter," Gino said. "Dillinger never opened his mouth. He just stood sort of in the background and let Homer do all the talking. And he signed the register for both of them, Mr. Smith and Mr. Jones, from Memphis, Tennessee."

"You don't know how lucky you are," Wes said. "You can always say you saw Dillinger and Van Meter."

"The only thing I know," Gino said, "is that if anybody calls the cops on them, he'll think it was me and he'll blast Angie and me."

"How's Angie taking it?" Missy asked.

"Well, at first she acted like the night them guys came into our place in Camden and said they were going to blow our heads off if we didn't hide them from the cops. But then she said she just wasn't going to let them scare her, so she cooks for them anything they want and they love it. Van Meter even kids around with her a little. They eat right in the kitchen, you know, with their goddam pieces on the table."

"I heard about that," Wes said.

Gino paused. "Then there's this other thing," he said. "Van Meter told me to fix them up to go out tarpon fishing on Thursday night. So I went over to Yent's and Pernell was there and I asked him if he wanted the job. He said, 'You're goddam right,' and went over to the hotel and talked to them, and made the arrangements for Thursday night. He wants to take them out in your boat."

"What do you mean he wants to take them out in my boat?" Wes said.

Gino shrugged. "He says you've got the only boat on the island you could take somebody like that out on. It's the only one with any class. He thinks if Dillinger gets a big tarpon he'll give him a thousand dollars or some goddam thing. He told me to ask you if it's okay."

"I don't know," Wes said. "I'd have to think about it."

"You could always say Dillinger went out for tarpon in your boat," Gino said.

"That's true," Wes said.

"Shall I tell him you're thinking about it?"

"Yeah, tell him I'm thinking about it," Wes said. Then he said, "No, go ahead and tell him it will be okay."

After Gino left, Wes said to us, "You know, this is a moment in history."

That night Pernell came to the house to talk to Wes. He came in when we were in the middle of dinner and sat right down and started helping himself to everything in sight, as usual. He ate mostly with his fingers and practically snarled over his food, but for some reason Wes, who was very rigid with us kids in the area of table manners, seemed to find Pernell's behavior at the table entrancing.

"Did you *see* the way he attacked that steak bone?" he would marvel after Pernell had left. "He ground it up with his bare teeth like a goddam *hyena!* Ha-hahahahaha! He ought to be in a *circus,* for God's sake!"

"Did you talk to *Dillinger?*" Wes said, watching Pernell stuffing fried chicken into his mouth.

"Yeah, I talked to him," Pernell said, leaning back and wiping his mouth with the back of his hand.

"Gino said he lets Van Meter do all the talking," Wes said.

Pernell went for another load of chicken, forking it onto his plate with total concentration.

"Maybe he wouldn't talk to Gino," Pernell said around a huge mouthful of chicken. "But he sure as hell talked to me."

"What did he say to you?"

"He asked me what the record was for the biggest tarpon ever caught around here. I told him ninety-eight-and-a-half pounds, Labor Day, 1927. Guy named Walters, from Paramus, New Jersey."

"Where did you talk to him?" Wes said.

"In the room," Pernell said, licking his fingers. "He was laying on the bed with his shoes on and he was wearing a shoulder harness, but his pistol was over on the bureau. Then he said, okay, if he caught a tarpon that was anything over a hundred pounds he would take care of me. You know what that means? A guy like him would give you a thousand dollars and never even blink an eye if you got him what he wanted."

"Okay," Wes said. "Just make sure you take good care of my boat."

THE NEXT MORNING around ten o'clock Wes told us all to get into the Packard, and we drove down the beach to the Gulf Shore Inn and circled around in back to the parking lot, and Wes said, "Well, there it is."

And he was absolutely right, there it was, a black Ford touring car with Tennessee plates.

"Tennessee plates," Missy said. "Where did he get those Tennessee plates?"

"Stole 'em," Wes said, always knowing everything. "You read about that in the papers, didn't you? He always has about ten sets of stolen plates in his car, and sometimes he'll switch 'em two or three times a day."

He drove right up alongside the Ford so we could get a close look at it, and I know all the rest of us had the feeling he shouldn't have done it, but of course you couldn't say anything, because questioning his better judgment was the quickest way to burn him up.

"Look for bullet holes," Wes said, and we all dutifully craned our necks looking the car over from end to end but didn't see any bullet holes.

"Maybe on the other side," Wes said, and he backed up and pulled the Packard around to the left side of the Ford, but we still didn't see any bullet holes.

Then, more or less all at once, we looked over the roof of the Ford toward the Gulf Shore Inn, which sat there brooding in the morning sun.

The Inn was a long, one-story building that stood on fairly low pilings. There were about twenty rooms, all of them giving onto the central hallway that ran the whole length of the building. The rooms on the Gulf side, with the "ocean view," cost three dollars a night, the ones in back a buck less. The rooms were all alike, very plain, with iron beds and dark brown bureaus with most of the knobs off and windows with sticks holding them open, one little round cloth throw rug on the floor between the beds, a lamp with the cord wrapped in friction tape in about ten places, one "easy chair," blinds with big round brown-edged stains all over them, walls with brown-edged stains all over them, little white curtains that had turned yellow, a nightstand with a Gideon Bible on it and a water pitcher and a big porcelain bowl to wash your face in. None of the rooms had a private bath. Men used the bathroom at the north end of the hallway, women the one at the south end.

Anyway, knowing so well what the rooms looked like I could imagine Dillinger in his room, laying there on the bed just as Pernell had described him, with his shoes on and wearing his shoulder harness but with his pistol over on the bureau. At least I hoped that was what he was doing. The thought that he might have been watching us out of his window was scary, and Pernell had neglected to say whether they had a front room or a back room. But actually, I thought it was a pretty safe bet that for a buck more John Dillinger would have gone for the ocean view.

"Maybe we should go on home now," Missy said in her most conciliatory tone.

"Not until I get a picture of this," Wes said. "Give me the camera."

Missy hesitated, and then opened the glove box and got out Wes's Kodak, which was one of those elaborate deals with a case that opened up and the lens slid out at the end of a black accordion housing. He cocked the camera and then backed up so that we were directly behind the Ford. He snapped a picture from that angle and then one from the right side of the car and then the left. Then he made a big circle and stopped the Packard at a distance of about thirty feet from the Ford, handed the camera to Missy and said, "Just one more," and got out of the car and strolled over to the Ford, put one foot up on the back bumper and posed there like a white hunter with his foot on an elephant as Missy snapped his picture.

Before returning to the Packard Wes ran his fingers over the dusty left rear fender of the Ford and rubbed the dust between his fingertips.

Missy put the camera back in the glove box, next to Wes's Smith & Wesson .38, which along with the official New Jersey state trooper's nightstick that had been given to him by a New Jersey state trooper he had once done some sort of a favor for, was the armament he relied on to deal with any kind of emergency from muggers to rattlesnakes to, I guess, bigtime bank robbers.

One thing about him, he was just about fearless.

From the parking lot we went across the street to the juke joint, and Marc and Sally and I stayed in the rumbleseat while Wes and Missy went in and talked about Dillinger with the crowd who had gathered in there.

Later that night Wes and Missy went back down to the juke joint to have a few beers and hear the latest rumors about Dillinger, and headed for home around midnight. They were driving home by way of the narrow dirt road behind the row of houses when the Ford touring car came out of the pitch blackness with no lights on and before they knew what was happening had forced them off the road and into the sandy ditch that ran along next to the road like a sandtrap. Then the Ford just vanished back into the night.

Luckily the Packard didn't turn over and neither Missy nor Wes was hurt, but the car was stuck so deep in the sand that Wes knew there wasn't a chance of getting it out until morning. So they locked up the car and walked the rest of the way home, which wasn't too far.

As usual when there was some kind of excitement they woke up Marcus and Sally and me to tell us all about it, and you could see that Wes was really happy now because he had a genuine Dillinger story that he could tell for the rest of his life.

But the next morning very early we were awakened by the milkman pounding on our back door. He told us the Packard's canvas top had been slashed wide open and it looked like the glove box had been jimmied.

Wes went with the milkman in his truck and came back a little later to tell us that his Kodak, with the film still in it, and his Smith & Wesson had been stolen, also his official New Jersey state trooper's nightstick.

Hardly had he gotten the words out of his mouth when Pernell stormed through the back door to inform us that Dillinger and Van Meter had cleared out in the middle of the night, and everybody was saying it was because they suspected that Wes was some kind of a G-man, so now his shot at getting took care of by John Dillinger was out the window.

He was so disappointed he just walked around in circles in the kitchen kicking at the chair legs and the icebox and everything else that got in his way, and even when Wes tried to make him feel a little better by fixing him his favorite breakfast—steak and eggs, with side orders of ham and sausage, pancakes, home fries and hot apple pie—he ate everything else but barely touched his hot apple pie, a sure sign that he was really hurting deep inside.

The net result of the whole episode was that Wes came out of it a big hero on the island—the man who had scared Dillinger and Van Meter out of town, and of course he gloried in the role.

But until the day he died he never really forgave himself for having neglected to take that film out of his camera.

&

EVENTUALLY MARC and Sally and I had to start going to school, and Missy enrolled us in the fall of 1934. Of course there was no school of any kind on the island, so we had to go by school bus all the way over to Fort Myers.

The trip each way could take sometimes two and a half hours because the bus had to go way back into the farmlands to pick up the farm kids, which meant crawling along dirt roads with the gears whining and the dust and the exhaust fumes choking you to death. But that was really neither here nor there compared to the harassment we had to take from the farm boys.

Wes insisted that we go to school in short pants, Buster Brown shoes and ankle socks and shirts with Eton collars and neckties. This to jounce around through the cornfields with a bunch of hard-knuckled totally humorless boys in bare feet and bib overalls who seemed to think of the whole experience of going to school as just a tedious interruption of the neat fights they had on the bus on the way there and the neat fights they had on the bus on the way back from there.

The first time they saw us they didn't laugh. They only looked at us steadily and suspiciously for the whole length of the ride as if they were positive this was some kind of a joke that they knew they would catch on to if they just thought about it long enough.

That was the first day. The second day they untied our shoelaces and our neckties and waited to see what we would do. We left our shoelaces and neckties untied.

After that they could see they had a pair of real beauties on their hands and that provoking us into a fight was going to take something a little less subtle, so in between rolling around in the aisle and under the seats punching each other and choking each other and trying to gouge each other's eyes out, they took turns lurching up to us and grabbing one or the other of us by the nose with one hand and with the other administering what they called a "washboard," which involved rubbing the top of your head vigorously with their knuckles.

Either one of those things would bring tears to your eyes. Together they left you feeling way down for the rest of the day.

When we didn't fight back they asked us if we were yellow, and when we said no, they said then come on back to the rear of the bus and prove it, but we always said we didn't want to. That really slew them, since I don't think one of them had ever backed away from a challenge in his entire life.

We always tried to sit as far up in front as possible, close to the girls and the bus driver. When the boys picked on us the girls told them to leave us alone, and that made them narrow their eyes, and the bus driver would look up in his mirror and say, "Hey, Joey, or Rusty or Wilbur, leave 'em alone. They ain't hurtin' nothin'." And that also made them narrow their eyes.

Anyway Marcus and I knew our day was coming, and we talked about it constantly. The main thing that bothered us was trying to figure out if we were yellow or not. Of course I was still a champion bed-wetter and still had all my fantastic insecurities, except a million times worse than ever now, and I was pretty sure I was yellow. Marc, never having been in an actual fight in his whole life, just had no way of knowing, but he was pretty sure he was too.

The worst thing about the situation was that Sally would come home and tell Wes about how we had been bullied and that she thought he ought to do something about it before we really got hurt.

Of course there was nothing in Wes's philosophy that could have made him sympathetic to Sally's pleadings. Besides having been a miler and a football player at Cornell, he had also been an outstanding boxer, with the trophies to prove it. On top of that, for a couple of years, he had served on the boxing commission of the state of New Jersey.

Therefore his approach to the problem was to buy two sets of kids' boxing gloves and start giving Marc and me instructions in the manly art of self-defense, along with very strong doses of the incentive to accept any challenge from anybody anytime and the will to win *big,* plus a couple of little tricks to pull out of the bag if the going got really rough. With enormous precision he would demonstrate to us how to throw a solar plexus punch that would leave any opponent practically for dead, how to bring your foot down on your opponent's instep in such a way that he would probably have to spend the next eight months in a cast up to his crotch, and how to break his nose with one lightning-quick twelve-inch blow with the heel of your hand.

The stuff we were learning fascinated Marc and me, but the idea of trying to apply our knowledge to a real-life situation terrified us. It just seemed to us that no matter how well we could box, all it would do was make things go that much harder on us when it came down to an actual fight with Joey or Rusty or Wilbur or whoever, since they all had so much more experience with fighting than we did and were naturally so much tougher and stronger than we were. And as for trying any of the *tricks,* I think we were both afraid that even looking as if you were going to attempt some of that stuff would just be an invitation to get yourself killed deader than a herring.

At noon we usually took our lunchboxes and went and ate our sandwiches in the playground. That was where all the serious fights took place, the ones where the boys would beat each other until one of them fell down and then the other would jump on him and sit on his chest and punch him with both fists back and forth until there was blood all over his face from his nose and his mouth, or, if there was a real grudge, grab a stone and just pound him senseless.

After we had witnessed one of those fights, Marc and I always slunk off to a corner of the playground and tried to fade into the scenery until the bell rang for our next classes.

But it wasn't too long before all the suspense came to an end, at least for me. One day in the playground a boy named Tim came up in front of me and put a pebble on his shoulder and told me to try to knock it off, and without even thinking of what I was doing I reached out and tried to do it. At that point I took two quick punches to the gut and then a straight left to the nose and the next thing I knew I was standing there with blood falling in huge drops on my white shirt and my green necktie with the little black and white Scotties embroidered all over it, and I was mostly thinking about what my mother was going to say when she saw that they both were ruined. Then Tim moved in with a blazing combination of punches that I never even saw coming, and all of a sudden I found myself sitting on the ground with my legs twisted in sort of a funny way.

Tim stood in front of me blowing on his knuckles. "Get up," he said.

But then Sally came flying up and pushed him away and grabbed me by the hand and pulled me across the playground to the girls' restroom, and dragged me right inside, not paying any attention to the girls in there who started giggling and squealing as she stripped off my tie and my shirt and made me stand there while she tried to wash out the blood with cold water before it stained the material permanently.

I went through the rest of the day in a damp shirt and tie, and when we got on the bus to go home I looked around for Tim, expecting further trouble. But he seemed to have lost all interest in me, and on the return ride spent most of his time with the other boys in their alternate activity, which was leaning way out the windows and yelling in disparaging voices "WREEEEEEECK!" at all the cars that came up behind us, even the ones that looked as if they had just come off the showroom floor.

When we got home Wes took one look at me and asked who had done it. You didn't lie to him or stall him. When he asked you something you just told him. So I told him who had done it and how he had done it hoping that would be the end of it except for maybe an intensification of our boxing program.

But then he said, "Listen, he was bigger than you, wasn't he?"

Again, you didn't lie to him. So I had to say that, no, Tim wasn't bigger than I was, and Wes got one of those looks in his eyes that you hated to see there and said, "Okay, go get in the car."

We drove very fast, and Wes said, "Just show me where he lives," and then he started telling me that he wanted me to remember everything he had taught me, and not to be scared, and just to wade in there and knock the little bastard on his ass.

I just kept nodding a mile a minute and saying "uhah, uhah, uhah," and too soon, much too soon, we were there, and Wes was pulling into the driveway where three or four skinny mongrels and six or seven inbred-looking cats and a whole bunch of hens took off in all directions to get out of our path, and finally the Packard came to rest in a cloud of reddish dust right in front of the house.

The house resembled all the other farmhouses out there in the fields. Two stories with a rusty tin roof, looked as if it hadn't been painted in fifteen years, had a little porch out front where there was a "glider" and a couple of rockers and an old overstuffed armchair with the stuffing and the springs coming out in about ten different places. Out back there was a henhouse and a pen for the pigs and a lean-to for the cow, and about eighteen old tires scattered around in the weeds.

All of those houses had at least three rusted-out cars up on blocks in the front yard and around by the side of the house there was always an old truck that had the radiator off, or the transmission pulled or an A-frame rigged up to haul out the engine block.

Somewhere in the backyard there would be a big shade tree under which no grass grew, but where the kids played, and which was where they picked up all their impetigo.

Wes and I got out of the car and went across the porch to the front door, where Tim's father was standing looking out at us through the torn screen door.

I don't know if he was a sharecropper, but I guess he was. I guess they all were.

"Yes, sir," Tim's father said. He was wearing bib overalls just like Tim's, over a faded-out red long-sleeved undershirt, huge black shoes, and, tucked into the collar of his undershirt, a white napkin.

Beyond him, we could see the mother and I guess the grandma and grandpa and about eight kids seated at the dining room table, and they were all sitting there staring at us.

I saw Tim looking at me, with his knife in one hand and his fork in the other, and his napkin tucked into the front of his overalls.

Wes was a little uncertain. I don't think it had ever occurred to him for a minute that we would find them having their supper at around five o'clock in the afternoon. It was uncivilized.

"I guess I've come at a bad time," he said.

"That's all right, what was it you wanted?" Tim's father said.

"Well, it was just that your boy had a fight with my boy here today," Wes said. "And we just came over here to see about getting a rematch. But I hate to interrupt your dinner—"

Tim's father looked back toward the table. "Tim," he said, "come on over here."

Tim put down his knife and fork and removed his napkin and when he came to the door his father said, "You know this boy here?"

"Yes, sir," Tim said.

"Did you have a fight with him today?"

"Yes, sir," Tim said.

"Well, they're calling you out," Tim's father said. "Are you going out?"

"Yes, sir," Tim said.

So his father opened the screen door and they came out, and Wes introduced himself to them and shook both their hands, and we went to an open space where Wes drew a big circle in the dirt with a stick. While he was doing that I took off my shirt and tie and my shoes and socks. Then I glanced at Tim and his father and saw that they were both gazing at the Packard, which looked very beautiful but also slightly menacing standing there. And I saw that the rest of the family had come out on the porch and were also staring at the Packard.

"Okay, this is the ring," Wes said. "Now I want you boys to shake hands."

Tim dragged himself away from looking at the Packard and turned to me. He was about an inch shorter than I was and had blond hair that was bleached out almost white from the sun, black eyebrows and lashes and very intense blue eyes. We shook hands and then Tim blew on his knuckles and put up his dukes and I did the same.

Wes said, "Okay, I want a good clean fair fight. Now go to it."

At that I suddenly burst into tears, but it wasn't from fear, just the excitement. Actually I felt ready to go. We circled each other and I saw Tim's four or five brothers gathering around to yell encouragement at him, but that didn't bother me too much. Of course it didn't help that I could barely see through my tears and my nose was so stuffed up that I had to breathe through my mouth, but one thing I noticed right away was that the moves I had learned in theory from my boxing lessons actually did work in practice. For example, when I feinted the way I had been taught, Tim usually reacted exactly the way he was supposed to, which of course meant that he was leaving himself wide open for an instant, and right away I began getting in some pretty good right hands.

I also noticed that the only thing Tim really seemed to know how to do was back off and then charge in throwing haymakers from both sides hoping that he would hit something, and that he almost always did it with his eyes closed. So I waited for him and slipped his left hand and brought in a short left hook that caught his nose. There was a good satisfying splat and then he was standing there with the blood trickling from his nose and wondering what had hit him.

That got him mad and he came at me again and this time the onslaught was a little more than I could handle and he hit me a terrific lick in my left eye that made me see stars, and then I started going crazy too and throwing punches wildly from both sides and I caught him five good lefts and rights to his three or four, and then suddenly we both seemed to run out of gas at the same moment and from then on neither of us could even hold his arms up much less try to throw any more punches, both having learned the first lesson of boxing, which is that the hardest part is simply to hold your arms up for more than about a minute and a half.

When we had stood in the middle of the circle and leaned on each other and pawed at each other a little longer and Wes could see that there definitely wasn't going to be any more action, he stepped between us and raised both our hands, and announced that he was calling the bout a draw.

Wes made us shake hands again, and then he went around and shook hands with everybody in the entire family, including the smallest girl, who was about two, and you could see that they all really liked him, even if he had busted in on them and gotten their dinners cold, and they ended up inviting us in for a glass of iced tea, and Tim's mother gave me a wet cloth with a chunk of ice in it to hold over my eye, and before we left Wes made an exclusive deal to buy all our eggs and vegetables from Tim's father, and they all came out on the porch to wave goodbye to us, and Wes was as good as his word and never did buy even a cucumber from anyone else but Tim's father for as long as we lived on Fort Myers Beach, although it meant going pretty far out of his way.

Going home in the Packard I said, "I'm not going to wear a tie to school anymore," and the minute I said it I was afraid I was going to burst into tears again because I was sure he would really get mad.

But he said, "Okay, Champ."

"Marc too?"

"Okay," he said.

And when we got home and Missy got a load of my eye, which by then had swollen almost completely shut, and was horrified, Wes said, very proudly, "Yeah, but you should see the other guy."

Marc had his first fight a couple of days later, and did okay for himself, and from then on we got into fights all the time, and of course they were never again like the fight I had had with Tim, with Wes to draw a circle and see that the Marquess of Queensberry rules were strictly observed. It was always just stupid lunging and grabbing and throwing wild punches and rolling around in the dirt, but when Wes asked us if we weren't glad now that he had shown us how to take care of ourselves we always said yes.

੨෧

EARLY IN 1935 we moved from the house that stood on ten-foot pilings to a house on Connecticut Street, that stood on four-foot pilings. Connecticut Street was the last named street to the south on Fort Myers Beach, and was also the point at which the back road came to an end.

Of course Connecticut Street wasn't really a street any more than Crescent Street and Carolina Street and Pearl Street were really streets. They were all just deeply rutted turn-offs in the soft sand where cars could cut over from the road to the hard sand of the beach—and where if they weren't very careful they could get stuck so bad it would take them hours to get out again.

Beyond our new house, which was roughly a mile from the main cluster of civilization at the north end of the island, there were no other inhabitants, except a recluse everyone called Dutch Futch, and an eccentric named Mr. McPhee. Dutch Futch's shack was visible in the distance if you stood out on the beach in front of our house, but McPhee's shack was hidden way back in the trees and you wouldn't even have known it was there if you hadn't known it was there.

We still had no telephone or electricity, although quite a few of the other houses had been hooked into the main lines from Fort Myers at that time. But the owner said he didn't want to go to the "enormous expense" of wiring his house, so we went on living by kerosene lamps and with an icebox instead of a refrigerator and always having to listen to the tic-tic-tic of the gasoline pump that drew up the foul-smelling water from the well.

But it really wasn't so bad because of course we were used to all that by then.

Up there when you went out on the beach in the morning it would have been swept absolutely clean of tire marks and footprints all the way up to the high-water mark in the night, and was strewn with lovely shells as yet unbroken by footsteps or tires.

At sunset we used to gather down by the water's edge. We had always done it, from the very beginning. It had something to do with regretting the last of the daylight, because right after sunset we would of course be driven by the mosquitoes and the sandflies back into the house, where our only light would be a flame. And the flame is a hard thing to live with. It has a life of its own. It fascinates you. You can't help gazing at it. You always fear it because it is fire. When you put out a flame you see its ghost rise in the wisp of smoke. Its light haunts a room. Our flames cast huge shadows that slid along the walls when anyone moved around. We saw things in each other's faces we never saw there by any other light.

Sometimes at sunset we saw the very tips of the masts of two or three sailboats appear on the red horizon. Wes called them "the Cuban smacks," and told us that he had it on very good authority that they stayed outside the three-mile limit until darkness and then came in close to the south end of the island, where they put their lifeboats over to run in across the sandbars.

"Chinks," he said. "They're smuggling in Chinks from Cuba. It's big business now. The Chinks are rich. They'll pay you a fortune to land them anywhere on American soil."

Also, at sunset, we often heard Dutch Futch's dogs barking faintly. He was a hallucinatory figure, filthy, clothed in rags, always barefoot, his mouth full of rotten teeth, his hair long and matted like Robinson Crusoe's. Every so often, always early in the morning, when we were playing down close to the water, he would suddenly be right there behind us, his approach unheard over the steady lapping of the waves. Perhaps his shadow would even fall on us as he passed by.

But he never glanced at us but just kept on going, an empty dirty brown gunny sack slung over one shoulder, and held with both hands in front of him, his sunken eyes with a strange fire in them, talking to himself in an angry, high-pitched voice that sounded as if he were vainly trying to explain away some terrible mistake.

Everybody said that he kept stray dogs in his shack that he picked up over in Fort Myers, and ate them, and that was how he survived. So when he passed by us one of us would say, "Well, there he goes over to Fort Myers to pick up some more strays."

Usually around sunset we would see him shambling back along the beach, and we would see that his gunny sack was always stuffed with *something.*

One night coming back from Fort Myers rather late we saw Dutch Futch right ahead of us. Wes drove slowly up behind him, keeping him squarely in the bright glare of the headlights, and all of a sudden Missy said, "Oh, *God,* that sack is moving. There's something *alive* in that sack!" And then we could all see that she was right, something in the sack was writhing about, and Sally said, "I'm going to be sick if we don't pass by him right now," and really meant it, so Wes stepped on the gas and went on by Dutch Futch, who never had looked back at us, and didn't look at us as we went by, but just kept right on trudging along, talking to himself a mile a minute.

As for Mr. McPhee, we saw him every Friday when he passed by the house in his gleaming black Model A on his way into Fort Myers to get his week's supply of groceries. The weird thing was that he not only drove a Ford Model A but looked just like Henry Ford driving a Ford Model A. He always wore a black suit, a narrow black tie, a high collar, pince-nez eyeglasses and a derby hat. This even in the middle of July when everybody else was dying of the heat and the humidity. In the back seat would be his mother and his aunt, both of them dressed up too. Everybody said they were actually very rich. At least they were friendly, and if you waved to them as they went by they would all smile and wave back to you, and Mr. McPhee would beep his horn.

Nobody on Fort Myers Beach ever laughed at Mr. McPhee. Somehow we all seemed to sense that before it was all over it would be demonstrated to us that he was not a man to laugh at.

ONE OF THE THINGS that intrigued Wes most of all about Fort Myers Beach was the abundance of coquinas along the shoreline. Coquinas are very small bivalve mollusks having prettily colored banded or striped shells. Most of the people who lived on the beach had a "coquina screen," which was a simple flat boxlike thing with a piece of window screen for a bottom. If you submerged the coquina screen in the water as a wave came in, when the wave went back out you would have yourself a whole bunch of the coquinas that had been kicked up in the cloud of sand that had been raised by the action of the wave. And after you had gathered about a kids' sandpail full of coquinas, what you did was take them home and drop them into boiling water and presto you had a really marvelous-tasting mess of what was called coquina broth.

The more Wes thought about it the more he began to believe that somehow or other a very good bet was being missed here. Basically, he felt that there had to be a commercial market for something as delicious as coquina broth, and the problem was just how to get the product to the New York market.

Of course the thing that appealed to him most of all about the proposition was the incredible availability of the basic ingredient. The shores of the Gulf of Mexico were teeming with coquinas that were owned by no one, unless it was the federal government, which was really the same thing, wasn't it? So there were no rights to be bought from anybody, no complicated deals to be worked out, no thirty-page contracts to sign, no fine print to read. All you would need to go into commercial production was a method for large-scale screening of coquinas and a way of putting up the broth for shipment.

It so happened that there was a very small, very primitive canning plant back in the woods near our house on Connecticut Street that had gone out of operation in 1930. Wes had always been fascinated by the plant and had often gotten the keys to it from the realtor who represented the owner, who happened to be Mr. McPhee, and we would all wade through the palmettos to the plant and go inside and look at the primitive little production line, which, according to the realtor, was still in perfect working order—just give it a shot of oil here and there and fire up the donkey engine that propelled the whole shooting match and you would be, in the realtor's words, "ready for business."

The production line charmed Wes beyond words. He could just stand and look at it. Finally he sought out the man who had been the foreman of the plant when it had been in full operation and paid him to come down from Bradenton and give him an estimate on how much time and money it would actually take to put the line back into running order.

The foreman spent a whole day in the plant and said it would take him about a month to get that thing back going again, but he sure could use the work so he would do it pretty cheap. So Wes hired him on the spot and then went to the realtor and told him to draw up an agreement for a six months' lease of the plant.

Unfortunately word came down from Mr. McPhee that he wouldn't consider anything less than a full year's lease, but by then Wes was so totally committed to the coquina broth concept that he said all right and went ahead and signed for a full year.

I should say that whenever people on the island asked Wes what he had done before he came there, he always told them he had been a "promoter"—without any explanation beyond the use of the word itself. Of course no one ever pressed him to tell them exactly what he meant. I guess they thought they knew.

I think I know. I think he meant that his talent was in taking hold of a concept that struck him as having possibilities and developing it to the point where he could present it to some big-time entrepreneur who would then, he hoped, take the project on from there to the stars, while he sat back and skimmed a royalty off the top.

It wasn't that he was alone in thinking this way. The thirties seemed to be a time when everybody had some kind of a hare-brained scheme simmering on the back burner and some of the ones we heard about from people who came to Wes as a potential investor made the coquina broth thing sound marvelously clear-eyed by comparison.

There were guys who wanted Wes to invest in the concept of putting springs in tires instead of inner tubes—"Say Goodbye to Blowouts Forever!" There were perpetual motion guys. There were guys who said they could make cars run on plain air with just a few minor modifications of the standard Ford carburetor. There were guys with new religions, guys with old religions, guys with visions, guys with oil rights, guys with mineral rights, guys with dog systems, guys with horse systems, guys with twenty-five thousand acres under two feet of water in the Everglades they wanted to sell to guys in Newark and Paramus as a "vacation paradise."

WES'S PLAN was to have a very limited run of about thirty cases of coquina broth—in other words just enough to give the product a fair test in the New York market. And then, if it was successful, he would assign the rights to a major soup canner.

The foreman from Bradenton went to work with a gang of laborers getting the production line back in running order while Wes had a bunch of people out screening masses of coquinas which he cooked up in test batches in huge pots in our kitchen. At first he seemed to have a very clear idea of what he wanted as an end result of his testing, but then he began to be afraid that perhaps coquina broth by itself was not a strong enough product for the New York market, and that what he really should be producing was a highly-seasoned gumbo with rice and tomatoes and okra, and that was what he ended up taking with him to New York—in cans with a label he had had printed up in Tampa that said "Big Marco Brand Genuine Coquina Gumbo."

He was in New York a long time, and when he came back he looked pretty glum and said that his mistake had been switching from the broth to the gumbo. At any rate for a long time we never had to wonder what we were going to have for lunch around our house because it was always Big Marco Brand Genuine Coquina Gumbo.

Of course he still had the remaining time of the year's lease on the canning factory, and in an attempt to save a total loss he got in touch with a man in Punta Gorda who had come to him with a theory that with the right kind of promotion you could get the American public to think of smoked snake meat as a "great delicacy," just as he said they did in the Far East.

This man had his own smokehouses in Punta Gorda all ready to go and he knew some snake men who could bring in a couple of hundred rattlers a week if the demand was there.

So Wes brought his foreman back from Bradenton and produced several cases of canned smoked rattlesnake meat under the label "Big Marco Brand Genuine Smoked Rattlesnake Meat," even though everybody he mentioned the idea to on the island promptly turned green.

He took his samples to New York saying that he was going to promote the product in the New York market with the slogan, "It Tastes Just Like Chicken." This time he wasn't gone very long and when he came back he said the trouble was that everybody said if it tastes just like chicken why not buy chicken, which was a hell of a lot cheaper?

The only good thing to come of it was that he never tried to get us to eat smoked snake meat for lunch. The left-over cans stayed on the back porch for a long time and then, when the labels had all peeled off from the rain and some of the cans had developed suspicious-looking bulges, he had Pernell come with a truck and bury them over on the bay side of the island right next to the Calusa Indian mound.

After that Wes closed down the canning plant and life returned to normal, meaning that he and Missy went back to working on their tans and their diets and their night fishing and their partying, and coincidentally, it was about then that we began to have the feeling that civilization had advanced as far as it ever would on Fort Myers Beach, and that, actually, the tide had started to turn the other way and that soon nature would begin to reclaim its lost ground all over the island.

The main reason for this was that all at once several families that had lived on the island for a long time had to leave. Wes said the Depression had caught up with them. Their pension funds had dried up. They would have to go where there was work. Some of them went back north, some to other parts of Florida, Miami or Tampa.

Anyhow we were more isolated than ever up at Connecticut Street because most of the families that left had lived in the houses nearest us. That didn't bother Wes and Missy too much. The truth was that those families with their financial problems had brought the whiff of the bitter realities of 1935 too close. Now the houses where they had lived stood empty and silent and their water pumps no longer went tic-tic-tic. Soon they would be completely forgotten and after a while the island would have it all back.

There was very little talk of the future. In fact the feeling was that there was no future, that we had all found our destinies on Fort Myers Beach, and that we would never change, and the island would never change, and we would all stay there forever.

و

BUT BY THE WINTER of 1936 the island had changed in ways we would never have imagined possible.

It happened so slowly at first that we really didn't notice anything until one day when Missy said, "I've never seen so many cars on the beach as there were last weekend. Down by the Gulf Shore Inn it looked like one great big parking lot."

Not long after that a roadbuilding crew came to the island and laid down a coat of asphalt on the dirt road behind the row of houses, and they didn't stop there. When they came to Connecticut Street instead of stopping where the old road ended they just kept on going and put in an asphalt road for about half a mile behind the high sand dunes to the south of us.

And not long after that some very rich people from Long Island bought some of the land among the sand dunes from Mr. McPhee and built a house there, and we watched the cars and trucks going by our house all the time, and saw the rich people, who always looked excited, and paid no attention to us whatsoever.

Then more rich people came—they were all connected somehow, according to Wes—and built more houses along the dunes.

These houses were not anything like the original ones on the island. They were "Modern" looking with lots of heavy beams and glass, and after each house was finished it was "landscaped." And the people who lived in them didn't fraternize much with the local people except in a patronizing way. They just stuck among themselves and made a speedway out of the back road as they continually roared back and forth in their expensive cars.

At the same time more and more people from the mainland began coming over to the beach on the weekends, and brought with them noise and trash and hot dog stands, and they cruised up and down the pure white sand of the beach so fast that mothers had to keep a close eye on their children if they didn't want them run over.

Then Mr. Hert, who owned the house on Connecticut Street, said he had decided to wire the house for electricity after all, because he had to keep his property "up with the times," and told us he wanted us to move out when our lease was up so he could get the work done.

Wes and Missy didn't even wait for the lease to expire. They started looking around and rented us a house in Venice, a town about twenty miles south of Sarasota. Venice was totally dominated by the winter quarters of KMI, the Kentucky Military Institute, whose immense barracks faced the little one-block "business section" of the town across the broad, sandy parade ground where the cadets drilled Sunday afternoons in full dress uniform before an audience of half a dozen town kids and a couple of dogs with nothing else to do.

Venice was a very different thing from Fort Myers Beach. It was a real twenties-style Florida resort. In other words it was one of those towns where there were only a couple of hundred year-round residents and where most of the houses were large and splendid and were owned by rich Northerners who occupied them during the height of the season only, roughly from Christmas to George Washington's birthday. Once they got back into their cars and went home and their servants had closed their houses up and gotten on the train and followed them, the town fell asleep and didn't wake up again until about Armistice Day.

It was also one of those twenties-style Florida towns which had had big plans for itself back in the great days of the Boom. You could tell because sidewalks and concrete-paved streets with silver-painted lampposts extended far out into the forest of scrub pine that enclosed it. In summer hot breezes blew along those desolate thoroughfares where the tar between the cracks in the sidewalks bubbled and glistened and clumps of weeds were coming up in the gutters and in every little fissure in the concrete of the streets.

I'm pretty sure it was in Venice where it first began to sneak in on Wes what a really long time he had ahead of him and what work it was going to turn out to be to spend it doing nothing, because it was then that he and Missy began going up to Ybor City in Tampa to spend whole days sitting around in what they called "boardrooms," big rooms in which the walls were covered with blackboards where men scurried around writing up in different colored chalk all the information about all the horses that were running at all the tracks around the country, and where you could get down a bet for as little as twenty-five cents or as much as you wanted.

Then practically all they talked about was horses and jockeys and *mud* and times for a mile and six furlongs and times for a mile and a sixteenth and the *Racing Form* and equivalent odds and *systems,* and about all the fascinating people they met hanging around the Columbia Restaurant.

They always seemed very excited then, so different from the way they had been in Fort Myers Beach, where every day had been the same. But I guess hysteria was more like what it really was. They had a whole new life, new friends, and were risking huge amounts of money almost every day. And losing it most of the time, of course—but always thinking they would make a really big killing on a long shot sooner or later.

One of the people they met in the boardrooms was a man named Cathcart. For a couple of weeks they talked about him all the time, and then one night when they came back from Tampa they brought him with them and in the morning there he was at the breakfast table, and Wes and Missy told Sally and Marcus and me that "Mr. Cathcart" was going to be staying with us for a while and to be very nice to him.

It was clear from the beginning that in Mr. Cathcart the two principal weaknesses that Missy and Wes shared had come together—a rampaging Lord and Lady Bountiful complex and their unswerving belief that there actually could be such a thing on earth as an infallible system for beating the horses.

Cathcart was a hard man to be nice to. He was always in a rotten mood, smoked cheap cigars in the house, complained all the time about everything, wore the same baggy brown gravy-stained suit and scuffed shoes every day, started drinking Wes's booze around ten-thirty in the morning and stayed more or less drunk the whole rest of the day and night, never said thank you for anything and generally treated all of us as if we should feel honored to have him there. He also looked as if he was going to die on us any minute.

After he had been living with us for a few days, Wes took Marcus and Sally and me aside and told us in the most respectful tones I had ever heard him use about anyone that Mr. Cathcart was "probably the most dangerous man in the world"—because after years and years of research he had finally worked out an infallible system for the horses, and was about to go down to Miami and break Hialeah Park.

The big debate going on was whether Wes and Missy should capitalize the venture, to the tune of about twenty-five thousand dollars. The main problem was that with Cathcart's system you had to have the patience and guts and cash reserves to be willing to lose maybe a couple of hundred dollars a day for a week, or even two weeks, and still have absolute faith that the system would *take hold* and start paying off.

They really believed in Cathcart, but one day he got mad and took the bus to Miami. They had hemmed and hawed too long about how they were going to raise the twenty-five thousand and he had decided to cut them out of the deal completely.

Wes never forgot Cathcart, never doubted for a minute that he really had been the most dangerous man in the world, or that he had found a backer with a little more faith in Miami and that together they had won a fortune at Hialeah, and he still talked about him years afterward, as if he had seen Our Savior's shining face on the Damascus road one day but had just passed Him by.

It was also in Ybor City that he started hearing about a young Cuban heavyweight by the name of Chino Alvarez who was killing everybody they put in the ring with him.

Wes watched him fight a couple of times and thought this was the fighter he had been looking for all his life, the first fighter he had ever come across he really felt had a chance to go all the way. So he bought up his contract and believed he owned an authentic heavyweight contender.

Chino Alvarez was a good fighter. He was very fast and very strong and had a right-hand punch like a kick from a mule. But something funny happened to him on the way to the heavyweight championship.

He got spoiled rotten.

Wes wasn't satisfied with just owning him. He had to give him the best of everything. He got the best manager money could buy, the best trainer money could buy, the best cut man money could buy, but that wasn't enough.

He bought him the best food money could buy and the best drink money could buy, and that still wasn't enough. He took him out of the crappy rooming house where he had been living and put him into a very nice apartment, and took him out of the weird clothes he was wearing and put him into beautiful tailor-made suits and silk shirts.

Chino fought a total of fifteen fights for Wes. I saw most of them either at the National Guard Armory in Sarasota or at the Garden Arena in Tampa. The first seven or eight were smashing first- or second- or third-round victories. But after that the fact that he was getting fat as a pig and wasn't training as hard as he used to started taking something away from him. He could still punch but he couldn't move. His eleventh fight was with a ferocious black from Philadelphia who lost the fight but was the first man who had ever put Chino on the canvas for an eight count. In his twelfth fight Chino got cut over both eyes, and that made him a different fighter because from then on it seemed as if he started concentrating more on protecting his face than on winning the fight. In his fifteenth start he got the life beaten out of him by a fighter who wouldn't have been allowed into the ring with him when he was at the top of his form. The fight went the distance and when it was over Chino was bleeding from the nose and mouth and both his eyes were practically shut, and he had to have something like thirty stitches over his eyes, and the next day when we went to see him in the hospital his head was the size of a basketball, and he said he was pissing blood, and after that he never got into a ring again.

❧

BY THE SUMMER of 1938 Wes and Missy had gotten bored to death with Venice and Tampa and Sarasota—in fact, with the entire west coast of Florida. Lately, they had been spending a lot of time in Miami and Miami Beach, and loved it over there, where there was always plenty of excitement, and they could go to Hialeah and Tropical Park. So, right after school let out in Venice, they put our furniture in storage and we all piled into the brand new royal blue twelve-cylinder convertible Packard touring car Wes had recently bought and headed for Miami, on the Tamiami Trail.

First, we went down to Punta Gorda, HOME OF THE FIGHTING SILVER KING! as the big sign that was painted on the railway trestle that spanned Charlotte Harbor proclaimed, and continuing south crossed the marvelously familiar Caloosahatchee River over the long bridge at Fort Myers. Then we went on down through Estero and Bonita Springs to Naples, which was a couple of gas stations and a general store at the edge of what the Seminoles called the Pa-hay-okee, the "River of Grass," and we called the Everglades.

From that point on, for the next hundred miles, we drove through some of the most beautiful and desolate scenery on earth, where the vistas were so long that you could see from one end of the horizon to the other, except when the view was interrupted by the dense hammocks of cabbage palms that stood like islands in the river of grass, and there was no evidence of the hand of man but the narrow road itself and the little signs nailed to stakes and tree trunks by the side of the road that advertised "666," a cold preparation that was very popular in those days, and the inevitable Burma Shave signs with their corny lines of doggerel that came at intervals of about half a mile for ten miles, and the Seminole Indian villages, with the Indians in their colorful costumes watching with their dark eyes as we went by, standing out there under the signs that said ALLIGATOR WRESTLING ON THE HOUR, and behind them the open-air thatched "chickees" they lived in that looked charming from a distance but up close turned out to be dirty and muddy, and overrun with chickens and cockroaches.

Ahead of us the road rippled in the heat, and now and then far off in the distance we saw a great dark mass floating on the ripples like a mirage, which, as we came closer, turned out to be a heap of twenty or thirty turkey buzzards feasting on a luckless cow that had been hit by a car during the night. Wes had to start blowing his horn at them from a long way off to get them to leave the carcass. Some of them made it into the air before we arrived, but others were so bloated that although they ran along the ground trying their best to get up flying speed it didn't work, and they finally gave up, and came to a stop, and just watched us sullenly as we went by.

About halfway across the Everglades was a gas station with a lunchroom attached called Weaver's. Out there, miles from civilization in any direction, the silence was eerie. The only sounds we heard were the calls of birds, the wind, and the ding-ding of the gas pump as Wes got a fill-up. We had sandwiches and Cokes in the lunchroom, and then we all went and gawked at the "wildlife exhibits," which consisted of a moth-eaten black bear, a moth-eaten yellow-eyed Florida panther and three moth-eaten raccoons, none of them looking the least bit happy to be there.

Then, back into the Packard and on to Miami.

WES RENTED an apartment at the Beachview Apartments, down at the very south end of the section of Miami Beach that is known as South Beach. The Beachview didn't actually have a view of the beach. It had a view of the Italian restaurant right across the street. But Wes and Missy were in heaven. Not only did they have two horse tracks to go to, there was a dog track only a couple of blocks away from the doorstep of the Beachview.

Also, there was a boardroom right next to the beach itself, where they could sit around in their bathing suits all day drinking beer and partaking of the free lunch, while they got down fifty-cent bets at horse tracks all over the country—a far cry from the formality of the horse rooms in Tampa. Whenever they felt like it they could cool off by throwing themselves in the ocean, and then come back all refreshed and ready to lose even more money. But perhaps the best part of living in South Beach, from Wes's point of view, was that there was a gym down there where fighters worked out, and pretty soon he began talking again of looking for a good young heavyweight.

South Beach was heaven for Marcus and me too, because we also had gotten bored to death with Venice and Tampa and Sarasota and the entire west coast of Florida. Here, we were in the midst of a fascinating city that was full of trolley cars and art deco architecture, and we had the Atlantic Ocean, which was so much more fun than the warm bathtub of the Gulf of Mexico.

We spent most of our days out on the beach, swimming and building sand castles, and stealing glances at the immense mural that was painted on the side of the South Beach Pier, which showed naked laughing female dancers hiding provocatively behind colored balloons, under a sign that said in huge letters MINSKY'S BURLESQUE.

Either that, or we went down to the Government Cut, a deep channel between two long piles of rocks that protruded into the ocean, where the big ships coming from or bound for New York, New Orleans or Havana went by. When the ships passed through the Government Cut they sucked up the water behind them, and it was possible for us to jump down onto the clean yellow sand at the base of the rocks and stand there for about a second and a half before the following wave came crashing toward us along the rocks, and would have killed us if our timing had been even slightly off.

WE STAYED all summer at the Beachview, but in the fall Missy, who was a Presbyterian herself but for some strange reason felt very strongly that she wanted her children to be exposed to alternate religions, packed Sally and Marcus and me off to a dot on the map of central Florida called San Antonio, where standing on the top of a hill was a Catholic girls' school called Holy Name Academy for Sally, and, across the road, a Catholic boys' school called St. Benedict's Prep for Marcus and me.

Later that fall Wes and Missy rented an apartment in Dade City, another dot on the map of central Florida, about seven miles from San Antonio, so they could be close to us.

Of course I was still wetting my bed every night when we went to St. Benedict's, but the sister in charge of the twenty little boys, aged about nine to thirteen, was a beautiful novice by the name of Sister Roseanna, who turned out to be amazingly kind and sympathetic and understanding, and forbad any of the boys either to tease me or complain about the stink in our dorm.

It was while I was at St. Benedict's that I began fainting fairly regularly, usually during morning Mass. Marcus and I had to go to Mass even if we weren't Catholics. That was part of the deal, and I would be sitting there, or kneeling there, and all of a sudden just topple over. This caused much consternation among the sisters, most of whom suspected that I was faking it.

We St. Benedict's boys went to Mass in the Holy Name chapel, and every morning at a certain time a train went puffing, puffing, puffing past on the far side of the lake at the bottom of the hill. I watched for the train every morning. It gave one plaintive whistle, and then disappeared among the trees, and directly after that the Holy Name girls, in their long navy-blue skirts and middies, went and took Communion, followed by the St. Benedict's boys, and I sat there on my bench, watching everything and secretly longing to become a part of the mystery.

In March 1939 I entered my first art contest. It was the March Contest in the *Young Catholic Messenger*. I drew some sort of a little picture, and Sister Roseanna sent it in for me, and one day about a month later she came running onto the playground, terribly excited, and told me that I had won an *Honorable Mention Award!* The Honorable Mention Award turned out to be a sheet of slick paper on which there was a portrait of Pope Pius XII. On one side of his face it said, "Our Holy Father, Pius XII." On the other side of his face it said, "Elected March 2, 1939." And then, below all that, "Honorable Mention, March Contest, 1939, *Young Catholic Messenger.*"

Of course the picture wasn't autographed or anything like that. There was no "To Doug, all the best, your friend Eugenio," but the more I stared at those dark eyes behind those steel-rimmed glasses, the more they seemed to be saying something to me, and what I was pretty sure they were saying was that He wanted me to become a Roman Catholic.

Once this obsession really took hold the fainting during Mass began to happen with alarming frequency, and finally I was excused altogether from having to kneel during Mass. Then one day I was hanging around alone out in front of St. Benedict's Prep, and I found myself mysteriously drawn to the little shrine to the Virgin Mary where all the Catholic boys were supposed to kneel down and cross themselves and say a Hail Mary at least once a day. I went over to the shrine and knelt down, crossed myself and opened my mouth to say a Hail Mary, but not a word came out. I jumped up, horrified, but the minute I started really thinking about it, I realized that this was all part of the Sign. I went and looked at my picture of Pius XII one more time and then found Sister Roseanna and told her I wanted to become a Catholic.

She was very sweet about it, and said she wanted me to go and tell Sister Theresa how I felt. Sister Theresa, in the order of things at Holy Name–St. Benedict's, was second in command to the Mother Superior herself. When I told her why I had come to see her, she smiled gently and said, "This is something you will have to discuss with your mother and father."

This response was not anything like what I had expected. I had truly thought they would be overjoyed at having a convert, especially one who had gotten an Honorable Mention in the March Contest of the *Young Catholic Messenger*.

But the next time Wes and Missy came over to see us, I took her aside and told her what was on my mind.

She said, "Dougie, when you're eighteen I promise you you can be anything you want to be and do anything you want to do, but I don't want to hear another word about this until then."

As if by magic, with those words, the obsession with becoming a Catholic was over, the fainting stopped, and I went back to practicing the Palmer Handwriting Method, playing softball with Sister Roseanna and the other boys and learning how to rollerskate.

IN THE SUMMER of 1939 we returned to South Beach, and lived in an apartment house on Ocean Drive called The Amsterdam Palace, which, unlike the Beachview, actually did have a view of the beach. During that summer, every evening around six o'clock, a newsboy hurried along the sidewalk below our front windows with the "pink sheet" of the Miami *Daily News*, yelling about Hitler, Danzig and the Polish Corridor, and the grownups, who had seemed so relieved back in 1938, after Munich, now were looking worried again, and kept asking each other, "Well, what do you think will happen?"

By the time the war actually broke out in September, we had moved to a house in the southwest section of Miami. Sally was going to Miami High and Marcus and I to Shenandoah Junior High. Now and then that fall, on the radio, a voice would say, "And now the chancellor of Germany, Adolf Hitler," and we would hear a rasping voice, with a voice-over translation that always began, "The Fuehrer has said—"

But Miami, like Fort Myers Beach, baking there in the tropical sun, was so remote from the real world that no one could stay worried very long, and after the invasion of Poland by Germany and the Soviet Union was completed, everyone seemed to breathe easier once again, feeling that perhaps Hitler would be satisfied now, with a Third Reich that had devoured all of Austria and Czechoslovakia and half of Poland.

But after the quiet winter of the "phony war," with the British and French holed up in the Maginot Line and the Germans holed up in the Siegfried Line, there was the surprise invasion of Denmark and Norway in April, and in May the Germans brought the blitzkrieg to Luxembourg, Belgium and the Low Countries and outflanked the Maginot Line. Then there was Dunkirk in late May, and soon after that, on June twenty-second, the fall of France, and, finally, even Miamians started worrying.

At Shenandoah Junior High all the little boys were making models of Spitfires and Hawker Hurricanes and talking about barrage balloons and the "Battle of Britain." But the big news as far as I was concerned was that all of a sudden, without any apparent explanation, I had stopped wetting my bed, and was the happiest boy on earth.

WHEN PEARL HARBOR finally happened, Miami practically dropped dead. Suddenly the country had a war to win, and tourism was a thing of the past. The hotels on Miami Beach all stood empty for a while, but the government quickly realized that Miami Beach, with its perfect year-round climate, would be an ideal place to train soldiers, and soon all of the hotels on the beach were filled up with Air Corps officers in training.

In early 1942 we moved from the house in the southwest section of Miami to a house in Surfside, a village at the northern extremity of Miami Beach, where at that time there was nothing but a Gulf station, a drugstore and a few houses. There, the Gulf Stream was only a few miles offshore, and when you stood out on the beach you often saw convoys stretching in an almost unbroken line all the way across the horizon, and at night we heard gunfire and saw the orange flames from torpedoed ships lighting up the sky. In the morning the ships that had been hit the night before drifted slowly northward before they finally slipped below the surface and joined all the other ships in the enormous graveyard of ships the U-boats were making of the bottom of the Gulf Stream.

We stayed in Surfside all through the summer of 1942, when the U-boat campaign was at its worst, and that fall we moved to the pink house beside the bay in Coconut Grove.

&

WRITING MY NOVEL was painful enough, but to make matters much worse when I had been at it for a while it got so that I couldn't sit down at my typewriter without a sick feeling coming over me which was the result of my fear about what was going to happen when I finished the first hundred pages. That was my goal, a hundred pages, and then it went into an envelope and was sent to a publisher in New York right away, before I could have any second thoughts about it and started rewriting or lost my nerve altogether and just decided to forget all about sending it anywhere.

Of course the sick feeling came from the realization that I was counting so much on something happening that obviously had no chance of happening at all.

I could see the whole sequence so clearly, and it was always exactly the same. Putting the hundred pages in an envelope, addressing the envelope, enclosing a stamped and self-addressed envelope, mailing the damn thing. Then the damn thing arriving in New York. Where? I had no idea where I would actually send it. But anyway it would arrive at some publishing house and somebody there would open the manila envelope, take out the hundred pages, light a cigaret, lean back, stare at the title page a minute, read page one . . .

But then what?

My cheeks would start to burn. The person, the reader, had stopped reading and was just sitting there amazed that anyone could have had the gall to send such an amateurish manuscript to a first-class publisher. A few more pages would be dutifully and distastefully skimmed, then the hundred pages would be jammed into the SASE along with a form rejection and as far as he was concerned that would be, thank God, the end of it.

And then what?

I could see the manila envelope waiting for me one day when I got home from work, but that was as far as I could stand to go with it. The envelope always remained unopened, the form rejection unread—except in my dreams. There the letter was read, over and over again, and it just said that they thanked me very much for having given them the opportunity to read my manuscript but they regretted to say they found it not suitable for publication at this time.

Anyway, I kept pushing on with it. Sometimes I only wrote one sentence in a whole evening, but then there would be weekends when I wrote two or three pages and it would sound pretty good and for a minute or two I would think maybe this wasn't really so hopeless after all, and that was one of the things that kept me going.

The other thing was that my writing was about the only way I had of escaping from the horror of the situation of our house.

Downstairs in the front bedroom Missy was lying there babbling and drooling and occasionally letting out a scream that would stop your heart cold.

Back in the kitchen Wes was sitting at the kitchen table in his undershorts trying to pass out on one slug after another of the absolute cheapest whisky money could buy.

The house where this was going on was the pink one, with blue trim, that stood right beside Biscayne Bay in Coconut Grove. Our front lawn sloped down to a seawall where a little Nassau dinghy was tied up to the dock. From my upstairs bedroom window I could see Key Biscayne in the distance and had a view of the entire lower end of the bay. At night it was either moonlight on the water and channel lights blinking, or in the hurricane season great storms sweeping in across the bay, wind lashing the palm trees and waves breaking over the seawall.

In this rather idyllic setting we three lived almost completely out of touch with each other. (Marcus had joined the Marines. Sally had gotten married and lived in California.) Wes spoke to me only when it was necessary to convey something that had to be said. The rest of the time he acted as if I weren't even there. The reasons for his doing this were that, first of all, he had told me that this had happened to Missy because I had disappointed her too often, particularly the last time. He said the shock of my having been expelled from Harvard had been too much for her. I kept trying to tell myself that surely brain tumors don't happen like that. But in my heart I guess I believed him anyway.

Then there was the fact that I refused to go in and see Missy. I just wouldn't do it, and that made Wes furious. In the very beginning I had gone in and seen her, but she had had lucid moments then and at least knew who you were. But when it got too horrible I simply couldn't bring myself to enter that room anymore. Wes said I was a mean little bastard, but I didn't care. He said he went in there all the time himself and talked to her and he knew that she heard him and it did her a lot of good. I didn't believe a word of it. I knew she wasn't aware of one damn thing that was happening. The truth was that as far as I was concerned she had died and gone to heaven and that thing lying in there in her room was nothing but a cruel insult to her memory.

Our daily routine was that I got up very early and took the bus to the yard in the center of Coconut Grove where the big red Midland trucks were parked, and at exactly eight o'clock we piled into the trucks and drove down south to the construction site where we piled out and started digging holes in the coral rock.

In the meantime Wes would have slept late because he would have been at the West Flagler Kennel Club the night before, and then would have stayed up until all hours figuring the horses for the next day.

Around noon he put on his powder-blue, gold and white uniform and took the bus out to Tropical Park, where he had gotten a job as a Club House usher.

The job wasn't for the money, which was nothing. It was for the possibility of picking up hot tips from jockeys, trainers, owners and hot walkers. In other words what was happening was that Wes, faced with huge bills for Missy's sickness, was kidding himself that he could get his hands on the money he needed to pay Missy's doctor's bills and the nurses' salaries and the bills for all the tubes and the needles and the Demerol by playing the dogs every night and the horses every day. But what was actually happening was that he was simply losing all the money that still came to him with unfailing regularity from the estate of his first wife. The fact was that if he had just worked carefully with the income he had he could have kept up with all the bills and the rent and everything else without too much trouble.

But of course there was more to it than that. I understand that now more than ever he needed the distraction and the false hopes and the day-to-day excitement that came from heavy gambling, just as he had to have someone to blame everything on. So he kept throwing his money down the ratholes of Hialeah and Tropical and West Flagler even if it meant that he couldn't afford a car anymore and had to put on his comic-opera uniform every day and we had to make out on a sort of dog food diet of corned beef hash and what they called in the army shit-on-a-shingle.

I knew he was cracking up. All those years of just hanging around the house all the time had prepared him for nothing. Missy had always been the financial wizard of the organization—meaning basically that she was the one who kited the checks when they got overextended. Hell, *he* didn't even know how to do that.

So there we were. Me plugging away at "Welcome Stamp Collectors" upstairs, Missy in her room taking her eternity to die, and Wes sitting in the kitchen in his undershorts in the glare of the overhead light pouring himself another shot of rye.

ಬ

THE NIGHT I FINALLY finished the first hundred pages of "Welcome Stamp Collectors" I was happy. But the next night when I read the whole thing through for the first time I didn't feel too well—the sick feeling but much worse than usual. The stuff just didn't sound so hot.

But I stuck to my promise to myself that I would send the book away as soon as I had finished these hundred pages, and the next morning I went to the Miami Public Library and asked for a book that had a list of New York publishers in it. With the book I went off to a table in a remote corner of the library and started looking for the name of a publisher that appealed to me. The trouble was I knew nothing about publishers. How was one different from another? In what way would one be better for me than another?

Finally I came to a name that rang more bells than most of the others I had come across so far. For one thing it had a famous logo that you saw all the time in ads for books. I wrote down the address and headed for home, stopping off on the way to buy two manila envelopes. At home I addressed the envelopes and then went straight to the post office in Coconut Grove and sent the thing off.

It was a Saturday and I had nothing to do for the rest of the day, so I just moped around in the Grove for a while and then went home and crapped out on the bed and started doing what I was going to be doing practically exclusively from then on, worrying about my book.

I actually hadn't the faintest idea what happened to a book when it arrived in the mail at a publishing house, but I was realistic enough to be aware that a lot of manuscripts came in the mail every day and that many of them came from writers who had already been published and that those manuscripts went on the top of the pile and the ones like mine, from people they had never heard of, went on the bottom. So obviously there was no way of knowing how long it would take to hear about my book. It could be a month. It could be three months.

I had resolved to keep right on working on my book after I sent it in, hoping that I might have two or three more chapters written by the time I heard from the publisher. But when I tried to go back to my typewriter nothing came and I was glad when that weekend was over and I could go back to breaking rock instead of sitting there in my room feeling guilty because I couldn't push ahead with my story.

The worst part of the waiting was the way I kept inventing little stories about how it would be if the publisher accepted my book. The thing that I wanted most of all to come of it was that I would be able to go back to Harvard, and I could see myself swaggering into University Hall with a contract for "Welcome Stamp Collectors" in my hand. How impressed they would be! And not only Harvard! Everybody! All my friends from St. Mark's. *St. Mark's* itself! Even the Boston debutantes whose parties at The Country Club I had crashed so many times!

Of course for every happy vision there was a correspondingly unhappy one, in which my book was rejected. If that happened I thought my life was as good as over, because there would be nothing ahead of me but more jobs just like the one I had now.

It took about a week and a half for the pessimistic visions to become the only visions. I told myself I was just being realistic. After all, here I was, a little nineteen-year-old jerk down in Miami who had never even had a short story published in the St. Mark's *Lion,* and I expected a major publisher to be interested in some farfetched story about a hotel in Florida in the thirties? This was long before Françoise Sagan, after all, and you still didn't hear too often about very young people publishing first novels. Therefore I thought of myself as being in competition with men who were all at least forty-six years old and looked like J. P. Marquand and had eleven very long and very successful novels under their belts.

As it turned out I waited thirty-seven days, and then I came home from work one afternoon and there was a letter bearing the famous logo of the publisher I had sent my hundred pages to waiting for me on the table in the hallway.

I took it up to my room and didn't open it immediately but just sat on the bed and looked at it for a little while—at the envelope, the logo and the name, my own name beautifully typed, the postmark with a plug for one of the publisher's hot new books—and when I did open it I did it very carefully, with a knife.

First of all I saw that it was a real letter, and skipping down I saw that it was signed by a woman editor by the name of Jean Luft. Then I read the letter, which was in three paragraphs, and what the editor had to say was that my novel had had several very enthusiastic readings, besides her own, and that while they were not prepared to offer me a contract at this time they wanted me to know that my story, my setting and my characters had charmed them and they were looking forward to seeing this manuscript again when I had gone a little further with it.

I paced up and down in my room, threw myself on the bed and lay there for a minute, then jumped up and paced some more, pausing occasionally to read the letter again.

Later on, when Wes and I were eating our dog food at the kitchen table, he asked me about the letter. Of course he knew that I had been working on a book and that I had sent it in. So I went and got it and showed it to him.

Both the race tracks were closed at the time so he was out of work and had nothing to do but hang around the house all day and brood about everything.

"That's okay," he said when he had finished reading the letter. "But if they liked it so much why didn't they put their money where their mouth is?"

"Because they have to see more of it," I said.

"That's what I mean," he said. "It makes it sound as if they still have their doubts about whether you really can write."

"I think I can," I said.

"Have you gone any further with it since you sent this part in?"

"Oh, a couple of chapters," I said.

Which was a lie. I hadn't written one sentence in those thirty-seven days. I could see that Wes wasn't really too happy about this success of mine. He had never even asked me what my book was about and he still didn't. I knew he was cracking up but it was almost impossible for me to talk to him at all when it was very obvious how bitter he felt about me. Anyhow it was hard to be sorry for him when I felt that I was myself in just about as bad shape as he was.

I had no social life at all. It used to be that the girls in the neighborhood came to our house all the time to go sailing in the Nassau dinghy, but they had all heard about Missy so they were reluctant to come around any more. One time one of them did come over on a Saturday and I took her for a sail over to Cape Florida, but when we got back to the house and were sitting around having a Coke, Missy let out a shriek that made the girl turn white, and of course she never wanted to come there again. And I was just as glad because it was a pain in the ass trying to pretend you were having a good time under those circumstances.

I had no male friends either, having lost touch with the boys I had gone to school with in Miami after I had gone away to St. Mark's. So the only people I really had much contact with were the guys I worked with on the line gang.

The linemen were very hard men. They had been working on line gangs all over the South most of their lives, moving around constantly, following the work wherever it took them.

They had three main subjects of conversation. The first was always whether the local of the International Brotherhood of Electrical Workers that we belonged to was going to be able to get us the raise in our hourly wage it was demanding from Florida Power & Light without our having to go out on strike again. We had struck Florida Power & Light unsuccessfully for higher wages three times since I had gone to work for Midland Constructors, the first time for a little over six weeks, the second for three months and the third for eighteen days, and nobody wanted to have to go out again, since that meant having to live exclusively on unemployment compensation, which in those days amounted to twenty-one dollars a week. Still, the linemen were working at one of the most dangerous as well as physically and mentally demanding jobs known to man for only two dollars and fifty cents an hour, which even in 1948 was a very low wage for any kind of skilled work.

Their second main subject of conversation was fighting. You had to be very careful how you spoke to them because they were easily offended, and the way they fought was with knives. After work on Fridays they went to Stone's Bar on West Flagler Street in Miami, which was a linemen's bar, and that was where most of their fighting took place. On the other hand, what was good about them was that if you didn't challenge them they were very considerate and polite and in general good guys and very easy to get along with.

Their third main subject of conversation was the size of their cocks. "This goddam thing is a solid ten inches," they would say. "That's *limp*. I don't know what it is hard, but I've never known the woman yet who could take it all." Or, "When she reached under the table and happened to touch the goddam thing, she said, 'Is that a foot?' and I said, 'No, ma'am, but it's about eleven inches.'"

The linemen were also fond of playing practical jokes on new men who were hired on as "grunts"—the lowest form of life in their view—to initiate them into life on a line gang. A particular favorite was to wire the truck to the ignition switch, the point being that it was a tradition that the men on a line gang always pissed against the side of the truck. What they did was open the side door of the truck to block the view and then fired away at a point just back of the running board. After a new man had been on a line gang for a while and had gotten used to pissing on the truck just like everybody else, one day one of the linemen would wire up the body of the truck to the ignition switch, and then the next time the new man came over to take a piss, the truck driver, who was supposedly sitting up in the cab innocently working on his time sheets, would turn the key in the ignition, which would make the whole truck as hot as a pistol so the instant the new man's piss hit the truck he would, in effect, be grounding the truck and the current would run right up his stream and give him a terrific kick in the balls.

After you had been a grunt on a line gang for a while you were expected to want to apply to the union local for your apprentice card and start learning to climb a pole so you could eventually become a full-fledged journeyman lineman. I had a fear of heights and the few times I put on a pair of hooks and a lineman's belt and tried to climb my knees started quivering when I was only a few feet off the ground and I came right back down. In order to make up for this obvious cowardice I volunteered to be the demolitions expert on our line gang, which meant having to rig up the dynamite charges we had to use when we came to a place along the road where we ran into a shelf of solid coral rock and our picks and mattocks and shovels and digging bars were absolutely useless. An apprentice on another line gang gave me the short course in how to prepare a dynamite charge, all the time telling me stories about the nice guys he had known back in Georgia and Carolina who had blown themselves to bits when they had made a little slip-up somewhere.

All you needed was three or four sticks of dynamite, a percussion cap, a flashlight battery and a long spool of the braided red and gold wire that was used to set off the charge. The important thing was to keep the dynamite and the percussion caps widely separated from each other until you began working on a charge. You didn't have to worry about the dynamite blowing up because it was very stable and it would have taken a hell of a jolt to make it go off on its own. But the percussion caps were frighteningly sensitive and when you handled them you were always afraid that one of them was going to blow your hands off.

You made a long slit in one of the sticks of dynamite, then attached the wire to a percussion cap and inserted the cap into the slit. Then you wired all the sticks of dynamite together, lowered the charge into a small deep hole you would already have bored into the rock with an auger and paid out the wire on the spool to a safe distance. After that you put a thick rope mat over the hole, went out to the end of the wire and touched the two bare tips to your flashlight battery, and there was a muffled crump, a slight moving of the earth and the mat jumped a foot or so and that was that, until I had to blow out the next level of solid rock.

The great advantage to me in being the demolitions expert was that the linemen themselves didn't like to handle dynamite, so although they knew I was afraid to climb poles I was known as a guy who at least had the balls to fuck around with explosives and that sort of evened it all out.

But basically the work we were doing was so monotonous and stupid and hard that we felt more like a chain gang than a line gang. We got off the trucks every morning and looked down the road ahead, which was a straight line of new asphalt that already, even early in the morning, shimmered in the heat as it stretched away toward the horizon. On either side of the road was a thirty-yard-wide strip of bare white coral rock, which was the power company's right-of-way. First we had gone along the whole length of the road and cut down the pine trees and burned off the palmettos and all the rest of the ground cover. Then we had started digging our holes, about fifty yards apart, following the perfectly straight line of the road. The holes were eight feet deep and just big enough around so the man in the hole had enough room to swing his mattock.

When we had dug down the eight feet a truck came with a brand-new pole that was still slick with fresh creosote and we set up the A-frame on the back of our truck and stuck the pole in the ground, festooned with ropes like a maypole, and then we all pulled on the ropes while the foreman went off at a distance and with his pocket watch dangling at the end of its chain sighted in the pole to the vertical position and then we pounded broken pieces of rock into the hole all around the pole until that pole was as straight and firm in the ground as it had been before they had gone into the forest and cut it down.

Then we picked up all our tools and moved down the road to the place where a supervisor had hammered a sharp stick into the rock to tell us where to start the next hole, leaving the linemen to go up the pole we had just set and bolt in place the crossarms and hang onto them the insulators and all the other fittings that would be used to hang the wires when it came time to sag in the new lines.

It might take a whole day for three or four of us to dig an eight-foot hole, or it might take two or three, depending on how hard the rock was that we had to break up. The farther you went down in a hole the more you felt the heat of the day, because down there no breeze ever cooled your sweat, and as the sun came straight up above you towards noon of course there were no trees left to give you any shade, and before long your arms and back and chest and even your face were covered with a thin white paste that was made of the coral rock dust mixed with your sweat.

Each man stayed in the hole for about half an hour and then the others hauled him out and the next man jumped in. The foreman and the supervisors didn't want to see the men who weren't in the hole looking as if they were enjoying themselves too much, so they made it clear to us that when we weren't actually working they wanted us to look as if we were anyway. Therefore we never sat down but just stood around the hole leaning on our shovels so that the foremen and the supervisors going past in their pickups would see that we looked as if we were, in their expression, "resting in a strain."

Anyway, no matter what I was doing I spent practically all of my time thinking about my novel and getting more worried every day because I just couldn't seem to write the few more chapters that Jean Luft had asked me for.

છે.

NOT THAT I didn't try. Every night I went to my typewriter faithfully and tried to push ahead with my novel, but I just couldn't seem to get back *into it*. Sometimes I spent whole weekends in my room upstairs smoking my head off and not producing more than half a page, which I tore up.

After that had gone on for almost two months I began to get really desperate, and out of that desperation came one of the worst ideas I have ever had in my life—although it did seem to have a certain logic to it when it first occurred to me. The idea was that maybe the best way to get back into my novel was to begin doing *now* some of the rewriting that I felt was necessary and would have to be done sooner or later in any case.

At first it felt good. Rewriting turned out to be a lot of fun. In the beginning I had really only thought I would clean up the grammar here and there and maybe cut or expand a few scenes, but now I found myself practically rewriting the book from page one. Of course I told myself I was improving the story immensely, but at the same time, as I went along, a still small voice somewhere inside me kept saying, "But they liked it as it was. They never asked for one syllable of this stuff to be changed. *Why are you doing this?*"

One night, when I had rewritten almost the entire first hundred pages, I decided to take the night off and read over my rewrite. As I sat there reading it seemed to me that the rewrite was much more different from the first draft than I had thought it was going to be. In fact it was almost like reading a different book altogether. And it wasn't the story itself that was so different. I hadn't really changed that very much at all. It was the whole *mood* of the thing.

I suddenly felt scared. The still small voice was saying what it always said, *"But they liked it as it was!"*

Frantically I went back to the original manuscript and read a chapter of that and then the same chapter from the new version, trying to compare. But it was impossible. The first draft seemed much more spontaneous, there was no question of that. However, it seemed to me that the rewrite was much more polished and far better developed. In the end I resolved to go ahead with the rewrite, having convinced myself that Jean Luft and her friends would be very impressed with how much I had improved my book when they saw it again.

But when I finished the rewrite, instead of then being able to plunge straight ahead into a brand-new chapter, as I had so fervently hoped I would be able to do, it was just the same as before. I stopped cold again.

After I had gotten the first letter from Jean Luft I had written her back immediately, thanking her for the nice things she had said about my novel and assuring her that I was forging ahead with it and that she would have several more chapters before long. Then she had written me a very cheering note saying how pleased she was that I was "forging ahead," and would I write her a nice long letter telling her all about myself? I wrote the letter, and got back another cheery note saying that it seemed to her that all the best people had gotten kicked out of Harvard so don't worry about it, and how much she looked forward to meeting me when I came to New

York to sign my contract, and that she wanted me to know she took a very special interest in me because I was so young.

Now, at this crucial moment another note came from Jean Luft. This one said that she just wanted me to know she was thinking of me and was waiting with great anticipation to see the new material.

I wrote her a letter back, telling her the truth—that I hadn't been able to write one word more of my book than she had already seen. And then I went on and told her that I didn't think I was actually ready to write a novel, didn't feel like a novelist and didn't think I really was one, and was positive I couldn't handle all the big scenes I would have to write if my book was going to have a chance of being successful.

But I didn't send that letter.

I sent her a letter saying that I had taken off a few weeks from "forging ahead" to do the rewriting I felt was necessary in the first hundred pages, and really thought that I had improved this section of the book enormously. Would she read this rewrite and see if she didn't agree?

Her return letter said in a nice way that she was very disappointed that I had wasted valuable time rewriting the first hundred pages of my book, which she had truly loved just as they were, and that she definitely did *not* want to see the rewrite now and urged me to forget all about that and go back to advancing my story because she really was dying to see even four or five more chapters.

So then it all began again, sitting there in my room trying to write and not being able to get anywhere and feeling sick about it.

ঽ⸱

BY THIS TIME Missy had been dying her slow death for almost a year, and I was very much aware that by then Wes's feelings toward me had gone from resentment and bitterness to something like hatred.

One day when I got home from work he was drunk and had the look on his face that had always terrified me. "Well, you've done it now, mister," he said, his voice high-pitched, always the sign that he was struggling to control his temper.

I asked him what he meant. At first he wouldn't tell me, but just kept standing there looking at me saying, oh, I knew all right, I knew. But finally, when I insisted, he told me a fantastic story about how he had applied to the Coral Gables Elks Lodge, of which he was a member, for some financial assistance to help him pay all his bills, and how after deliberating for a hell of a long time they had voted to give him an outright grant of seven thousand dollars. But this morning, he said, when he had gone to the lodge to pick up his check the Grand Dragon, or whatever he was called, had told him that in the meantime someone had called him and told him not to give any money to Wesley Bunce, who was actually a very rich man, but to save it for the members who were really needy.

"I know you were the one who called," Wes said.

"That's crazy," I said. "I didn't even know you had asked for that money."

"You found out somehow," he said.

"Listen, I didn't make any phone call like that," I said.

"I tell you I know it was you," he said.

"How do you know?" I said.

"Because Martha told me she overheard you when you did it," he said.

"And you *believe* her?" I said.

"You're goddam right I do," he said.

Martha was Missy's nurse, and Wes had become absolutely dependent on her. She was only a "practical nurse," but she had seemed God-sent when she had first come on the job, replacing the RNs who had worked three eight-hour shifts and not only had cost Wes a fortune but were always quitting because they didn't like to be involved with terminal cases. Martha worked very cheap, and stayed on duty twenty-four hours a day, sleeping on a cot in Missy's room. The only time she left our house was for a couple of hours once or twice a week, when she went home to visit with her brother.

She was over six feet tall, with heavily muscled shoulders and arms and huge hands and feet. She had a big square face, a guttural voice and her forearms were covered with thick black hair, and she looked and sounded and moved around like a truck driver dressed up in a nurse's uniform. But she was a living doll compared to her brother, who Wes said was a "giant." Anyway he had strange skin that looked like wax and walked around like Frankenstein's monster, and the two of them to me were hallucinatory figures, like Dutch Futch.

Martha and I had been instinctive enemies from the beginning, because from the beginning she had known that I knew what she was up to. She wanted to get Wes into her power knowing that somehow out of it all she would profit far beyond what she would from any ordinary nursing job. Of course Wes, in a daze all the time by then from all the booze and all the pills he was taking—Martha had seen to it that he had first become addicted to barbiturates and then, very subtly, to Missy's Demerol—couldn't see what she was doing, and really wouldn't have cared anyway. The only thing he knew was that he had to keep her happy so that she wouldn't desert him at a time when he was so broke that if she had walked out on him he would have had to start taking care of Missy himself.

"Can't you see?" I said. "Martha made that call herself. She doesn't *want* you to get that money, because then you wouldn't have to depend on her so much."

"What an ungrateful little bastard you are," Wes said, his voice getting higher. "This woman is making tremendous personal sacrifices to help me and help your mother, and you can talk that way about her. Go on! Beat it! Get the hell out of my sight!"

"Okay," I said.

I started to go up the stairs to my room, but he said, "Wait a minute." I turned and looked back at him.

"You can stay here as long as your mother is alive," he said. "Then get your ass out of here, mister."

I HAVE ALWAYS thought of it as a miracle that it was only a couple of days later that I met Michelle, because if I hadn't met her just then I can't imagine what might have become of me.

It was a windy Sunday afternoon and I was trying to work our dinghy along the seawall to the safety of the canal about a hundred yards to the north of our house, because I was afraid it might break loose from the dock in the night and smash itself to bits against the seawall.

It was hard going because there was heavy action in close to the seawall, with the waves smashing against the seawall and then curling back onto the next wave that was coming in, so that the dinghy was either wallowing in a trough or rising up on a wave and battering into the seawall and scraping the hell out of its gunwale on the barnacles.

I decided that when I came to the dock belonging to the last house before you came to the mouth of the canal I would pause and rest for a minute. This house had always been something of a mystery in the neighborhood because no one seemed to know who really owned it, and most of the time it was empty, and when it was rented out it always seemed that the tenants were there one day and gone the next. It was a vast old house, painted white but with the paint peeling off in a lot of places from the wind and the salt spray, and surrounded by a lawn that was brown from the salt spray which was never washed off with a hose or sprinklers, and it seemed to brood there at the end of the seawall, its long front porch and wide upper windows dark behind blackened screens.

As I had approached the house I had seen a dark-haired girl in a vivid bathing suit sunning herself on a chaise on the dock. When I reached the dock the girl sat up and shaded her eyes, looking at me.

"Are you all right?" she yelled.

"I guess so," I yelled back. "Can I hang on to your dock for a minute? I'm trying to get this boat into the canal."

"Sure you can," she said.

Just then two huge German shepherds came out from under her chaise, where they had been sprawled in the shade, and came over and looked at me at very close range as I bobbed up and down in front of them. Then the girl sat right next to me, dangling her legs over the side of the dock, and made the dogs lie down one on either side of her.

I was dazzled by her. She was one of the most beautiful women I had ever seen in my life, and I was amazed at how friendly she was. In my experience girls who were that good-looking had never seemed to be really friendly with anyone but their fathers. I thought she was about the same age I was, twenty, twenty-one, twenty-two.

We had a short, difficult conversation, carried on over the wind and the sounds of the waves sloshing against the seawall and slapping up under the stern of the dinghy, and with me trying desperately to keep a grip on the dock. She asked me my name and I told her, and where I lived and I said in the pink house down there. She said her name was Michelle Lorimer and that she and her husband Steve had just come here from California.

By then I couldn't hold on to the dock any longer and I said I was going to have to hurry up and get the boat into the canal.

"Listen, Doug," she said, "come and see us, will you? We don't know anyone here."

I said I would love to, and it seemed as if from that moment on all I could think of was Michelle.

&

I HAD GONE to the sink to get a glass of water when Martha came into the kitchen and said Missy was gone. It was about eleven o'clock on the Saturday morning after the Sunday when I had met Michelle. The only thing I felt was just that I was very glad it was over.

Wes was sitting at the kitchen table playing Canfield. He turned around to me and said, "Okay, you're all through here now."

I had already told Mrs. McGowain, a woman who had been a friend of Missy's and lived in a house on Crystal Court, a couple of blocks from our house, that I thought I was going to have to be leaving home pretty soon and wondered if she had a room she could rent to me. She said she would be happy to have me, and she would rent me the spare bedroom upstairs for ten dollars a week, and I could use their kitchen whenever I wanted to.

After the silver and black hearse came and they took Missy away to the place where she was going to be cremated, I moved out, taking only a few books and my clothes and the rented typewriter and my novel. I left all the other junk I had accumulated over the years right where it was.

Before I left the house with my last cardboard box full of stuff I stood in the living room for a minute or two, looking at Missy's bedroom door. It was almost impossible to believe she wasn't still in that room. But just then Martha opened the door and came out carrying a bundle of sheets, and I could see into the room. For the first time in months the curtains were pulled back from the picture window and the room was full of light. The stripped bed looked so ordinary. I couldn't help thinking that if someone had been dying on it for a year it should at least have been aglow with an unearthly luminescence. But it was just a bed with a badly stained mattress cover.

On my way out of the house I passed by the bedroom in the rear of the house where Wes had slept all that year. I saw him lying on the unmade bed with his clothes on and his mouth open and his face looking gray, and his arms and legs twisted awkwardly as if he had been flung down there by someone, and I knew he was in a stupor from either the booze or the Demerol, or both.

He had told me there wasn't going to be a funeral service or anything like that, and he told me to call Sally and Marcus and tell them not to bother coming down because as soon as Missy was cremated he was going to close up the house and get the hell out of there. I called them and told them what he had said, and I knew they were both very relieved that they didn't have to come to Miami. They both just said that they were glad, for me and for Wes, that it was finally over with. They asked me what I was going to do and I told them about going to live at the McGowains', and they thought that sounded very sad, and I said maybe but I was just so glad to be getting out of that house.

But that night when I was alone in my rented room, which was furnished very depressingly, to say the least, and had no marvelous view of the bay but only a couple of narrow windows that looked down on the street, my heart began to ache with nostalgia for my room in the pink house.

To make myself feel better I thought of Michelle. It was clear to me by then that I had fallen in love with her. I wanted very badly to see her again, but I was afraid that once she found out about me—that I was just a guy who dug holes in the ground for a living and didn't even live in the pink house by the water anymore but in a little rented room on Crystal Court—she would lose all interest in me very quickly.

A couple of days later when I got home from work Mrs. McGowain said Wes had called and wanted me to come over to the house and pick up Missy's ashes. Missy had made me promise before she went into the operating room that if she died in there I would scatter her ashes over Biscayne Bay, which she had truly loved. So I went back to the pink house. It was getting dark and there weren't any lights on inside, but the back door was open. I walked on through the house and saw Wes sitting on a chair out on the front lawn. I stood looking at him through the front window for a minute, thinking how different this was from the beautiful man who had punted his football back and forth so happily in the mornings on Fort Myers Beach. The year of living there in that house while Missy died had aged him ten years. His hair had gone completely white, and his blue eyes, which had always been a very light blue, now looked as if almost all the color had been washed right out of them. And of course he was in simply terrible mental and physical condition from the cheap booze and the addiction to Demerol and living on the dog food for such a long time.

Looking at him sitting out there on the front lawn in the dusk I tried to feel sorry for him, but just couldn't do it. I kept remembering that everyone—the doctors, the RNs, even Sally and Marcus when they had come to Miami to see us—had told him that once Missy no longer even knew where she was, he should have moved her to a nursing home, where she would have had much better, and a lot cheaper, care, and where he would not have had to be so intimately and painfully, and horribly, involved with her dying. But he had always told them that this was Missy's home and if she was going to die it would be here, and that was all there was to it.

But I had always thought the truth was that just the fact that Missy was nearby—never mind that she really didn't even know he existed anymore, or that *she* existed—was the only thing that had held him together, because her being there was the only thing that had always held him together.

I went outside and he looked at me coldly for a minute. Then he said, "Do you have anything to say?"

I didn't know what he meant, but I could see he was drunk or doped up and I didn't want to mess with him.

"Nothing?" he said. "Well, that's about par for the course, I guess"—one of his favorite expressions.

"What do you expect me to say?" I asked.

"Oh, Christ Almighty," he said. "Your mother is dead. Even you ought to be able to think of something to say, you miserable little mutt."

"I'm sorry," I said, "but I really just don't have anything to say about it."

"No?" he said, starting to get mad. But then he just let it go. "I've given everything in that house to Martha," he said. "It looks to me as if you've left some of your own stuff in your room. If you want any of it you'd better take it right now because her brother is going to start hauling everything out of here first thing tomorrow morning."

"No, I've taken everything I want," I said.

"Okay by me," he said.

"I just came for the ashes," I said.

He shrugged. "The urn is on the table by the window," he said. "Are you going to scatter her ashes over the bay as she asked you to, or are you just going to throw them in the garbage can?"

"I'm going to do what I promised," I said.

"Where are you going to do it?"

"From the drawbridge of the Rickenbacker Causeway," I said.

"Because if you're just going to throw her ashes in the garbage can I'll scatter them right here from the dock," he said.

"I'm not going to throw them in the garbage can," I said.

"Okay," he said. "Well, you can go now."

I turned and went toward the house.

"I'm getting out of Miami tomorrow," he said. "I'm going back to Montclair."

"Goodbye," I said.

He snorted. "That's all you've got to say to me after all this?"

"Well, and I wish you good luck," I said. I knew it sounded stupid but I just couldn't think of anything else to say to him.

He snorted again. "You too. And believe me, mister, you're going to need it."

I went up the three steps to the front door and looked back at him again. "I didn't make that call to the Elks," I said. "You know that as well as I do."

"It doesn't make any difference whether you did or you didn't," he said. "In my book you're still just a mean little bastard."

There wasn't anything I could say to that. In the first place I wasn't entirely sure he wasn't right. I knew there were things I could have tried to do to keep our relationship from turning so bitter if I hadn't been too preoccupied with my own survival to bother all that much.

On the table by the window in the living room I found the "urn," a round cardboard carton that looked like a quart of ice cream without the label. I picked it up and took the lid off and inside there were some ashes that looked as if they had just been shoveled up out of somebody's fireplace, except that there were little bits of what was obviously incinerated bone in the dust. I didn't believe for a minute that they were really Missy's ashes. I knew they were probably a hundred people's ashes all mixed up together.

I put the lid back on the urn and looked around our living room for the last time. The furniture was all very beautiful. Most of it was antiques that Wes and his first wife had bought in Europe when they were on their Grand Tours.

When I got back to my room at Mrs. McGowain's I didn't know what to do with the urn, so I stuck it in the bottom drawer of my bureau. But for some reason that made me feel guilty so I took it out of there and put it up on the top shelf at the back of my closet. The next day I told the driver of our truck there was something very important I had to do and I wanted to take the next day off, and asked him if he would mark me present anyway, because I couldn't afford to lose the day's pay. He said okay, and the next morning I took the bus into Miami and rented a car. Then I went back to my room and got the urn and drove out on the Rickenbacker Causeway, which had only recently been completed, opening up a connection between the mainland and Key Biscayne, until then an inaccessible island famous only as the main location of a war movie called *They Were*

Expendable and as the site of the world's largest cultivated coconut plantation.

I drove to the high drawbridge and stopped about in the center of the span. There weren't any cars coming in either direction. There never was much traffic on the Rickenbacker Causeway in those days because there wasn't much of anything on the island then to attract people except a beautiful but very lonely beach and a little zoo where they had a few moth-eaten monkeys and lions. I got out of the car and went over to the railing and stood looking south in the direction of the pink house, which I could actually see in the distance. A strong wind was blowing from the north and down below me the current was also running swiftly south, and I thought that between them the wind and the current would carry the dust a long way.

I was about to open the urn when all the bells on the drawbridge suddenly started ringing loudly and frighteningly. I looked toward the concrete blockhouse with blue glass windows where the bridge tender manned his controls and saw that he had come out and was yelling at me and signaling wildly for me to get off the bridge. I knew it was illegal to stop a car on the bridge, but I had thought I might be able to get away with it. I opened the urn and was going to fling the ashes over the side when it occurred to me that if I did it the bridge tender might call the police and have them arrest me for some kind of unnatural behavior when I tried to get off the causeway.

So I took the urn and got back in the car and drove on over to Key Biscayne and sat on the lonely beach for a while, and then went over and looked at the animals for a while.

Then I got in the car and drove back to the mainland, and went to a side street that ran along the north end of what we used to call the Deering Estate but is now known as Villa Vizcaya. There was a high wall surrounding the whole place, and I got out of the car, looked around to make sure no one was watching, and then tossed the urn over the wall.

After that I drove to the street where Michelle lived and parked at a slight distance from the white house. Under the porte-cochere I could see a tomato-red 1948 Buick convertible, which was the most aggressively vulgar, flamboyant, outlandish, obnoxious, crazy-looking and generally offensive design that ever came out of Detroit. It resembled a great, swollen baroque bathtub on four wheels with a grille like a gigantic set of chrome-plated gnashed teeth. But after the austerity of the war years the American public had been starved for extravagance and it seemed that everybody in the country wanted one of those Buicks.

To make matters worse, the Buick under the porte-cochere had matched pairs of three-foot chrome-plated airhorns mounted on both front fenders, which made you wonder a little. But I really wanted to see Michelle, airhorns or no airhorns. The only trouble was that for some reason I couldn't seem to make myself drive on up to the house. I waited a long time, hoping she might come outside, which I thought would make things easier for me. But she never did, and finally I just went on back to Mrs. McGowain's.

Two days later, on a Saturday morning early, I went down to the post office in Coconut Grove and mailed the rewrite of the first hundred pages of "Welcome Stamp Collectors" to Jean Luft. I did it compulsively, as you might wolf down a whole pound of chocolates or a whole blueberry pie— not giving a shit about all the harm it was probably going to do you. Just ravenously wanting the immediate relief from frustration or sadness or disappointment or loneliness you know the simple act of having done it will bring.

⁊❧

RIGHT AFTER I sent my manuscript away, living in the little spare bedroom suddenly started being too much for me. It got so I could barely face going back after work to a room where nothing was familiar and there was nothing of my own but the few clothes hanging in the closet and stuffed into the drawers of the bureau. And my whole existence suddenly seemed so stupid. Got up early in the morning and took the bus down to the yard, worked my ass off in the sun all day, then took the bus back to that little room, hung around there for a while, showered, took the bus back down to Coconut Grove where I ate every night sitting at the counter of a greasy spoon called the Clipper Inn, the exact same place where I had my breakfast every morning. Then took the bus back to Crystal Court and fell into bed so I could get up very early the next morning and do the same damn thing all over again.

And yet going to work was far less of a horror than the weekends, when I had nothing to do but hang around the room. I had told Mrs. McGowain I was working on a novel, not really trying to impress her but just to make her think that I was doing something in my room when actually most of the time I was just crapped out on the bed smoking and staring at the ceiling or sitting in the armchair smoking and staring at the walls.

Mrs. McGowain had a son named Bob who was twenty-six, slept in the room across the hall from me, was a teller at the bank in Coconut Grove and had a very good-looking girlfriend, Nancy. Mrs. McGowain and Bob and Nancy were all quite close, and Nancy spent a lot of time at the house in the evenings. She would come over and they would have dinner and then play cards or some game, like Monopoly.

I had the feeling in the beginning that they were debating whether or not to invite me to have dinner with them some time, and Mrs. McGowain always seemed to be on the point of asking me when I ran into her downstairs on the way to or from my room, but then she would hesitate and the moment would pass, and I would be just as glad knowing that if she had invited me it would have been because they all felt sorry for me, and I hated pity.

I was envious of Bob. He was a nice enough guy but I couldn't see how he could deserve such a girlfriend. It wasn't just that she was good-looking. I could often hear her talking up in my room and she sounded marvelously bright and cheerful and funny. One evening when I was passing through the living room, on my way down to the Clipper Inn, she was sitting there all alone and said hello to me. I said hello and kept on going, but then I heard her say, "What kind of a novel are you working on?"

I stopped and came back a ways. Mrs. McGowain was out in the kitchen fixing dinner and Bob was upstairs taking a shower. This was the first time I had ever been alone with Nancy. She sat there looking at me with a beautiful smile.

"Mrs. McGowain told me you're working on a novel," she said.

"Yes, that's true," I said.

"What sort of a novel is it?" she said.

"Well, it's about a young couple who buy a small hotel in a town over on the Gulf coast," I said. "They have a lot of problems, but in the end they make a success out of the hotel. It takes place in the thirties, in the middle of the Depression."

She was still smiling. "What's the title?" she said.

I said, "It's called 'Welcome Stamp Collectors,' because the main thing they're trying to do is get a convention of stamp collectors to come to the hotel."

"How much of it have you written so far?" she asked.

"About a hundred pages," I said.

"Well, it sounds good," she said. "Has anyone seen any of it so far?"

"I sent it to a publisher in New York," I said.

Her eyes shone. "Really? What did they say?"

"Well, they said they liked it."

"Really?"

"Yes," I said. "Would you like to see the letter?"

"Oh, *yes,"* she said. "I think this is very *exciting."*

"Well, wait just a minute," I said.

I hurried upstairs and got the letter and hurried back down to the living room, but when I got there Nancy had disappeared. I waited a minute, and then Bob came downstairs and saw me standing there, and I felt very awkward. At the same time I heard Nancy laughing out in the kitchen. Bob didn't know what I was doing there like that, with the letter in my hand, and I didn't know what to say. So I just went past him, back upstairs, hung around in my room for a minute frantically trying to collect myself, and then went downstairs again, leaving the letter behind. By this time Nancy had come back from the kitchen, where I gathered she had been helping Mrs. McGowain with something, and she and Bob were standing in the living room holding hands and looking at me with big smiles.

"I was just telling Bob about your book, Doug," Nancy said. "Where's the letter?"

"Oh, I thought you were busy," I said. "I took it back upstairs. I'll show it to you the next time you're here."

I knew by the way they were looking at me that they could see how flustered I was.

"Well, I'll see you later," I said, and sailed past them out the front door, burning up. I was sure they were amazed at what a fool I had made of myself, and I truly regretted having spoken to Nancy because I knew it looked as if all I had been doing was trying to impress her. Besides, I felt that the integrity of my relationship with the McGowains had come apart now that I had demonstrated that I was willing to talk about my personal life, and I had liked it so much better when they had thought I just wanted to be left alone.

The Sunday after I sent my manuscript to New York I went over to the pink house in the morning. Already out in front there was a FOR RENT sign. I went around the side of the house, to the front lawn, and walked out on the dock and looked back at the house. I could see that it was empty. I went over and looked through the picture window at the empty rooms, and then I went back to my room at the McGowains', and thought about my manuscript up there in New York.

I didn't have so long to wait this time. About ten days later when I came home from work there was a letter from Jean Luft on the hall table outside my room. I took it into my room and sat down and started to open it, but something made me pause. I decided I would take my shower first and then read it. But even after my shower I hesitated, and sat in my armchair smoking and watching it start to get dark outside.

What she said was that, very simply, I had ruined my book for her. She said I had taken a story, which as I knew, she had found wonderfully fresh and charming and original and had over-written it right into the ground. She said I didn't know how much it hurt her to have to write me this letter but she had no choice except to be totally honest because anything else would only do me more harm in the long run. She said she realized now that I probably had never written even one more chapter of this book, and that was the thing that disturbed her most of all. If you had only forged ahead as you promised me you would, she said, instead of doing *this*. She said that she somehow felt totally responsible for what had happened, and deeply regretted now not having stayed in closer touch with me. She said the worst part of it all was that almost the same thing as this had happened to her twice before in her experience as an editor—two novels had come to her that she had loved with all her heart, and then in the rewriting the authors had insisted on doing against all her pleading to the contrary, they had lost all of the qualities she had so loved about them in the beginning. And now here it was all over again, she said.

At the end of the letter there was a paragraph that sounded different from the rest, as if it had been written much later, when she had been feeling more detached. She said that of course all editorial opinions are highly personal and that no one is God, and that perhaps someone else might react very favorably to my novel as it now was written, and recommended my trying it at some other house. As for her the trouble was that my book was just not the same, and she knew she could never feel the same about it again. And she was returning my manuscript under separate cover.

I could have stood her criticism of the book and accepted it no matter how much it hurt, but her saying I should send my book to another publisher was really saying that she was abandoning me now completely. Of course she couldn't have understood to what extent it was only her interest in me and my book that had kept me going all this time. I stayed there in my room letting it sink in that she was no longer going to be waiting in New York for the great day when I would send her the next section of my novel, that she was no longer "my editor." That I had gone very suddenly in her judgment from someone with enormous promise as a novelist to just another terrible disappointment, that no one cared any longer whether I wrote or didn't write.

I thought there was only one thing to do. I hurried downstairs and almost ran through the pine woods that separated the McGowains' house from the old house on the bay where Michelle lived.

As I approached the house I saw the tomato-red Buick under the porte-cochere, and it looked as if every room in the place was lit up, and I could hear music playing even from a distance. When I came near the house the dogs began barking, and I saw them standing behind the screen of the front door. Then Michelle appeared at the door and the dogs shut up right away.

I said hello, and she came out, with the dogs leading the way and raising their nostrils to catch my scent. She was wearing a pair of white shorts and a tight-fitting white top that showed off her breasts, and with her tan and her long dark hair and her green eyes she looked stunning.

"Oh, *Doug!*" she said. "It's *you!* I'm so glad to see you! I wondered why you never came back! Come in! Come in! I really am so glad to see you!"

I followed her into the house and my whole life changed. I didn't have to come home from work and hang around that spare bedroom all alone anymore. I went to Michelle's. I didn't have to eat all alone at the Clipper Inn anymore. Michelle fed me. I didn't have to die for love anymore. Michelle loved me. I didn't have to crawl with envy every time I saw a man with a good-looking girl anymore. Michelle was better-looking than the whole bunch of them put together. I didn't have to lie in bed at night galled by erotic fantasies anymore. Michelle made love to me in every possible way. I didn't have to worry about impressing people anymore. Michelle adored me just as I was, she said that from the moment she had started talking to me that day she had known we were "two kindred souls."

OF COURSE there was a terrific price for all that. The terrific price was that I never knew when Steve was going to blow my head off with his famous Colt .45.

He was thirty-two, tall and slender, with straight blond hair and black eyebrows and eyelashes and dark blue eyes, and had a stainless steel plate in his head from the time he crashed his P-51 into an ME-109 after he had run out of ammunition for both his cannons and his machine guns and that was the only way left for him to bring down the son of a bitch.

"And, Doug, they never even gave me my DFC," he said bitterly. "In fact for a while they were trying to get me court-martialed for reckless destruction of a brand-new aircraft. Me laying there in that goddam hospital with half my brains blown away and them talking about sending me to Leavenworth for fifteen years. But, shit, they knew they could never make it stick. Not with me such a big hero all over the ETO. Forget Douglas Bader! Forget Cobber Caine! Forget Paddy Finucane! Forget Adolf Galland! Those guys were all basically just company men. You know what I was? I was a throwback to the *real* aces—guys like Albert Ball and Frank Luke and Ernest Udet and Guynemer. You know what the Germans called me? The Avenging Angel of Fighter Group Fifteen. I'm not kidding. I shot down this German one time and when he cracked up in a cow pasture I went down and took him prisoner myself, like Richthofen used to do. And it turned out he could speak pretty good English and that's what he said—all the guys in his Jagdstaffel knew about me and that's what they called me. And the miserable pricks never even gave me my DFC."

Just being in the same room with him made me nervous. He never seemed to be able to sit still, and never seemed to be able to stop talking. All that intensity, and ego, practically made me want to throw up my hands in front of my face to protect myself from it.

After a while I realized that when he was talking, no matter what the subject seemed to be, actually all he was doing was trying to explain himself. He was a mass of conflicting desires and feelings of guilt and self-doubt and ambitions that clawed at his entrails like demons. He only wanted to understand himself, that was basically what he was trying to get across. For instance, he wanted to know why he loved violence so much. "That's why I became a fighter pilot," he said. "The only trouble with it was that the experience only reinforced my perception of myself as a killer. I mean, when I had a German plane in my sights and I knew I was about to send the pilot to hell I was happy. And after a kill all I could think about for days was how good it felt and how bad I wanted that feeling again, at the same time feeling like shit because of how good I felt. I didn't want to be a war lover. I'm very honest when I say that. I didn't want to be like all those guys who hung around the OC telling each other they just didn't know what the fuck they were going to do when it was all over and they couldn't fly combat any more, but in my heart I knew I was worse than they were because with them ninety percent of it was bullshit but with me combat actually was something I didn't think I could live without.

"And there were so many other unanswered questions." He stared at me with his dark blue eyes. "That was why I decided to try acting. Understand? I thought that maybe the experience of projecting myself into the personas of *other people* would help lead me toward the light about *myself*. But just as I had failed to come to understand myself through my life as a fighter pilot, so did I fail to come to understand myself through my career as an actor."

I didn't care about him and his problems, but I had to have Michelle. After it began, the third night I went over there, on the bare terrazzo floor of the front porch with the cold night wind blowing over us, I couldn't have given her up. So I was willing to put up with anything, even Steve endlessly explaining himself, which was all the more excruciating because of his conviction that I *loved* hearing all about him. He thought I couldn't get enough of it. I think that was because every once in a while I would ask him a stupid question, which he always took very seriously, as if, almost innocently, I had dazzlingly illuminated whatever facet of his character he was driving into the ground at the moment, when actually it was just that I knew I had to say something now and then or he would have begun to catch on that I didn't give a damn about him and his problems.

He would look at me, and then say, "You're *brilliant,* Doug," or "You really *do* understand, Doug," or "Doug, not *one* person has ever thought to ask me that."

The worst part was that sometimes he would break off right in the middle of one of his monologues and go and get his huge .45-caliber Colt automatic (his "personal weapon" from back at Fighter Group 15) and go out on the dock and pump a full clip into a piling, chewing great pieces out of it, and then come back into the house and sit there and wait for the City of Miami cops to come and warn him again about discharging a firearm within city limits. They were never really mean about it though. They seemed to understand why he would have to go out there and start blasting away, and they would accept a shot of Old Fitzgerald (the only thing Steve ever drank) and stand around kidding, looking at Michelle as if they wanted to eat her alive.

Michelle said they met when they were both in a war movie at MGM. Steve had a small part as an idealistic Marine lieutenant. She was a Navy nurse who got killed in the first ten minutes, which was what always happened to her. For some reason, even though she was so good-looking, nobody out there had ever taken much interest in her as an actress. Anyway they started having lunch together at the commissary, and then dating, and about a month later they got married. After that Michelle said she more or less stopped working in movies, but Steve went on with it another year, until he finally got a part as an idealistic intern that he honestly thought was going to make him a star. It was his seventh movie but the first one in which he felt he would have an opportunity to show the industry how good he really was. Then, halfway through the shooting, first the star and then the director walked off the picture over contract disputes and the next thing Steve knew the studio had canceled production on the picture altogether. That was when he got mad and said he was through with Hollywood forever, and told Michelle they were going to Miami, where he was going to throw in with a friend of his from the Air Force who was starting up a new airline.

The "new airline" consisted of two DC-3s and four Lockheed Lodestars, plus a couple of Stearman biplanes they made a few bucks with on the side skywriting and towing signs advertising dog tracks and restaurants back and forth along Miami Beach. They weren't licensed to carry anything but freight so far, therefore Steve, the great fighter pilot who had always looked down his nose at transport pilots as nothing but glorified bus drivers, was flying strawberries to Boston and cantaloupes to Newark.

"I don't really know why I married him," Michelle said. "Well, I thought he was very handsome and exciting, of course. But, also, I guess I thought maybe I could help make him feel better about himself. I could see how unhappy and confused and bewildered he was, and I was naive enough to imagine that all he really needed was love and understanding. It took me about ninety days to see how wrong I was. That's when I found out about his passion for waitresses. With some men it's secretaries or nurses or something. With him it's waitresses. He can't resist a cute waitress. If we go somewhere and he spots one he likes, I know he'll be back there the next day trying to date her up. And if she's married or something and he can't have her, that gets him mad and he's mean around here for days. He's seeing three different waitresses right now. I know because he told me, just like he always tells me. He says there's nothing he can do about it, it's part of the problem. But I know there's some girl somewhere who's holding out on him. That's why he's shooting off his gun so much lately."

She was stretched out naked on the couch in the living room, drinking a Coke. It was late on a Sunday afternoon and Steve had flown to Chicago and wasn't supposed to be back until late Monday. But all the time I was listening with one ear for the sound of his pickup coming down the street.

"But he has his own way of looking at things," she said, "and I promise you that if he ever found us making love he'd shoot both of us in cold blood."

For some reason it drove Michelle wild if I let her make up my eyes with mascara and put all her gold and silver bangles on me before we made love. I didn't mind. I always thought, what the hell, if it makes her happy. What scared me shitless was the possibility that Steve might burst in on us sometime before she could get the mascara and the bracelets off me, because I was positive he sure as hell would be able to figure out what that meant.

"You should leave him," I said.

We had been making love on and off more or less all afternoon. I was lying there nude beside her on the couch, in the mascara and the bracelets, dripping with sweat, and probably with the mascara running all over the place.

"One of these days he may kill you just because he's in the mood for it," I said.

"Where would I go?" she said. "What would I do? Have you thought about that?"

Of course I hadn't thought about that. But she was a beautiful young girl and I couldn't imagine that she would have too much trouble finding her way in the world.

"Anyway," she said, "now I have you, and I'm happy."

All of the twenty or so rooms in the house were empty except the front bedroom upstairs where they slept on a couple of mattresses on the floor and the living room, where they had put the couch and a couple of tables and chairs and lamps they had bought from somebody who advertised in the paper, and wherever you were you heard all the vague flutterings and murmurings and the banging of doors that you do in houses near open water where the wind is always sailing through, and when we were making love I often thought I heard a door open somewhere and then someone moving and distinctly felt a *presence,* and wanted to look around, expecting to see Steve in the doorway with his .45.

Sometimes I had a very strong and dizzying intuition that he knew *everything.* When I asked Michelle about it she said no, she didn't think so. That didn't do any good. I still listened all the time and tried to stay alert no matter what we were doing, which usually was very difficult. I kept an eye on the dogs. If they so much as twitched a whisker, I was ready to get the hell out of there.

Once in a while she would surprise me by driving out to the road where we were digging the holes, in the Buick, with the top down, in one of her fantastic bathing suits and with the two dogs in the back seat, and drive slowly along the line until she saw me, or if she didn't see me keep asking until somebody told her what hole I was in, and they would haul me out and when I went over to the car she would take my face in her hands and kiss me and then lick the sweat off my face, while all up and down the line the linemen up on the poles and all the grunts on the ground watched with their mouths open. Then she would just turn around and drive slowly back the way she had come, with them all staring at her in silence, and none of them ever kidded me about it, but they all looked at me in a strange way, as if trying to see what there was about me that could have made a beautiful girl like her come all the way out there just to lick my sweat.

On Saturdays, if he wasn't flying, Steve would take me with him out to the airport for a flight in one of the Stearmans, and that was the happiest I ever saw him, looking like a World War I ace in his leather jacket and leather helmet and goggles, in the open cockpit, sailing around in the sky doing chandelles, Immelmann turns, falling leaves, lazy eights, aileron rolls, split "S's," dead-stick loops and wingovers just like his heroes Richthofen, Albert Ball, Georges Guynemer and Frank Luke.

For a climax he would climb to ten thousand feet and level off there and just hang for a minute and turn around in his cockpit and look back at me and grin, and that meant just one thing—that we were about to go into a power dive. He would turn back around and raise his gloved hand, and then shove the stick forward and down we went, full throttle, with the struts and wing brace wires screaming and the earth coming up to meet us faster and faster, and every time I always thought this is the one, this is the time he won't pull back on the stick at the last possible moment but will take us straight to hell to meet all those Germans he sent there. But then, at the last possible moment, he would haul back on the stick and we would flatten out a hundred feet off the deck, and head back to the airport, where he would set the plane down very sweetly. He was a great flyer, there was no question about that, but I wished that I could have found it in me to refuse to go up with him when he asked me to. However, I knew that somehow a condition of my being able to continue coming to their house was that I go flying with him, and pretend that I loved it, just as I had to pretend that I loved hearing him talk about himself.

"Michelle won't go up with me," he said. "She's afraid."

Of course, after I had known them a while, I realized that Steve thought I was very much like him—that I too was full of conflicting desires and feelings of guilt and self-doubt and ambitions, and that was why I understood him so well. In other words, he also felt, in his own way, that we were two kindred souls.

"I would never go up with him," she said to me, "because I know what he would do. He would dive the plane straight down into the ground and kill us. That's his dream."

❧

THEY ATE all kinds of crazy stuff. Tons of baloney, peanut butter, tons of canned chili, Corn Flakes, tons of hot dogs, Moon Pies, all kinds of junk fried in deep fat, and neither one of them ever seemed to think there was anything the least bit wrong with it. Of course it didn't bother me too much either—it was just like home. But the weird thing was that at the same time they were wolfing down all that swill, they were telling me about the great restaurants back in L.A., and saying that in their humble opinion there wasn't one single really first-class restaurant in the entire city of Miami.

One Sunday afternoon I went over there because Michelle had called me at Mrs. McGowain's that morning to say that she was cooking a roast for Sunday dinner, and I was pretty excited about having something other than the peanut butter sandwich and a chocolate bar or bowl of chili and a Moon Pie I usually got over there.

When I approached the house I saw both the Buick and the pickup parked under the porte-cochere. I knew Steve had the whole weekend off, a rare thing for him. I didn't see either Steve or Michelle anywhere around, but the two dogs were standing behind the screen door wagging their tails. They usually growled fiercely when anyone came near the house, but by then they had gotten to know my footsteps and could tell it was me coming even when I was a block away, and they had taken a liking to me to the extent that I could even give them orders. Also by then I was used to just going into the house without knocking or anything, so I went in and looked around for Steve and Michelle, followed closely by the dogs. When I didn't see anybody downstairs I took the opportunity to go into the kitchen and slip half a dozen slices of baloney to each of the dogs, a little trick that accounted for about seventy-five percent of my popularity with them.

But one thing that struck me as funny was that when I entered the kitchen I wasn't immediately knocked out by the glorious aroma of roast beef simmering in its own juices. The fact was that nothing at all was going on in the kitchen. There was nothing in the oven, no sign of preparations of any kind whatsoever on any level. I went back into the front hallway and was about to yell upstairs that I had arrived when something made me pause, and all of a sudden I knew why nothing was happening in the kitchen—because there was a hell of a lot happening upstairs.

I went up the stairs very quietly and looked down the hall, and saw that the door to the room at the far end of the hall, where Steve and Michelle slept on the mattress on the floor, was closed. The dogs had followed me, and they stood looking at me for a minute, and then went along the hall to the closed door and both lay down there. I went back downstairs and sat in the living room trying to figure out what right I thought I had to feel so fucking *hurt*. Okay, they were screwing up there. I knew perfectly well she screwed him all the time, she had never for a minute pretended that she didn't. In the first place if she hadn't, Steve would have guessed there was something going on between her and me. She had told me that about ten times, and of course I knew she was right. Okay, it was just that this was the first time I had ever been in the house when they were actually *doing* it. She had always been very careful to see that that had never happened before.

Then, sitting there, something else began to creep into my consciousness—the suspicion that there was much more going on here than just the screwing. Michelle had invited me over for a big elaborate dinner. Steve knew that. Well, obviously there wasn't going to be any big elaborate dinner. Therefore Steve was doing about ten different things to me all at once, the most important of which was proving to me that his wife thought it was more fun screwing him than cooking for me.

Thinking in that direction kept leading me back to my intuition that he *knew,* and that got me up and started me walking through the empty ground floor rooms, trying to decide whether to stick around or go back to my room. Finally I went out on the dock and sat on Michelle's chaise. After a while Steve came out of the house and ambled across the brown lawn smoking a cheroot and looking pleased with himself, and wearing nothing but one of his southern California bathing suits that were only about the size of a jockstrap and were meant to show off your wang. He was one of those guys who had to shave twice a day if they wanted to look like anything, but he clearly hadn't shaved at all so far that day and had a thick dark stubble. He said hello and stood looking out at the water for a minute, and I could see he had some very nice claw marks on his back, and knew he wanted me to see them.

Then he sat down next to me and said he was going to have to go out to the airport pretty soon because one of their pilots had suddenly quit and he was going to have to make the flight to Dallas he had been scheduled for. After that he went back to the house to get ready to go, and a few minutes later Michelle came and sat where he had been sitting. She had combed her hair and everything, but all around her mouth it was red from rubbing against his stubble.

She said she was going to drive Steve to the airport and asked if I wanted to come along, and we could stop on the way back for a hamburger at one of the drive-ins out on LeJeune Road. I didn't know what the hell I had expected from her, an apology or something? Anyway I said all right, I'd go along, and when we came back she posed for me and I worked on the portrait of her I had started. She didn't care about writing. I had shown her the letter from the publisher and she had said that was very nice, or something like that, but I could see it really didn't mean anything to her.

However, she was impressed with the way I could draw. I had kept right on drawing ever since I had copied the comic strips at Maridor, and by this time I was very good at it. She was immensely pleased with my picture of her and said that when it was finished she was going to put it in a beautiful frame.

We had the roast two nights later, when Steve came back from Dallas, and then things just went on as before. Michelle and I made love whenever we had a chance, rode around in the Buick on warm evenings with the top down, all over Miami and up and down Miami Beach, went swimming weekends on the remote beaches of Key Biscayne, or sometimes I borrowed a boat from someone and we went sailing on the lower bay, all day, all alone, and I was happy. But Michelle had changed me from someone who felt terrible about himself to someone who really felt very good about himself, and one of the things that came along with that new-found self-confidence was an increasing restlessness.

I had the urge to *do* something, although at first I didn't know what.

One night I wrote a letter to Jean Luft telling her that I had gone back to work on "Welcome Stamp Collectors" and had written several new chapters and would she look at this new material? I was hoping that if she said yes it would inspire me actually to go back to work on my novel. I was very disappointed when a couple of weeks went by and I realized she was never going to answer my letter.

The other thing I had been thinking about was Harvard. It was going on two years since I had left Cambridge, and the more I thought about it the more I began to ache to go back. I asked my supervisor at Midland to write a letter to the Dean of Admissions for me, and the next day he handed me a letter saying that I had been a good and dependable worker and recommended that I be allowed to return to Harvard. That night I wrote to the Dean, telling him that not only had I worked very hard at Midland Constructors but I had also been working on a novel that had been received very well by an important publisher in New York, and enclosed the letter to prove it. By this time I had managed to save about five hundred dollars, which I figured would be just about enough to get me to Cambridge and cover my first term bill, which of course was payable at registration.

About three weeks later I got a letter from the Dean saying that after due consideration the College had decided to allow me to return to Harvard in the coming fall term. Of course I was very excited. I immediately wrote to some of my old friends in Cambridge and said I would be seeing them in the fall, and back came letters from them saying how glad they would be to see me again after all this time, and suddenly the world seemed like a very fine place indeed. My plan was to work very hard when I got back to Harvard so that when the next term bill came due I would be able to apply for a student loan. There wouldn't be any problem, I thought. I knew I could get good grades if I really tried hard. Furthermore I had it in the back of my mind that up there, in Cambridge, in that atmosphere, I would go back to work on my novel, and this time I would get it right and some other New York publisher would love it just as much as the first one had, and before I knew it I would be signing a contract for "Welcome Stamp Collectors" after all.

Then, in June, there was the Berlin crisis. Selective Service started taking itself very seriously again, so one night in July I went to the National Guard Armory and joined the big crowds of guys who were signing up. Everyone said that in the event of general mobilization the Guard was always the last of the reserves to be activated. I didn't have any trouble passing the physical. The doctors wanted to pass as many men as possible so they could bring this unit up to full strength, and the entire procedure only took about ten minutes from one end of the line to the other, including the Wassermann. At the end of the line we took the oath and got sworn in to the Army of the United States, and a couple of weeks later they equipped us with uniforms, rifles, helmets, bayonets, entrenching tools and full field packs and transported us in a truck convoy to Fort Jackson, South Carolina ("Home of the Red Diamond Division") where we were to go through basic training with the Fifty-first ("Bushmaster") Division of the National Guard. At Jackson, when we weren't collapsing from the heat we learned to shoot an M-1 rifle and how to march in close order and went on route marches and bivouacked in the mud and crawled through a field where they were firing live machine guns about six inches over our heads and all the rest of it. At one point there was a wildfire rumor sweeping through the barracks that they were going to give us a two-day pass to go home and say goodbye to our loved ones and then we were going to get shipped straight to Germany, but six weeks later they just put us in the trucks again and brought us back to Miami.

By then it was late August. I hadn't told Michelle yet that I was going back to Cambridge, but right after I returned from Fort Jackson I told her. She said she had known for a long time that she was going to lose me, but she made me promise that I would write to her all the time, and that I would come and see her during the next summer vacation. I promised, and then one beautiful morning in September she drove me to the train station in Miami and we kissed goodbye.

&

CAMBRIDGE SEEMED very much the same. I was happy and excited to be there again, but felt just as intimidated by the place as I had when I had first arrived there in 1946.

Most of my friends from St. Mark's were still around, and were very glad to see me. But of course they were seniors now, and they all belonged to final clubs, and had tutors, and were much more serious than they had been when we had all been freshmen together.

I was given a room in Claverly Hall, one floor below the room from which I had thrown the beer bottles. My roommate was a small, thin, frighteningly pale young man named Jerry, who yawned all the time. He, too, had been expelled from Harvard and then allowed to come back. But his offense had been much worse than mine—a nervous breakdown. As he kept saying, it was much harder to get back into Harvard if you were a psycho than if you were a drunk or a cheat or a straight F student. He was very self-conscious about his yawning. He said he did it because he was so afraid he was going to crack up again before midterms, and he knew this time they would never let him come back.

I wanted everything to be different. I wanted to settle down and really work hard so I could get good enough grades to qualify both for membership in a House and for a loan from the University, which I had to have, since all my money had been used up paying registration fees and for my books.

And I wanted to go back to work on my novel.

I found out somehow—it wasn't in the catalogue—that Archibald MacLeish was giving a course in which all you had to do was work on a novel. I took my Letter and went to Widener Library, where I was told he had his study. After much wandering around in the marble halls, I came to his number, and was surprised to see that his door was wide open. A man was sitting at a desk at the far end of the room, a long distance away. I tapped on the doorjamb and he looked around at me, but didn't speak or beckon me forward. Just stared at me.

I smiled and sort of raised the Letter. "Mr. MacLeish—?"

"Yes?" he said.

I hovered on the threshold. "I wonder if I might talk to you about joining your novel course—?"

"No," he said.

I continued hovering, half through the doorway, with my smile, and the Letter poised in the air, confident he would say more than that. But that was all there was, just the "Yes?" and then the "No." Then he returned his attention to whatever he was doing, and after a minute I just drifted away.

I thought of going back and making a big scene and trying to practically force him to read the Letter, but decided against it.

In the end I signed up for Carpenter's Advanced Drawing in the Fogg Museum, and the famous gut Roman Law, and another famous gut that was officially listed in the Harvard catalogue as History 1380: European Oceanic Discovery, Trade and Settlement, 1680–1815, but everybody just called Boats. I also signed up for a course in International Law, Twentieth-Century Art History, and a course in theater I had heard about where you never had to go to any lectures because there weren't any. All you had to do to get your credit for the course was turn in one paper about some aspect of the theater at the end of the term. The professor had his office in the Houghton Library. He asked me what area of the theater I was interested in and I said set design, and that was it, I was in.

In other words, I wasn't making any effort to devise a meaningful curriculum for myself. All I was doing was putting together a string of miscellaneous courses out of which I was pretty sure I would be able to pull high enough marks to insure myself a House and a loan.

Of course I showed the Letter to everyone I knew in Cambridge, and they were all very impressed. They asked me how much longer it would take me to finish the book, and I said I was in the final stages right then, and was working very hard on it because I was under a lot of pressure from my editor to finish soon so they could bring it out next fall. My friends said they thought I was going to get rich and famous, and I said well I sure hope so.

It was on the strength of the Letter that some of my friends got me elected to the Signet Society, a highfalutin club on Mt. Auburn Street where all the supposedly brightest people in Cambridge gathered for lunch. A stiff white envelope was pushed under my door one day. Inside was the invitation to join and a white feather. The invitation said I would be expected to give a very funny speech on the day I was initiated. But I couldn't afford the initiation fee so I didn't join. I was elected to the Hasty Pudding, but couldn't afford that either.

I also was "punched" by a couple of the final clubs on which I had friends. This involved going to a series of cocktail parties and outings at graduate members' country houses throughout the fall, where you were looked over by the membership. I went to the parties and the outings, even though I knew I would never be able to join any of the clubs if I were elected.

EVERY ONCE in a while that fall I told myself here you are doing the same damn things that got you into trouble last time—hanging around with rich kids, drinking too much, wasting precious time on social activities that were fine if you had a home and a family and lots of money behind you but were just an insane self-indulgence if you were homeless and broke and absolutely depending on getting a loan from the college.

Then there was the lying about my novel. It had been thrilling at first to see how impressed people were by the Letter, but then it got so that having to talk about my book all the time—and my friends seemed to think they had to ask about it *all* the time—the lies left a bitter taste in my mouth.

My worst moments usually came in the evenings when Jerry and I were studying in our room. His yawning would get me to yawning, and I would sit there and gaze at him for a while through the cigaret smoke. He smoked more than I did, which was really going some. And his eyes were always rabbit-pink behind his thick glasses because they were very sensitive to smoke. There he was, concentrating so hard on his work that he was oblivious to everything else. He didn't get any invitations to swanky punches. He definitely wasn't "final club material." He didn't even have any friends. But none of that bothered him. All he wanted to do was keep from slipping back into the darkness, and you didn't have to be a psychiatrist to see that the odds against it were very narrow. Still, I envied him his singlemindedness and his ability to carry on alone, without all the socializing I couldn't seem to resist but which I knew so well only distracted me from what should have been my one true purpose, staying in Harvard.

Sometimes, there with Jerry, both yawning and smoking, in that dismal brown room with the two desks, the two traditional black Harvard chairs, the two traditional ugly, cumbersome, totally uncomfortable and therefore totally useless wooden armchairs, the empty fireplace, and nothing else, and with the steam heat flowing up from the registers in the floor stupefying me little by little, and outside my windows Harvard boys yelling and kicking beer cans up and down Linden Street, I was overcome by nostalgia for Michelle, the red Buick, Moon Pies and all the rest of that, and wished I had never left Miami, because the fact was that for all my longing to return to Harvard, actually it was a big let-down. I wasn't having a very good time, or learning anything I cared much about, and the ominous sense of standing still, or actually going backwards, was even worse than it had been in Miami, because *here* I was supposed to be getting somewhere.

The only course I was taking that I really enjoyed was Advanced Drawing. I used to tack some of my work to the walls in my room and friends of mine who were on the *Lampoon* said they needed people who could draw on the magazine, so I started going to the candidates' meetings. I didn't want to write for the *Lampoon,* but I hoped I would be able to get some drawings in the magazine, and maybe even do a cover. I knew the *Lampoon* was as much a club as a magazine, if not more so, and that the members had a reputation for delighting in blackballing candidates for very whimsical reasons even after they had worked their asses off for a whole term trying out for the literary or business boards, but after I had my first drawing reproduced in the magazine in the November issue, I thought I had a real chance of being elected, and when they told me I was to draw the cover for the next issue, I was pretty sure I would make it, and I was right.

Then there was Fools Week, when the newly elected candidates made fools of themselves all over town, and then initiation night, when we were forced to get disgustingly drunk, and then took the oath, and finally got packed one by one into a dumbwaiter and hoisted up to the Great Hall, where we made speeches while the members threw rolls at us. Then we were officially members of the *Lampoon,* and were given our keys to the building, and it was strange because in the building I felt at home—the first time I had really felt at home anywhere since I had left the pink house.

❧

I'll climb upon the mantelpiece
And fill my eye with candlegrease,

And when I see you passing by,
I'll give you a little wink,
With my greasy, greasy, eye.

THAT WAS one of the songs we used to sing when I was on the *Lampoon*. We always sang our songs after the traditional Thursday evening dinners in the Great Hall, standing at our places up and down the long table, in the yellow light of the candles glittering in the chandeliers high above us, under the vaulted ceiling, with the smoke from our cigars and cigarets and from the always very badly made fire in the colossal fireplace turning slowly in the air. First, we got drunk on the unlimited free booze that came with the five-buck price of the dinner, then we had dinner, then we threw rolls at each other, and then we sang our songs: "The Lampoon's Out Tonight, Boys," "Cats on the Rooftops," "I'm Mighty Sorry I Came to Town, Cuz the Boys Started Kicking My Dog Around," "Everybody Knows Goodtime Charlie, Charlie Is the Perfect Clown," and all the others.

One Thursday night toward the end of the spring term, I began telling everybody that I was seriously thinking about spending the summer in the building, trying to make it sound as if I were going to make the one big final push that was all I needed to finish my novel, and how I thought that living all alone there in the building with a whole long summer before me would be the ideal time and place to do it. Actually I wasn't just thinking about it. I had already made up my mind that I was going to spend the summer in the Lampoon, for the simple reason that I knew I wouldn't have anywhere else to go when the college closed at the end of the term. So this was a trial balloon to see what kind of a reaction I would get from the membership. The reaction was that everybody said how goddam *grubby* it sounded. Where was I going to sleep? Where would I *bathe,* for Christ's sake? Besides, didn't I know that living in the Lampoon was not only against the rules of Harvard University, but also against the rules of the Trustees of the *Lampoon?* The answer was, yes, I was aware of all that—but I knew I had one thing, definitely, working in my favor, which was that there really was no one around who had the authority to forbid me to spend the summer in the building.

A day or so later, Fred Gwynne, who was the current president of the *Lampoon*, said he had heard I was going to live in the building that summer, and he was going to join me, because he had just gotten a job for the summer as an apprentice at the Brattle Theater, and the day after that George Plimpton told me he thought it would be fun to spend the summer in the building with Fred and me, and maybe work on a novel, too.

Frankly, I wished they hadn't decided to join me. Feeling as insecure as I did at the time, I would much rather have been alone in the Lampoon. Besides, I knew there would be inequities. For instance, they both belonged to clubs, where they would have all the conveniences, like hot showers and hot water to shave with, and of course they wouldn't have to be worrying about money all the time either. But, anyway, Plimpton and Gwynne were rather glamorous figures around the Lampoon then, and suddenly all the members who had been saying how *grubby* living in the building sounded began saying how *romantic* it sounded, and that they might like to do it themselves some time.

However, most of them were going to Europe that summer, and were talking excitedly about meeting each other in Paris, Rome or Pamplona. These were the years when the massive postwar summer invasions of Europe by American students were in full swing and the great transatlantic liners jammed the Hudson River piers in New York and every crossing was booked to capacity.

I wished I could be going to Europe, too. Well, anywhere, for that matter. I went to the Student Employment Office faithfully a couple of times a day, still hoping to land a job on a boat or at a summer camp—anything to get out of Cambridge. But it always seemed that I arrived a minute too late for all those jobs. Finally, just as I was beginning to think that I actually might starve to death after the Harvard dining halls closed up, I was offered a job repairing furniture for the Harvard Department of Building and Grounds, at my eternal dollar and a quarter an hour, and of course I jumped at it.

At last the end of the spring term came, and there were no more meals being served in the dining halls, and I had to move my things out of Claverly Hall and carry them across the street to the Lampoon. There was a brief flurry of activity in the building on that last day as the members rushed in and out, leaving messages for each other in the Common Book and tacked to the bulletin board in the Public Room, and then all the shouting stopped, and the slamming of the Bow Street door stopped, and the Lampoon was silent and empty, except for me.

I remember sitting in the Great Hall toward evening. Plimpton and Gwynne had gone home for a few days, so I faced spending my first night there in the building all alone. I had brought up one of the typewriters from the Business Office, and had the most recent draft of my novel stacked up beside the typewriter. I had resolved to go to work on a total rewrite immediately, but I couldn't seem to do anything but sit there staring straight ahead of me, smoking one cigaret after another and thinking about how hopeless everything looked.

Then, in the gathering dusk, as if drawn there by destiny, I walked down the length of the Great Hall to the foot of the winding stone stairway that led up to the Ibis Room. I ascended the steps slowly, and when I reached the Ibis Room I went and sat down on the dusty couch, and lit another cigaret. It was a strange feeling being up there in that room, where neither I nor any of the other members usually went very often. It was an unfriendly place, isolated from the rest of the building, and yet I knew this was where I was going to sleep all that summer, mostly because I knew that once I had locked the heavy wooden door at the bottom of the steps behind me, I would be safer up there than anywhere else in the building.

After a while I lay down on the couch, just flat, seeing what it was going to be like. From the Mt. Auburn Street side of the room there was the sound of fairly heavy traffic passing by. The Bow Street side was quieter. Looking out the windows on the Mt. Auburn Street side I could see Lowell House, looking lonely with no lights in the windows. On the Bow Street side there was Adams House, also, of course, with no lights in the windows. Lying there, I thought about the fact that all the money I had in the entire world was something like thirty-five cents. That morning I had gone to one of the bookstores in the Square and sold a twenty-five-dollar thesaurus my mother had given me when I had gone off to Harvard the first time, in 1946, for five bucks. But then, after I had bought some breakfast, and then lunch, and my usual two packs of Pall Malls to see me through the day, I had wound up with the thirty-five cents as my total remaining capital.

I got up and went down to the Business Office and opened the drawer in the desk where I knew all the money that had been collected by one of the Business Board members from all the little newsstands around the Square had been left in a gray metal box for Wensley Barker, the *Lampoon*'s accountant, to take to the bank the next morning. I knew the money was there because I had seen the guy put it there, and I had looked at it when I had gone to the Business Office to get the typewriter I had taken up to the Great Hall.

I opened the box and took out the money. It came to a little over a hundred dollars, in a neat stack of mostly ones, fives and tens, but with a couple of twenties on the bottom, held together with a thick rubber band, and with a piece of paper on top where the total had been scribbled by the member who had collected the money.

I removed the piece of paper and crumpled it up and stuck it in my pocket. Then I took a twenty off the bottom and stuck that in my pocket, too, and wrote the new total on another piece of paper and slipped it under the rubber band.

This was the first time in my life I had ever stolen any money, and I went back to the Great Hall and sat down at the end of the long table again to see how it made me feel. I felt exhilarated, and excited. To me, I told myself, this twenty bucks would make the difference between starving and not starving, because the job I had been promised with Building and Grounds didn't start for a week, and then I knew I would have a whole week after that to wait before I received my first paycheck. Whereas, to the *Lampoon,* it was just bookkeeping. I went up to the Square and stuffed myself with ham and eggs and English muffins and coffee, and then opened the fresh pack of Pall Malls I had bought on my way to the restaurant and sat there smoking and feeling good.

However, when I returned to the Lampoon, I couldn't stop thinking about the money in the cash box. I tried to do some writing, but couldn't. Finally, around three o'clock in the morning, when I hadn't been able to fall asleep, I rose from my couch in the Ibis Room and went down to the Business Office in my bare feet and stole another twenty, and after that, slept like an angel.

る

I WAS ALONE almost every evening in the Lampoon. Gwynne usually had a part in whatever play the Brattle Theater was doing, and Plimpton was off somewhere with his friends, or at Braves Field. Often they both came back to the building at around the same time, and then we had a few beers together and talked, but the rest of the time I was alone in the President's Room, with my typewriter and the silence.

Every day while I was fixing furniture I thought about my novel, and felt sure that tonight everything would go well, and looked forward to the moment when Fred and George would leave. Then I rolled a piece of paper into my typewriter, thinking that this time it would be different, I would know exactly what to say. But I would work furiously for a while, and it would be all wrong—and then the arguments would begin. What's the point of going on with this thing, for God's sake? It's just a dead end, for God's sake. Why not start something brand-new? How about a humorous novel? How about a crime novel? How about an adventure story? How about sex? Look at what happened to *Forever Amber*. What was it Scott Fitzgerald said? Anyone can make a lot of money in writing if they can just think of an original way of saying the opposite of what people generally think? But what do people generally think? God knows. And who wants to start all over again anyway? Page one? New characters? New situations? New backgrounds? A whole new story? With time so precious? No, much better to go with what we already have here, when we have such an enormous emotional investment in *these* people and *this* story—and when there's so little time left.

So I would let it go for the night, and start my wandering. Go into the Business Office and stare for the millionth time at the framed group pictures covering the walls of *Lampoon* staffs going back to the very beginning. Then in the Public Room, plenty of dusty old cabinets to open and look into, poke around in. The bulletin board with stuff still up there from last December. Read all that stuff again. In the Narthex more cabinets, dusty old armchairs, dusty bookshelves lined with dusty books. In the Sanctum a dusty couch, more cabinets, pages from stories, notebooks, cartoons, back copies of the magazine, make-up pages, squash rackets, neckties, tennis shoes, raincoats, beer glasses, crumpled cigaret packs.

Up the winding stairway, softly into the Great Hall, which was all dark except for the pale glow from the streetlights. Glide along, feeling my way in the darkness, behind the red ash of the cigaret stuck in my mouth. Flicked a shoulder at the bell rope. Stood before a tall window gazing down at the street. A few people were strolling by, under the streetlights, a few cars rolled past. Church bells sounded the quarter hour. A gust of wind moved the heavy curtains, which were slowly disintegrating, like cardinals' hats, and ruffled the pages lying at the end of the long table— *George's novel.*

He worked there sometimes in the afternoons. There was his typewriter, his ashtray, his pencils, his eraser. Was it going well? He never really said. He invited me to read a couple of pages once. Not the way writers usually invite you to read something—half whining, half challenging, ready to jump down your throat if you don't like it, but knowing you won't like it, so sitting there watching you, telling themselves they really couldn't care less what you think, because what do you know about writing anyway?

George wasn't like that. He was completely good-natured about it.

The nine or ten pages I read were the beginning of the novel, which as I remember it had no title. It was a night scene. A country club had caught fire while a dance was in progress, and people were all over the place, running around, screaming, running back into the blaze to try to save friends and relatives who were trapped inside. There was a nice effect of the contrast between the white moonlight and the orange flames.

I told him I liked the moonlight and the orange flames thing, and I thought he liked that.

I tried to press him a couple of times after that about his novel, wanting very much to know what it was about, but he really didn't seem to want to talk about it, so I stopped trying.

In fact, the only time George ever really talked to me about *writing* was once when he made a rather long and convoluted speech about Hemingway's "shock of recognition." I wasn't sure I knew what it meant, but it was the first time I had ever heard the phrase, and I loved it.

One Saturday afternoon I stood in the shadows at the top of the stairs and looked at George for a while as he sat there in his usual place at the end of the long table, tossing a sock into the air, over and over, trying to make it catch on a petrified blowfish that was suspended by a thin wire from the ceiling above him, and never quite making it, but looking very peaceful and happy, anyway.

Finally, back to the President's Room, and the typewriter and the balled-up pieces of paper all over the floor. Later, Fred would come in, still with traces of mascara in his eyelashes from the play. Then George would come in, perhaps very happy because the Braves had won. They would ask me how many pages I had written that night, and I would say five or six or something, and they would say, *"Terrific!"*

THE SUMMER, which had promised to be such a good long time in the beginning, so many good long hot days ahead of us, back in June, drifted away. In August I got laid off from my job. At almost the same time George said he was going to have to go home soon to get ready to leave for England, and Fred's season at the Brattle Theater was over.

First, George said goodbye. Then Fred.

Suddenly the Lampoon became terribly lonely and frightening, and I began to spend whole days without saying a word to anyone. I stopped working on my novel altogether. Killing time was my principal fixation. I slept late every day, usually not getting up until noon, when the August heat drove me out of the Ibis Room. Then I dragged myself up to the Square for a cup of coffee, and dragged myself back to the Lampoon, where I sat around the rest of the day smoking and thinking about how lonely and frightening it was in the building. For a while I took the subway to Boston every night and went to a movie, but if you keep that up for very long you run out of movies, so then it was back to wandering aimlessly through the building most of the night.

The worst part was that I began to let myself go, sometimes not bothering even to shave for two or three days at a time.

Now and then members came into the Lampoon—on their way home from Bar Harbor or somewhere. They always seemed to barge into the place late in the morning, when of course I was invariably still in bed. The locked door at the foot of the stairs to the Ibis Room frustrated them, and made them feel they had to pound on the door with their fists and yell, *"Who's up there? Bunce, is it you? Open up this door, you little bastard!"*

I didn't want them to see my three-day beard, and I didn't want them to see the filthy way I was living, so I never answered, but just stayed very quiet, until finally they gave up and went away.

Then there was my "relationship" with Elmer Green, the janitor of the Lampoon, who had lived in the basement for over twenty years. Nobody had any idea how old he was, or much of anything else about him. He was small and thin and very pale, and wore glasses that seemed to reflect light more dazzlingly than any glasses I had ever seen before. When you spoke to him he was always very polite, and he loved to laugh.

For some pitifully small salary he swept the floors and cleaned up after the Thursday night dinners, and never complained about his living conditions, which were simply abominable. He slept on a cot in the darkest corner of the basement. Down there you saw two or three sad suits and an enormous square-shouldered overcoat on hangers lined up on a bare pipe, a couple of pairs of scuffed shoes under the cot, and that was all he seemed to own in the whole world.

I had never paid much attention to him, but when everybody left and I was living alone in the building with him, I became very conscious of him, and had the feeling that he had also become very conscious of me. I kept thinking that he was wondering why I hadn't left too. What was I doing there now all by myself? I began to have the distinct feeling that he was worried about me, even felt sorry for me, and that depressed me beyond belief.

Maybe to cheer me up, he began stopping by the President's Room almost every night when he returned from wherever he had been, to have a little chat. I had started on the cover for the Freshman Number of the *Lampoon,* and he would stand in the doorway flashing his glasses at me, and talking in his high voice and laughing at anything I said, whether it was funny or not. Mostly, we talked about the Boston Red Sox, deploring the fact that with all Yawkey's money they hadn't been able to come up with two really front-line pitchers since Ellis Kinder and Mel Parnell—and going on from there to wallow in the memory of the great tragedy of '46 when they had finally gotten into a World Series and Ted Williams hadn't been able to buy a hit and the whole thing went down the spout.

I had already taken the material that was to appear in the Freshman Number to the printer. The Freshman Number was traditionally a reprint issue, consisting mostly of a lot of old stuff by Robert Benchley '12, Gluyas Williams '11, Edward Streeter '14, J. P. Marquand '15 and Robert Sherwood '18, all of which was supposed to impress the incoming class of freshmen and make them want to try out for the *Lampoon.*

Soon the printer called and said the galleys were ready, and I took the subway over to his shop near South Station and picked them up, and spent the whole night proofreading and making up the issue. The next morning I delivered the dummy and my completed cover to the printer, and right after that I began to have a tremendous urge to get out of Cambridge. Michelle had written me several letters asking me to come down to Miami, as I had promised I would, so that afternoon I bought a round-trip Greyhound ticket for Miami, and then called Michelle and told her I was on my way. She was very excited and said she was really looking forward to seeing me.

ROARING ALONG the highway in the bus, I was happy. I loved the motion, the rushing onward, watching Connecticut and New York and New Jersey go past. I loved the whole experience, even the wolfing of stale egg salad sandwiches and Cokes at the rest stops. It just felt so good to be going somewhere away from Cambridge, from the Lampoon, from my novel, which I had left behind in my footlocker in the Lampoon with everything else I owned in the world.

ॐ

THE MORNING looked sullen, with the wind blowing hard sometimes and then falling off altogether and leaving the air still and ominous. The sea was dark blue and restless, and I remember the clouds as very low, swift-moving and yellowish-gray. The radio was saying there was a hurricane churning around a couple of hundred miles east off the Bahamas.

Steve and Michelle and I spent that whole day there on the beach near Cape Florida, and every once in a while one of them would wet his finger playfully and touch my back with it and go "Sssssssssssss!" and we would all laugh. I hadn't been wearing anything but a pair of bathing trunks all day and knew I was getting sunburned, but it was such a cloudy day I really hadn't worried too much about it, even though this was the first time that summer I had spent a lot of time out in the sun and I was very pale when the day began. Besides, the wind had kept me cooled off most of the time.

But toward evening I began to hurt, and the pain quickly became agony, and it gradually dawned on me that I was hideously sunburned. At the same time I remember that one of the things my mother always used to say was that it was on overcast days that you got all your truly wicked sunburns—and that I had never really listened to her.

When we got home and I looked at myself in the mirror I knew that I was in terrible trouble. I had never seen anyone turn such a frightening color before. There were large splotches all over my body where I was actually becoming purple. As I looked at myself in the mirror a chill went over me that I could feel in spite of the burning, and I was suddenly so weak and dizzy that I had to sit on the edge of the bathtub to try to collect myself.

By seven o'clock the pain was unbearable, and they called a doctor, who stood looking down at me as I lay on my bed, and said while it wasn't the worst sunburn he had ever seen—that was on a man who had drifted on a life raft for six days in the Gulf Stream before they had picked him up—it was a very bad one. Then he said that if I didn't start blistering within the next couple of hours, which would mean a second-degree burn, I might not have to go to the hospital. The treatment would be the application of cold compresses soaked in a solution of baking soda, and cold baths, also in a solution of baking soda. No Vaseline or other lubricants during the first twenty-four hours, no products containing benzocaine ever. Plenty of aspirin. He said the worst pain would be in the first forty-eight hours, and left me twenty Seconals.

Michelle was my nurse and applied the cold compresses and drew the cold baths for me. For the first two days I lay alternately on my left side or my right side. I could not endure lying on my stomach or my back. I took a sleeping pill practically whenever I woke up, so I slept almost all the time, except when Michelle woke me up to take me to the bathroom, or to the bathtub, or applied the compresses, or fed me orange juice, limeade or grapefruit juice through a straw. She brought me an electric fan that played a cool breeze over me. On the fourth day the pain diminished, and the itching and the peeling began.

I had been staying with them for almost a week when I got the sunburn, and up until then Michelle and I hadn't made love once—no bangles, no mascara, no nothing. She kept saying just to be patient, and it was true that Steve was around almost all the time, but from the first I had sensed that there was something very different not only in our relationship, but in their relationship, too. Very clearly, they seemed much closer, much more affectionate, much more involved with each other than I had ever seen them before.

One day, when I had almost entirely recovered from my sunburn, Steve left on a flight to New York, and that evening I made my first serious pass at Michelle. She got very nervous, and after a lot of stammering, and pushing away of my hands, and generally acting as if she were going to die of embarrassment, she asked me if it would be all right with me if we didn't do any of "that stuff" anymore.

"See, the thing is, Steve and I are getting along much better than we used to," she said.

"I've noticed," I said.

"I mean, for quite a while now we've been getting along real fine."

"Well, I'm very glad to hear it," I said, beginning to realize that I might have made a terrible mistake in coming all this way.

"So, if you and I—well, you know, if you and I started doing all that stuff again, it would sort of upset me, you know. Make me feel guilty and everything. Understand, Doug?"

"Oh, sure," I said, wanting to bite off my tongue.

"You mean it?"

"Hey, don't worry about it," I said, dying.

She came and put her arms around me and gave me a big hug, and a kiss, on the cheek. "I knew you'd understand," she said happily. "You *know* how I love you, don't you? You *know* how much I care about you—?"

"Of course I do," I said.

"And you're sure you're not disappointed?"

"Listen," I said, "I'm just very happy for you, that's all."

And I really was happy for her, and for Steve, and for their dogs, but this was *not* what I had come fifteen hundred miles for. I had come fifteen hundred miles for somebody to adore me the way I had been adored before, which was what I really felt I had to have after almost a whole year of practically no contact with women because I couldn't even afford to take one to a movie. Jesus Christ, I thought, for this I spent a small fortune for a round-trip bus ticket to Miami, Florida?

I didn't think for a second that she actually believed me, but knew she realized she better pretend to because that would make the situation easier all around.

"What an *angel* you are," she said, giving me another hug, and another kiss on the cheek.

"The thing is, he's given up all his waitresses," she said. "Can you believe it?"

"That's marvelous," I said.

"And he's been so *sweet.*" She shuddered, just thinking about it. "And you know what?"

"What?"

"He's even said that maybe we could start thinking about having a *baby!*"

"Say, that's really great," I said.

"Oh, you don't know how much I'd love to have a baby," she said, her eyes glistening. "I think that would be the most wonderful thing that could possibly happen to me!"

Then she told me that one thing she truly hoped for was that she and Steve and I would be friends for the rest of our lives, and I said I hoped for the very same thing, but what I was really hoping for was that I would be able to get out of there soon. The trouble was that things I had been able to put up with before, when there was something in it for me, now were simply intolerable. For instance, Steve. Listening to him talking endlessly about himself had been exquisite torture before, now it raised the bloodlust in me. And many of Michelle's little habits, which I had never even paid any attention to in the past, now began to drive me crazy. I let a week pass, and then I started saying that I was going to have to be getting back to Cambridge pretty soon, if I expected to register for the fall term, and I asked Steve if by any chance I might be able to hop a ride north on one of his flights. He said he didn't think he would be going either to New York or Boston any time soon, but promised to ask around at the airport and see if he could get a ride for me with someone else.

❧

BOTH MARCUS AND SALLY had written to me that Wes had soon gotten tired of Montclair and had come back to Miami, and they had given me his address. I didn't want to leave Miami without seeing him, but it took me a long time to bring myself to do it, because I had no idea whether he would ever want to see me again.

I found him living in an apartment that was located on the second floor of a very pleasant old mansion off Brickell Avenue, near the mouth of the Miami River. The place had beautiful grounds, and vast screened-in porches. When he came downstairs to meet me, he had a rather shocked look on his face, and for a minute there was an uncomfortable silence, but then he said, "Well, this is a really nice surprise, Champ."

It was my turn to be shocked, because I hadn't heard him call me by that name in I didn't know how many years, but then he was leading me upstairs and showing me around his apartment, which looked very comfortable, and from the window had a fine view of Biscayne Bay.

Then he said, "Come on, I want to show you something very pretty."

He led me back downstairs and through a long cool hallway to a door at the rear of the house. Outside, at the foot of the back steps was a brand-new, block-long forest-green convertible Coupe de Ville with a tan top and red leather interior. "What do you think of it, Champ?" he said, proudly surveying the car.

"It's beautiful," I said.

"All the new ones have these fins," he said, running his fingertips over the left rear fin. "Say, you know who'd love this car, don't you?"

I nodded.

"She would really love this car, wouldn't she?"

"She sure would."

"I thought of her when I bought it. Remember that last Packard I bought her? She'd like this car even better. She always secretly wanted a Cadillac, you know. And I think she would have liked this color, too, don't you?"

"I know she would have," I said.

"I paid cash for it," he said. "They made a cash settlement to get me out of their hair in Pennsylvania, so I decided to buy a new car. It's been a hell of a long time since I've had a new car."

He opened the door for me. "Go ahead, sit in it," he said, and I got in and sat in it, and looked it all over. "Later on we'll go for a drive," he said. "You get a wonderful ride in these cars, you know. I've always been a Packard man of course, but your mother was right. When it comes to the *ride,* there's no car in the world like a Cadillac. Say, listen, I want you to come back upstairs with me now, because I've got another little surprise for you."

In the hallway we encountered some of the other tenants, and Wes introduced me to them as "my boy Dougie." I could tell that, of course, as usual, they all liked him and were charmed by him. When we entered his apartment, he said, "The sun may not quite be over the yardarm yet, but how about a touch of schnapps?"

"Okay," I said.

"Well, name your poison," he said, leading me into the kitchen and showing me his liquor supply, in the cabinet above the kitchen sink. I saw that the days of the rotgut were over, now that he had come into his "cash settlement." The cabinet was stocked with nothing but J&B and Black Label and English gin. I asked for some scotch and he poured me a healthy slug, and one for himself, and then said, leading me back into the living room, "Remember that novel of yours, Champ? What ever became of it, anyway?"

"Oh, nothing much, really," I said. "The fact is, I'm still working on it."

"*Still* working on it?"

"Yes."

"Forgive me for sounding stupid," he said. "But how can you *still* be working on it? How many years is it now since you began it?"

"I know," I said. "It's been a long time."

He studied me for a moment. "Well, tell me, how near are you to finishing it, right now?"

I shrugged. "Oh, I don't know," I said. "It's just hard to say."

"Well, what about that editor in New York who wrote you that letter? What's become of her interest in the book?"

"I'm afraid she isn't interested in it any longer."

"Not interested? Why?"

"Because she thinks I ruined it."

"My God," he said. "Is she right? Did you ruin it?"

"Yes, by rewriting it until there wasn't anything left of what she had liked about it," I said. "And ever since then, what I've been trying to do is get it back to the way it was in the beginning. But I just never seem to be able to do it."

"Well, where does the matter stand now?"

"Pardon me?"

"Where does the matter stand now? Are you going to send it to her again when you finish it?"

"No, I'll never send it to her again," I said. "She told me she never wants to see it again."

"In other words, you're not in contact with her at all anymore—?"

"No, not at all."

He stared at me again. "Well, I'm really very sorry to hear that," he said, sounding terribly disappointed. "Really, very, very sorry to hear it."

I had begun to have a very strange feeling about him. For instance, he hadn't once asked me anything about myself. What I had been doing since he saw me last, how I had managed to survive all this time, what I was doing now. But here he was, paying all this attention to my novel, which I never thought he had cared that much about before.

"I don't understand," I said. "What difference does it make to you?"

He said, "Well, come on, look at this."

He led me into what I assumed was the spare bedroom, and in there was a card table with a typewriter on it and stacks of yellow paper all around, and an overflowing wastebasket, and my heart sank, because all of a sudden I knew what the other surprise was.

"I've been working on a novel of my own," he said proudly. "I can't type of course, so I just write the stuff out in longhand and a girl comes in twice a week and types it up for me. She's very nice. Very expensive, but very nice. And very helpful, too. She has a degree in English from the University of Miami, and she's working on her master's now, and she makes a lot of very helpful suggestions about grammar and syntax, and between the two of us the book has come right along. In fact, I think I'll probably finish it before Christmas. You know what I'd like you to do? Just take a look at some of this stuff and let me know what you think of it."

He went over to the card table and picked up a thick manuscript and handed it to me. "That's how much I have right at this moment," he said, and I sat down in the chair in front of the typewriter and started reading page one, but it was very hard to concentrate with him standing right there breathing down my neck. All the words just seemed to run together, and after three or four pages I stopped trying.

"Well, what do you think of it so far?" he asked.

"I'm afraid it's pretty difficult to make any sort of judgment from reading just these few pages," I said, and hoping not to have to read any more right then, I asked him to tell me what it was about.

"Well, I guess you'd have to call it a comedy," he said. "Kate, that's the girl who does my typing—laughs right out loud all the time as she's typing along. Of course, I don't know how good her sense of humor really is, but she sure gets a kick out of all the crazy stuff that happens. But you'd have to read it yourself to know what I mean. Anyway, I was hoping that you might recommend me to that editor in New York, and now you tell me you're not even in touch with her any longer . . ."

I nodded.

"That really would have been a nice entree," he said. "You know, I've been getting one of those writers' magazines and in a recent issue they said that your chances of getting a novel accepted by a major publisher are pretty remote, unless you have a literary agent to send it in for you, or you have some other form of an entree, like being recommended by someone whose work they're familiar with. This really would have been a hell of a nice entree, if you could have written a cover letter for me, so I didn't just have to send the damn thing in, as they say, 'over the transom.'"

"I'm really sorry," I said.

"Well, that's okay," he said. "Ready for another drink?"

"Not quite yet," I said.

He stood up and started toward the kitchen, and then paused and looked back at me. "Well, hell's bells," he said. "Just because she isn't interested in your book anymore doesn't necessarily mean that she wouldn't accept a recommendation for someone else's book from you, does it?"

I absolutely couldn't think what to say to him. I was amazed that he could think that what he was suggesting was reasonable. I looked at him as he waited for my answer, and had the feeling again that there was something very strange about him, but I still didn't know exactly what it was.

"Well, what do you say?" he said.

"I just don't think I could do it," I said. "I mean, she was very disappointed in what I did to my own book, so how could she accept a recommendation from me for someone else's book?"

He came back and sat down across from me, holding his empty glass in both hands in front of him and rolling it back and forth between his palms.

"Look," he said, "let me tell you how important this book is to me. This settlement they made in Pennsylvania, it didn't amount to all that much to begin with, and I've had some bad luck at a couple of tracks since then. The fact is, I don't have all that much left out of the whole schmeer after buying the Cadillac, and I'm not well. I've been having some trouble with my heart. I have to sleep sitting up in bed, because if I don't the blood rushes to my head and I get very bad attacks of vertigo. Besides that, I'm having problems with my legs. In other words, I don't think I could handle a job at the track or anything like that in the shape I'm in now, but if I can't sell this book that's what I'll have to do. What else am I good at?"

He really didn't look too well, and I suddenly felt very sorry for him, and before I knew what I was doing I heard myself saying, "Okay, I'll write to her for you when you're ready to send your book in. I think you're right. I think it might get you a lot better treated than if you sent it in cold."

He was very happy. "Listen, you don't have to worry that I'm going to embarrass you," he said. "It's a hell of a story. It may even turn out to be a bestseller!"

After that we went for a drive in the Cadillac, and as I had guessed we would, eventually wound up at the pink house down on South Bayshore Lane. "I come here all the time," he said. "There's nobody living in the house right now, so I just walk around to the front and sit there on the front steps for a while, and, you know, I swear to God sometimes I can hear your mother's voice, calling me, or you kids, and I look around and think I'll see her standing there in the doorway behind me, and it will turn out all this was just a bad dream, and it's all back like it was."

We went around to the front of the house and sat on the steps side by side, and both lit up cigarets and sat there smoking and looking at the bay. When I glanced at him I saw that his eyes were shining, and I realized how lonely he was, and how much he did wish it could be all back like it was. But I knew that what he really meant by back like it was, was back like it was in Fort Myers Beach.

Returning to his place, he finally asked me what I'd been doing since he last saw me, and I told him about my having gone back to Harvard the previous fall. He said he thought it was very nice of them to have let me return, considering everything, but he didn't ask me how I had managed to pay my way through the year or anything like that. Then he asked me what I was doing in Miami, and I told him I was visiting some friends, who, incidentally, lived in the big white house down the seawall from the pink house, and he said that sounded very nice, but, again, I knew he was only asking the questions because he felt he had to and didn't actually care very much what was happening to me.

All he really had on his mind was his book and his loneliness, and when we were back in his apartment he sat me down at the card table again and asked me to read the first three chapters of his book. He gave me another drink and an ashtray and said he was going to leave me "strictly alone" so I could give him an "honest evaluation" of his work. Reading along, something began to nag at me, and all of a sudden I remembered a fact I had almost forgotten, which was that for many years he had kept a bunch of little notebooks, where he had recorded what he had used to call the "felicitous phrases and expressions" that he had run across in his reading. What I was reading now was full of "felicitous phrases and expressions," and looking up from his manuscript I saw the very same little notebooks stacked neatly beside the typewriter.

When I had read the first three chapters I went into the living room, where he was waiting for me with a numb look on his face.

"Well?" he said.

I had fully intended to tell him what I honestly thought of his novel, but when I opened my mouth what came out was, "I think it's really very good."

He looked happy. "Well, what did I tell you? Didn't I tell you it was a hell of a story?"

"It's really very nice," I said. "At least what I've seen of it so far."

"Well, it only gets better and better, believe me," he said. "How did you like the style?"

"I think the style's just fine."

"Does it read smooth enough for you?"

"It reads very smooth."

"Did you get some laughs?"

"Yes, I think you have some very funny stuff there."

"Listen," he said, "tell me the truth now. You *really* like it?"

"I really do."

"And you're going to write that letter to the editor in New York for me?"

"Absolutely."

"Well, look," he said, "rather than waiting until I'm finished with the book, how about writing the letter now?"

"I don't understand," I said. "If you're not going to finish the book for several months, why do you want me to write the letter now?"

He sort of hesitated, and then said, "Well, so I can be in contact with her. I mean, so I can then write to her myself, and establish a rapport with her before she actually sees the book. So we can get to know each other a little. I think that might be very helpful not only to me but to her, too. "What do you say?"

"Okay," I said.

"Well, why don't you just go in there and use my typewriter? And I'll go down and sit on the porch and wait for you."

"Right," I said.

"You'll let me read it, of course, before you seal it up?"

"Of course," I said.

The only thing was, I told myself as I settled down at the typewriter, there was no possible harm I could do myself in writing the letter, because God knew I was already dead there.

I wrote a very nice letter to Jean Luft, telling who it was I was recommending to her, and saying that I had read a portion of the book myself and had really found it extraordinarily good. I didn't say anything at all about "Welcome Stamp Collectors," but just said I truly hoped all was well with her.

He liked the letter. I sensed that he wished I had gone a little bit more, in the expression he loved, "overboard," but he was, by and large, very pleased with what I had written. By then it was getting rather late in the afternoon, and he said that he would like to take me to dinner somewhere—I could name the place. I said all right, but I had better call the people I was visiting and let them know I wouldn't be home for dinner. While I was calling Michelle, he made us a couple more drinks, which we took back down to the porch, where a cool breeze was sweeping up from the bay.

Gazing out at the bay, he said, "You know something, Champ? Correct me if I'm wrong (another of his favorite expressions), but isn't it possible that the reason things didn't turn out as you had hoped with your novel, was because nothing has ever happened to you in your life so far? I mean, I believe that in order to be able to write about life, you have to have *lived*. Understand, I don't mean this in a derogatory way, but the truth is, you have led a very sheltered existence. Will you agree with that?"

"I guess so," I said.

"And that's why this book of mine will probably succeed where yours failed—because I've had such an enormous amount of *experience* to draw on. Do you follow me?"

"Yes, I do," I said.

"Not that plenty of things won't happen to you in your life. They probably will. But until then you'll never be a writer, because you won't have the writer's stock in trade, his *experiences.*"

After dinner he began drinking stingers (always a big favorite of his), and we stayed in the restaurant until almost closing time while he grew very mellow reminiscing about Fort Myers Beach. Just before we finally left the restaurant he asked me how I was managing to pay my way through Harvard, and I said that I had gotten a student loan for the spring term and was hoping to get another for the coming fall term.

"Well, I'd like to make a contribution to the cause," he said, and took out his checkbook.

"No, that's all right," I said. "You need your money. I'll get by one way or another."

"No, listen," he said, already scribbling in his checkbook, "I sincerely want to make a contribution to the cause."

"Well, okay," I said. "I really would appreciate it."

"You did something for me, didn't you?" he said. "Why shouldn't I help you out a little, too?"

He tore out the check and stuffed it into my shirt pocket, and then said, "I guess I'd better be getting you back to your friends."

When we reached Steve and Michelle's house, he asked me if he would be seeing me again before I went back to Cambridge, and I said I would like very much to see him again. He shook my hand warmly and swung the car around in the street, and I watched until the taillights disappeared around the corner up on South Bayshore Drive. Then, in the light under the porte-cochere, I took his check out of my shirt pocket and looked at it. At first, I couldn't believe what I was seeing. It was a check for twenty-five dollars! I wanted to run after him and tell him that for God's sake he must have left off some zeros! Did he mean two hundred and fifty dollars? Or twenty-five hundred dollars?

Steve had heard the car arrive, and he came out of the house and told me that he had a free ride for me all the way to Boston on a plane that was leaving at one o'clock. He said Michelle had packed my stuff for me and we could make the airport without any trouble if we left right then. I was in such a daze that I could barely talk all the way to the airport. Twenty-five dollars! Even two hundred dollars or three hundred dollars or five hundred dollars would have been an enormous help to me. But twenty-five dollars! I kept thinking that maybe I should call him up from the airport and come right out and ask him if that was what he had really meant to give me. If it was, nothing at all would have been much better, because then he wouldn't have had the satisfaction of thinking that he had actually made a "contribution to the cause."

Michelle and Steve said how much they had enjoyed my visit and before I left them Michelle told me again how much she hoped that the three of us would be friends forever. In a daze I climbed aboard the plane and took my place on a jump-seat in the cockpit, and as soon as we were off the ground I took the check out of my pocket again and looked at it to see that if maybe in the bad light under the porte-cochere I hadn't seen the other zeros. But there it was, twenty-five dollars, big as life. By the time we were about halfway to Boston I knew there had been no mistake.

æ

I ARRIVED BACK in Cambridge to see copies of the Freshman Number of the *Lampoon* with my drawing on the cover on the newsstands all around Harvard Square, as well as on posters plastered up everywhere.

That was very exciting, but my excitement was short-lived because when I went to the Student Loan Office to apply for another loan from the University, I was refused, on the grounds that my grades in the spring term hadn't been good enough to qualify me for any more money—and, as a matter of fact, the man I talked to said the University would like to have some idea of when I would pay back what I already owed. I told him I was very sorry but I was afraid it might be some time.

I couldn't imagine what to do next. I had honestly felt that I had a good chance of getting another loan, and this left me with only a few dollars to my name, and no place to live. When I told my friends on the *Lampoon* what had happened, and that I would have to use the last of my money to go back down to Florida and try to get my job back at Florida Power & Light, they were very upset because they said the magazine really needed me, and suggested that, what the hell, why didn't I go right on living in the Ibis Room?

The thought of it appalled me. Living in the Ibis Room for a summer was one thing, but living there when the college was in session and the building would be full of people all the time was quite another. I said I simply couldn't do it, but in the end I did it, because I didn't want to go back to Florida. The only thing I wanted to do was stay in Cambridge and be among people who respected me for the things I could do well. And so I can't say I let them persuade me to go back to the Ibis Room. I persuaded myself, and that was when the stealing of the subscription money, and the raiding of the cash box in the Business Office, and the semihysteria, and the quivering, and the chain-smoking, and the stinking, and the wearing of cast-off clothes began in earnest.

RIGHT AFTER we Fools had been made full-fledged members of the *Lampoon* the previous spring, the older members had, in effect, handed the magazine over to us and left us standing there with the responsibility of putting together the next issue, although none of us had had any experience with even the basics of magazine production. But that was the *Lampoon* way in those days, and these older members who were doing this to us had had the same damn thing done to them in their time. The attitude was, let the new guys handle all the boring part of it from now on. Let them do all the slaving over dummies, proofreading, coping with printers, etc., while we concentrate on our tutorials, and our drinking, and our girlfriends, and worrying about what the hell is going to become of us when, *much* too soon now, we are to be thrust out into the real world beyond Harvard Square.

So one night we sat down and taught ourselves how to construct a dummy out of the long yellow galleys, and when we were through with all our line-counting and pasting-up and inserting of cuts and runarounds, we had a not-too-bad-looking magazine, which we delivered to the printers' the next morning, feeling very proud of ourselves.

The next thing we had to do was learn how to develop a forthcoming issue out of the time-honored *Lampoon* institution of the "gag session." The main problem with the gag sessions was that most of the members of the literary board of the magazine didn't really give much of a damn about the quality of the material that went into the magazine. But then it was a very old tradition of the *Lampoon* that a serenely blasé attitude toward the subscribers, as well as to the public at large, was the only possibly correct attitude, which of course derived from the traditional *Lampoon* concept that it was basically vulgar for the magazine to make money. For what purpose, after all, make money? What would we have done with it if we had had it? All we had to do, really, was cover our printing costs and our light bills and pay Elmer Green, and even as ineptly managed and under-subscribed as the *Lampoon* was, we were usually able to break about even every month.

Furthermore, very few members of the literary board had any serious literary or artistic aspirations, in the sense that they ever actually intended to write another line of prose or compose another stanza of light verse or draw another cartoon after they left Harvard. What they honestly wanted to do when they came to the building, to put it very simply, was just horse around and have a good time. As a result of this, the gag sessions in the Sanctum, during which we were all supposed to submit our ideas for the approval of the board, always deteriorated very quickly into scenes of hilarity out of which, more often than not, nothing whatsoever that could actually be used in the magazine emerged.

So then, as the deadline for the next issue came closer, we would have to gather in the Sanctum once more, and perhaps begin proceedings this time by opening the drawer in which the candidates deposited their contributions, and would grab those flimsy manuscripts and sit down and start to read, in hopes that just this once, for Christ's sake, one of our little geniuses had turned in something we could use.

A few minutes would pass by and then someone would say, "Oh, my God, I have never seen such *shit!*" and then would read a passage of enormously well-intended but perfectly sappy prose and that would start all the rest of us reading aloud from *our* pieces of shit, and once again the proceedings would deteriorate into another wild katzenjammer, with the inevitable result that the night before the deadline we would suddenly have to get very serious and stay up until three o'clock in the morning deciding what material we were actually going to deliver to the printer the next day.

The truth was that most of the stuff we ran in the *Lampoon* was mediocre at best, but who cared? The point of belonging to the 'Poon was to have a good time, wasn't it? Not print great literature. Leave that to the *Advocate!*

I had liked all of the new members who had been elected at the same time I was that spring, but the fact that at twenty-four I was three, or four, or even *five* years older than some of them, had made it difficult for me to feel close to them. When one of them told me once that, collectively, they liked my being older than they were because to them I represented "sanity in a world gone mad," I was charmed, but in my heart I never got over feeling uncomfortable around them.

That fall of 1950 I was free of course to devote most of my time to the magazine. What else did I have to do, after all, except work on my novel late at night, after everyone else had gone home? I drew most of the covers and contributed a large number of cartoons and stories. I also assumed the job of making up the magazine, and took care of most of our dealings with the printer, and, in general, made myself indispensable. All of this naturally lightened the burden for everyone else, and left them free to work harder at their studies. The point, obviously, was to make not just myself but all of the other members, too, feel that I was, in a sense, "paying my way." But I was painfully aware that it was not really a healthy situation. Here I was, an old guy, not even in college, living this creepy existence in the Ibis Room, and wasting valuable time working very hard at an enterprise from which there was not the remotest possibility of any profit for me.

Soon the money that could have bought me a bus ticket back to Miami was gone, and then I knew I was really trapped. Also, the weather began to turn very cold, and when the steam heat went off in the building around eleven o'clock every night, and the Ibis Room became nothing but an extension of the enormous drafty barn of the Great Hall, I lay there under the Inverness capes and the top hats and wondered what was going to happen if I got sick, and every time I coughed I broke out in a sweat.

Occasionally, someone would invite me to dinner at one of the House dining halls, but most of the time I ate in the cafeterias around the Square, if I had been able to score on the subscription money, or the cash box. If not, I made it on cigarets, hoping for a better day tomorrow.

ॐ

THE FIRST TIME Alex Latta made a serious impact on my consciousness was one night in the middle of the fever of Fools Week, when I pushed open the side door of the Lampoon building at 44 Bow Street, and upon entering the Public Room saw him perched, swaying precariously, on top of an antique Dutch cabinet, roughly eight feet off the floor. He was pathetically drunk and several of the members, also very drunk, were urging him to jump headfirst into The Boot, which stood on the floor below him.

The Boot was an enormous black rubber boot that was stolen every Fools Week from the place where it hung above the entrance to a rubber boot manufacturer's main office, somewhere near South Station. It stood about a yard high and I guess would have fitted a man eighteen feet tall very nicely.

When I arrived in the Public Room it looked as if Alex would jump at any moment. He had a crazy look in his glassy eyes and seemed just as enthusiastic to jump as the members were to see him do it, even though to anyone who was at least halfway sober, as I was, it was obvious that if he jumped he would kill himself. As I was standing there afraid to look, I was grabbed by one of the drunken members and ordered to go off and perform some stupid errand, so I left.

The next day I heard that in the end Alex had not jumped, but instead had been taken by the members to the Boston Garden, where, during the first intermission of the Harvard-Princeton hockey game, he had clumped out onto center ice in The Boot and before several thousand cheering Harvard fans had gotten sick on the red line.

LATER, I NOTICED that Alex was one of the few new members of the *Lampoon* who spent as much time in the building as I did, and it gradually came to me that perhaps he felt more at home there than anywhere else in Cambridge, just as I did. I knew he was the son of William Latta, a partner in one of the largest publishing houses in New York, but it wasn't until he told me that his ambition, too, was to be a novelist that I knew I had finally found someone whose heart was in exactly the same place mine was.

Of course, one of the first things I did was show him the Letter. He was very impressed, and asked me if he could take it down to New York with him that weekend and show it to his father. I said okay, and on the following Monday he came around to the building first thing in the morning.

"Douglas, the Old Man says you don't get letters like that from editors unless they really mean it. He says it sounds to him as if you have a very good novel in the works, and he said to tell you that if things don't work out at this place, he'd love to see the book himself."

"That's very nice, Alex," I said. "Who knows? Maybe I will send it to him if things don't work out at that place."

Alex hesitated. "Actually, he really was *very* interested. In fact, he asked me to find out anything I could about the book—the setting, some sort of general idea of the story line. Do you want to tell me any of that? I wouldn't blame you if you'd rather not—"

"Well, maybe not right this minute," I said.

It was about eight o'clock in the morning, and he had come pounding up the stairs to the Ibis Room and shaken me until I had popped my head out from under the covers.

"Well, okay," he said, "but *sometime—?*"

"Sure."

"You don't know what a crazy business this is," he said. "They can reject dozens of perfectly good books without a qualm, but if they hear there's something around that somebody else is very excited about, they'll try to do anything to get a look at it. Oh, by the way, you don't happen to have an agent, do you?"

"No, I don't," I said.

"That was something else he wanted me to find out."

"I've never tried to get an agent," I said. "I wouldn't know how to go about it, actually."

"You could get one," he said. "They can be very snooty if you're unpublished, but I don't think you'd have any problem once they knew about all this enthusiasm for your book."

He lit a cigaret. He smoked even more than I did. "You know, the fact is, if the Old Man really liked this book, he might make you a fairly large offer. He likes the idea of discovering new talent. He's brought along some very famous writers in his time."

"Well, actually I feel sort of committed to this editor," I said. "I just feel that since she was the one who encouraged me to go on with the book to begin with, I have to stay with her."

"But what if, when you finish it, she turns it down for some reason? They do that, you know."

"Okay," I said, "but if she turns it down, the chances are your father would, too."

He laughed at that. He had sort of an insane laugh when he was really amused. "Hey, you're not as dumb as you look," he said. "I'll have to tell the Old Man what you said. He'll get a kick out of it."

He was a strange little thing, skinny, with squinting eyes, a pretty big nose, a puffy, touchingly vulnerable mouth, stiff straight black hair that he seldom seemed to bother to comb, or get cut very often either, so was always sticking up all over his head, a small chin, alarming moles on his cheeks that made you think how excruciating shaving must be for him, and a face that turned dark red, particularly the nose, when he got excited, but the rest of the time was pale, if not actually pasty.

The impression of himself that he projected was of someone slightly mad, very funny, perhaps suicidal, whose shirttail was always hanging out.

He had gone to Groton, where, I heard, he was not too popular. I also heard that he had come out for the *Lampoon* twice before this time, and had been blackballed on both occasions, but simply had come out again anyway, even though there was supposedly some sort of a tacit understanding that if you had been balled once you weren't to try again, and had only made it this time because the magazine was getting very low on talent, and there was no question that he was a very good writer.

"Okay, we'll forget about your book for now," he said. "Understand? I just like to give the Old Man a bone to snap at now and then? It makes it so much easier to get money out of him."

"I understand," I said. "Now I'd appreciate it if you'd get the hell out of here."

"All right, all right," he said, and ran back down the steps.

I was very glad that I had gotten out of that. Obviously, all I needed was for William Latta to run into Jean Luft at a publisher's cocktail party—where in my overactive imagination people like that spent most of their lives—and have her spill the beans to him about what had happened to "Welcome Stamp Collectors." I had only shown the Letter to Alex to impress *him,* and that having been done, I fervently hoped this would be the end of it.

That spring, as I got to know Alex better, I found that my feelings toward him were confused. Mostly, I liked him, and thought he was funnier, brighter, more glamorous, more sophisticated, and cared much more about writing than anyone else around the *Lampoon.* But he could also be fantastically annoying. For one thing, he was obsessed with always having to be the first to know everything. The day the weekly news magazines were delivered to the newsstands in the Square, he was always there early and had read all the book and movie and theater reviews before anyone else, so that if you happened to say, "I wonder if this book (or play or movie) is any good," he could say, "Oh, I hear it's meant to be okay," or "Oh, I hear it's meant to be terrific," or "Oh, I hear it absolutely eats *shit.*"

That was always how he said it—"Meant to be this or that," never any other way, and sometimes you seriously had to struggle with yourself to keep from going for his throat.

Also, he could be very hurt when things didn't go his way, and he could be very selfish, and he was a shameless opportunist, so that in any situation he was involved in, if you watched carefully what was actually going on instead of what *appeared* to be going on, you would see that he would have unerringly done what was best for himself.

Furthermore, I was, of course, envious of him. Envious of his influential father, his duplex on Fifth Avenue, where, you gathered from listening to him, people like John O'Hara and Bennett Cerf and Richard Rodgers were always dropping in for a drink, and, most of all, his authentic familiarity with the whole world of books and agents and publishers and publishing. For instance, one time he came back to Cambridge from a weekend in New York and said he had run into Monica McCall at 21 and she had made him promise her faithfully that when he wrote his first novel, he would let her represent him. I knew the names of very few agents, but I had heard of her, so of course I was really snowed. And he could say things like, "Well, if I had my *choice* of British publishers, I guess it would always have to be Heinemann's."

LATE THAT SPRING, at a *Lampoon* dance, he got very drunk and climbed up on the mantel in the Great Hall, and it was The Boot scene all over again, except this time he also had beautiful girls to play to. People started chanting, "Jump! Jump! Jump!"—never, I was positive, really imagining for a minute that he would actually do it—and when he took his swan dive there were screams, and I, and several of the others, tried to break his fall, but he fractured his wrist anyway, although he wasn't even aware of it until the next morning when it was swollen up twice its normal size, and he came around to the building and showed it to everyone as if it were a museum piece. "Just *look* at this, would you?" he said. "I repeat, just *look* at this, *would* you?" and then almost fainted from the pain, and somebody had to run to get a car to rush him to the infirmary.

∂⅋

IN THE FALL of 1950, as things went from bad to worse for me, I realized that Alex Latta was the only person I knew in Cambridge who understood that there was nothing funny about my predicament any longer. As the weather turned colder and colder he invited me over to his rooms in Adams House to take hot showers, and would have let me sleep on the couch in his living room, except he said his roommates would have objected. And he sneaked me into the Adams House dining hall as often as he could get away with it.

One night, in the Lampoon, when I started coughing, he said, "Is it time now for me to start seriously worrying about you?"

"Not yet," I said.

"Tell me this one thing. When are you actually going to finish this fucking novel? You've been saying any minute now ever since I've known you, but when do you think you're actually going to do it—I mean, within a million years, one way or the other?"

"I don't know. It seems to go on and on. And, unfortunately, I'm a very slow writer."

"You're not kidding. Three years now? How long is the damn thing going to be, anyway? Some kind of a thousand-page epic that you're going to have to haul down to New York in a footlocker, like Thomas Wolfe?"

"It's going to be pretty long, I guess."

"Well, to begin with, you shouldn't be writing it on your own. I cannot understand why you haven't asked this editor of yours to go in there and get you some money. Haven't you told her you're starving to death?"

"No."

"Well, tell her, for Christ's sake."

"I'd rather not."

"You'd rather live like this?"

"Yes."

"Why? Some sort of idiotic *pride?*"

"I guess."

"That's crazy. Tell me, how much money do you have at this precise moment? I mean, what is your total capital in the entire world right now? About thirty-five cents?"

"Something like that."

"Look, go to that phone. Call her collect. Tell her to get her ass in there and get you a thousand bucks. She can do it, you know, if she really likes your book as much as she seems to."

"Leave me alone, Alex," I said.

He stared at me for a minute. "Listen, has she seen any more of this book since you sent it to her that first time?"

"No."

"Is that the truth?"

"Yes."

"You're sure?"

"Of course I'm sure."

"Well, what's happened since then? Has she stayed in touch with you? Have you stayed in touch with her?"

"Yes, she writes to me now and then, and I write to her and tell her how it's going."

"But you haven't sent her one more word than she's already seen? That's unusual, you know. You know what I think? I think you're afraid to ask her for any money because she might say she would have to see some more of the book first, and you're afraid she might be disappointed in the new stuff and lose interest in the book altogether. Am I close?"

"Will you leave me alone, Alex?"

"Okay, but now I really am worried about you."

THE IRONY of it all was that I was actually much more worried about him than he was about me. He had an Austin-Healey that he never drove unless he was drunk, because he said he was scared to death of traffic. So he took off for New York almost every weekend to see a girl he knew who was going to Barnard, and I could just imagine him on the Merritt Parkway, flying blind, and obviously headed sooner or later for a classic ten-car pile-up.

∂

THE SAME with Moran Phillips.

One night in late November when I wanted to do some work on my novel outside of the pandemonium of the Lampoon building, I went to the main reading room of the Widener Library. As I was sitting there at one of the long tables the first snow of the year began to fall, and several people jumped up and went to the windows to watch it drift down through the floodlights outside, and I did, too.

Then I came back to the table and began scribbling on my yellow legal pad, and a few minutes later Moran sat down across from me. She was a Radcliffe girl I knew vaguely from Hasty Pudding and *Lampoon* dances, and also as a rather electrifying presence in Mt. Auburn Street and Harvard Square, where you either saw her being escorted by some elegant final club man or tearing around corners in her shiny black MG. She was blond and had the bluest eyes I had ever seen in my life, and was very good-looking in a way that was, miraculously, at once angelic and sort of tough.

When she sat down I caught her eye and gave her a little wave, and she gave me a little wave back. She slumped way down in her chair and began reading *The Golden Bowl*. After a while, something made me look at her again, and I saw two very large tears running down her cheeks. For one moment I thought maybe a passage in the book had broken her heart, but then I thought that was crazy, nobody's heart could possibly be broken over anything in Henry James, and, furthermore, her eyes weren't moving. She was just staring at the page in front of her. As I looked at her, fascinated, her eyes came up and met mine, and with the back of her hand she brushed the tears away.

I returned to my writing, but of course I couldn't concentrate, with her sitting there like that, the tears continuing to run down her cheeks. Finally, I leaned across the table and whispered, "What's wrong?"

"Oh, nothing," she said.

"Nothing?"

She shrugged, and brushed with the back of her hand at the tears again.

"Look, I'm going out in the hall for a cigaret," I said. "Want to come along?"

She nodded and slung her bag over her shoulder. Out in the hall, she went right over to the steps and sat down and dug in her bag for her cigarets. I sat down beside her and offered her one of mine, but she said, "I can't smoke Pall Malls. I don't see how anybody can. I have to have a filter."

She found her L&Ms and I gave her a light.

"Listen, you *remember* me, don't you?" I said.

"Yes, I remember you," she said. "I just can't seem to think of your name."

I told her, and she said, "Right. And you're the one who's not even in college, but living in the Lampoon, and you're writing a novel. Somebody was talking about you the other day. He said you exist by stealing money from the *Lampoon*. Is that true?"

"Yes."

"Good for you. I used to steal money all the time when I was at Farmington. This hood-type from St. George's School taught me how to jimmy a Coke machine. Of course this was before they had to *remove* all the Coke machines at Farmington. Guess why."

"Why?"

"Come on. You're supposed to be a writer, aren't you? Use your imagination."

"I'm sorry, but I honestly can't think why they would have had to remove all the Coke machines at Farmington. Tell me."

"Because *some* of the young ladies were using Coke bottles for purposes other than what the manufacturer specifically had in mind, and a rumor started going around that someone got a bottle stuck in there because of the suction, so the school had to bring in a *worker* to drill a hole in the bottom of the bottle so they could get it out. *Not* a good experience for anyone concerned—except the guy who did the drilling, of course. He probably hasn't stopped talking about it yet down at the old neighborhood tavern."

I said I wouldn't be surprised.

"Of course it may be mythology. No one seemed to have the faintest clue who the girl with the problem was. As a matter of fact, no one seemed to know how the rumor got started in the first place. Maybe they just wanted to keep all our teeth from falling out. All I know is, it sure made life a lot duller at Farmington when they took the Coke machines away."

"I'll bet."

"Anyway, I wanted to tell you, I found stealing the coins from the Coke machines very *exciting* in a way. It was also very *sexy,* in a way. Is it like that for you?"

"In the beginning, maybe. Not so much anymore."

"How old are you?"

"Twenty-four."

"I don't know, you look older than that. Tell me, do your fingers quiver like that all the time?"

"More or less."

"I think it's because you're so scruffy-looking."

"What do you mean?"

"That you look older than twenty-four. And you're sort of beat-up looking, too. Don't get me wrong. I like it. It's a nice change after all these clean-cut types I go out with most of the time."

"I was a little worried about you in there," I said.

"Oh, that? It seems to be happening to me all the time now. Half the time I don't even realize I'm doing it, and then I'll find these great tears dripping off the end of my nose. You know what it is? *Pressures.* I'm just feeling a lot of pressures from a lot of different directions right now. My father. My mother. *Men.* I mean, all this is over and above simply trying to survive at Radcliffe, which I'm also not doing too marvelous a job of. You know, I wish I were you. I think that would be so nice—just working on a novel, and stealing from the rich to give to the poor. You probably don't even have a father and a mother, do you?"

"Not to speak of," I said.

"Count your blessings," she said. "Then there's this man who says he's going to kill himself if I don't come to Paris and marry him over the Christmas holidays. He's a French boy. Very sweet, very *beautiful.* But I only knew him for about three days last spring, just before he went back to France. Of course we made mad, passionate love practically for the entire three days, and it was so nice, but I don't really want to marry him. Still, knowing him, he *might* kill himself. Or does anyone actually do that anymore?"

"Do you think they ever did?"

"For love—?"

"Would you?"

"I can't say because I've never known anyone I liked that much. In fact, I don't know if I've actually ever been in love. You tell yourself you are, you know. But are you? *Really?* What about you? I have a feeling you've been in love hundreds of times."

"No. A couple of times, maybe."

"I don't believe you. You look to me like one of these types who are always worshiping someone from afar. Like the ones who are always staring at you at the Bick. I'll bet you do that, sit there at the Bick and stare at women. Right?"

I shrugged.

"I thought so. Listen, this guy was saying you live in the Ibis Room at the Lampoon, and he was telling everybody what it's *like*. He said everybody says only a *goat* could live there. He says it smells awful, and you sleep on a grubby couch under a pile of top hats. Is that true?"

"Yes."

"Well, I don't know. It sounds kind of fun. Is it?"

"No."

"Well, what about your novel?"

"What do you mean?"

"Well, how's it coming along? What's it about? When are you going to finish it? This guy said everybody expects it to be a bestseller, because you have this letter from some editor in New York who's crazy about it. Is *that* true?"

"Yes."

"Well, come on, don't you want to tell me about it?"

"Tell you about my novel? No."

"What's the matter with you, Douglas? I thought all you writers loved to talk about your work."

"I used to," I said.

She smiled. "But not so much anymore?"

"That's right," I said. "Not so much anymore."

She put her cigaret out. "I have to go back in there and try to wade through at least another chapter of *The Golden Bowl.*"

I went back into the reading room, too. About ten minutes later Moran slapped her book shut with a report that made half the heads in the room turn to look at her. She gathered up all her things and came around to my side of the table and said, "I like you," and leaned down and kissed me quickly on the mouth, and then walked out of the reading room, and I was left with half the people there staring at me.

❧

THREE DAYS LATER, around four o'clock in the afternoon, the phone on the wall just outside the Business Office of the *Lampoon* rang, and whoever was nearest to it picked it up and said, "Douglas, it's for you."

It was Moran.

"I'm in Massachusetts General Hospital," she said. "I have mono. I want you to come and see me. You don't have to worry about visiting hours. I have a private room. When will you be here?"

I said in about an hour, and went up to the Square and took the subway across the river to the Charles Street station. It was a horrible dark day with snow falling intermittently from clouds that looked like charcoal smudges and were only about five hundred feet up.

I was wearing a chesterfield someone had left in the building. It was way too big for me, but much warmer than my own coat, which was just a raincoat with a thin alpaca liner. I was also wearing a pair of sneakers someone had left in the building, because both of my pairs of leather shoes had holes in them, and I couldn't risk getting my feet wet, the way I was coughing. Between the subway station and the hospital I slipped and almost fell three times on the hard ice on the sidewalks because the soles of the sneakers were so slick.

I got lost trying to find Moran's room and had to go back to the reception desk twice to ask for better instructions how to get there. I finally found her in a bleak room with a worn-out linoleum floor, badly stained walls and an iron bed in it that looked as if it had come straight out of a nineteenth-century prison ward. She was standing over by the window in a pale blue nightgown that you could see right through, looking at the snow and the black river.

She came and put her arms around me and kissed me. "It's all right," she said, "they say I'm not infectious any longer." But she kept clinging to me, and when I began to get excited, she said, "Not right now, some of my friends are coming any minute now. Later, okay?"

I was thinking, you *mean* it? Right here in the hospital?

She got back into bed. She hadn't noticed that my coat was way too big, or that I was going around in sneakers on a day like that. She just told me to sit on the bed beside her, and took my hand.

"I think I'm in love with you," she said. "I've been talking about you to everyone I know. That's a sure sign. I even told my mother about you. But not the part about the Ibis Room, of course. I don't think she could stand it. Not that she's as bad as my father, but she does have her limits. I just told her you're working on a novel that's going to be a bestseller. What about you? Have you been talking to anybody about me? Have I made any sort of impression at all on you? I have to know."

"I think I'm in love with you, too," I said.

"You don't have to say that."

"Of course I don't have to say it."

"I don't think either one of us really means it. We only sat there on the steps together for what? Ten minutes?"

"I think I mean it."

"I think I do, too. Well, we'll see what happens after my friends leave. That's always a sure sign. If I can really let myself go with a man."

"Are you serious about this?" I said. "What if a nurse comes in to take your temperature or some goddam thing when we're right in the middle of it?"

"Oh, I'll talk to Lucy Prentice. She's very sweet. I'll ask her to put the NO VISITORS sign on my door. Look, I've only got infectious mononucleosis, not the bubonic plague. Don't you want to?"

"Obviously I want to."

"All right, then."

We heard voices approaching, and her friends swarmed into the room, with a hamper full of glasses, and half a dozen bottles of red wine from SS Pierce. I knew some of them from the same places I knew Moran from, *Lampoon* and Hasty Pudding dances. They were perfectly nice, but they stayed a long time. Much too long a time, because when they finally left, Moran said, "It's beginning again," and told me to put my hand on her cheek, which was burning up.

"Every evening, just about now," she said, "this happens. I was hoping it was over with, now that I'm in here. Look, I'm afraid I'm just not going to feel like it. Do you mind? I mean, my eyes are actually swimming. I can barely see you. You understand, don't you?"

"Of course," I said.

"You'll stay though, won't you? I want you to have my supper. I can't possibly eat this food, but you'll probably love it. Will you stay?"

I did eat her supper, and it wasn't all that bad. She had the dessert and the tea. Then she began telling me how her parents had gotten divorced when she was ten and each had been trying to alienate Moran, their only child, from the other ever since, even though they had remarried (he only once but she twice) and both had had several children by their subsequent spouses—and their way of going about it, apparently, was by striving to outdo each other not only in the area of vilification but also in the area of writing checks to Moran for extravagant amounts of money, which she spent on stuff like skiing in Val d'Isere.

"Basically, they both have this terrible need to make me believe that the divorce was the other one's fault, although, frankly, I don't care—and never have cared—whose fault it was. I only wish they'd leave it alone. Ten years, but to them it's like yesterday."

Her mother lived in Boston, her father in New York, where he was, I gathered, a powerful figure on Wall Street. She began telling me how intensely he would dislike me, and how intensely her mother, if perhaps to a slightly lesser degree, would dislike me, and then the junk they had given her to bring her fever down started making her very dopey, and it was late by then, so I told her I had better be going.

She took my hand. "Douglas, just tell me this," she said. "Your book really is going to be a bestseller, isn't it?"

"What do you mean?"

"Well, I have to have *something.*"

"I just don't know what you mean," I said.

"Well, I have to have *hope.*"

"Hope?" I said. *"You* have to have hope?"

"Yes, if I'm going to let myself be serious about you. I mean, it's all right for you to be this way and live this way as long as there's hope that you'll be successful in the end. Don't you see?"

I nodded.

"So tell me."

"I can't," I said. "I don't think my book is going to be a bestseller. The truth is, the most I'm hoping for is that someone will just publish the goddam thing."

I saw the two tears run down her cheeks.

"And I thought you were going to be the one who would save me," she said.

"Moran," I said, "I know your eyes are swimming, but do I really look to you like somebody who could save somebody?"

She shook her head.

"I'm sorry," I said, "but you'll have to find someone else."

BACK TO the Charles Street station where I almost froze waiting for the train. In the middle of the night I awakened feeling strange, and pretty soon I was burning up.

❧

"ALEX, I'M DYING," I said.

"I'll be right over."

He took one look at me in the morning light and said, "Here's my Bursar's Card."

"THE BLOOD TEST comes up pneumonia, Alex," the doctor at the Student Health Center said. "I want you to report to the infirmary right away."

Alex drove me to the Stillman Infirmary on Upper Mt. Auburn Street in his Austin-Healey. I was put to bed in a twenty-bed ward that was about a third full. It was like heaven. Alcohol rubs. Oceans of hot water to bathe and shave in. The clean sheets felt so good. Meals brought to me on trays. I lay there and watched the snow fall. But when the nurses began saying, "Alex, you're beginning to look human again," with nice big smiles, I thought, "Please, God, save me somehow from going back to the Ibis Room."

ALEX SAID, "Moran called. I told her what happened. She's coming to see you tomorrow."

MORAN SAID, "I'm going to Paris. I know André really wouldn't kill himself, but I feel I should make this gesture. I've got permission to take off for Christmas vacation early. I'll see you when I get back."

"Bon voyage," I said.

"Remember when I said I was in love with you?"

"Yes."

"I'm just not so sure about that any longer. It may just have been the fever. Understand?"

I nodded.

"What about you?"

"It may just have been the fever with me, too."

"I have been thinking about you though. So how can I be sure? What about you?"

"Yes, I've been thinking about you, too."

"I told my mother what you said. That you don't really think your book is going to be a bestseller. She said she wants to meet you, when I get back from Paris. How would you feel about that?"

"I don't know," I said. "I may not be ready for that."

"My father, too. He wants me to bring you down to New York."

"I definitely don't think I'm ready for *that,*" I said.

"I already told them both okay. Look, don't worry about it. You may *love* them. They may love *you*. We'll talk about it when I get back."

"No," I said.

"Don't say no," she said. "Don't say no."

≈

IN THE ELECTION of officers of the *Lampoon* that took place just before the break for Christmas vacation in December 1950, I was elected president. I imagine this had to have been the first time in the history of the *Lampoon* that someone who wasn't in college had been elected president.

Anyway, it was something I had dreamed of, had wanted more than anything in my whole life, except, of course, to have my novel published. Something I knew I would have with me all my life, even if I failed at everything else. It was pretty much a foregone conclusion that I would be elected president if I could simply assure the membership that if I were, I would find a way to get back into Harvard for the spring term of 1951.

The day after my election I went to the Student Loan Office and told the man who interviewed me what had happened, and how much it meant to me, that it was something I would have with me all my life, and he was remarkably understanding, and said he would see what he could do, come back and see him in the morning. The next morning he said it hadn't been easy but he had persuaded the Dean of Harvard College to let me register for the spring term, and the loan was being put through immediately.

I applied for membership in Lowell House the same day and was accepted, and suddenly life seemed not so bad after all.

IT SO HAPPENED that my ascendancy coincided with the beginning of the end of an unusual period in the history of the *Lampoon*. Ever since the end of the Second World War the *Lampoon,* like Harvard itself, had been awash with students who had left Harvard to go and fight for their country, and, after their time was up, had come back to Cambridge sadder, wiser, and twenty-three or twenty-four years old. The result was that from 1946 to 1950 the *Lampoon* was dominated by the tough, cynical men who had beat up the *Wehrmacht* rather than by the traditional fresh-faced boys who came to it straight from high schools and prep schools. However, by the end of 1950 most of the veterans were graduating, and the *Lampoon,* like Harvard itself, was being returned to the fresh-faced boys.

I had turned twenty-five on December 20, 1950, and yet, technically, I was only *beginning* my junior year at Harvard—although it seemed to me as if I had been around Cambridge forever.

Of course it was marvelous to be back in college, having rooms of my own again, and eating in the Lowell House dining hall. However, the excitement of being president of the *Lampoon* soon passed, and gave way to my old deep dark fear that I was doing absolutely everything wrong in my life. Also, I knew that it was in reality a very short way from the beginning of the spring term till June sixth, and then what? Another summer in the Lampoon? The very thought of it could make me smoke ten cigarets in an hour. But the thing that troubled me most of all was my spending so much time hanging around the Lampoon with people who could not possibly understand what my life was like for me. Of course I didn't blame them for it, or hold it against them, but when all the talk began again of another summer in Europe, I couldn't help being fiercely envious, because all I had to look forward to was the fact that at the end of the term I would be that much deeper in debt to Harvard—money that as far as I could see I might never be able to pay back. I began to reproach myself for having accepted the presidency of the *Lampoon,* because very soon after I had it, I saw that all it really meant was that I would have the privilege of devoting so much time to running the magazine that there would probably not be much left for my studies.

Sometimes I seriously wondered about my sanity, and kept going back to my "neurotic symptoms," and thought that when you looked at it objectively, there was really nothing about my life so far that was "sane."

WHEN MORAN came back from Paris she told me she was pretty sure she was in love with André after all. Then, like everybody else, she began holing up in the libraries during the couple of weeks known as "Reading Period," and I didn't see her again until after her exams were over. By then I had moved out of the Ibis Room and into Lowell House and there was a phone in the rooms I shared with a very bookish young man by the name of Bob Evering. Bob was a Latin scholar and was working on a new translation of Virgil, and the one thing he could not tolerate was "his" telephone ringing all the time. He called it "his" telephone because he was paying the bills for it and so of course had every right to, and when Moran began calling me at all hours to talk about her *men,* or her mother, or her father, I didn't blame Bob a bit for threatening to pull the phone right out of the wall, and I tried to explain the situation to Moran, but she would go ahead and call me at three in the morning anyway from New York or Philadelphia, or anywhere, after a date that had gone sour, or if she just happened to be feeling down.

We made love in my bedroom on Sunday afternoons, when Bob always went to see his girlfriend at Wellesley. It was not what you would call great sex. It was always a quick, intense, almost violent scene that ended abruptly right after Moran had gone through a series of rapid, sort of scary convulsions. Then she would say, "Well, I'm all done. How about you?" More often than not, no, I would not be all done, but she would have lost interest, and was dying for a cigaret. Then she would be famished and we would have to go up to St. Claire's for tea.

She lived in a strange dark red house on Massachusetts Avenue, about half a dozen blocks from Harvard Square. The house was separate from the main Radcliffe campus, as if the girls living there for some reason had been exiled. When I went to the house to see Moran and had to wait around for her to come downstairs, some of her "friends" would try to warn me about what a big mistake I was making getting "involved" with her. What they didn't understand was that I got more from her than she from me, because she brought excitement and fun to my life that simply wouldn't have been there without her, and that I needed very badly. They also didn't understand that I truly liked her, and was truly interested in her, although I never seemed to know for sure if I was actually in love with her. Sometimes I was sure. For instance, she sang in the Harvard-Radcliffe Choral Society, and one night when I was watching her in a rehearsal for their spring appearance with the Boston Symphony she looked like an angel, and I *knew* I was in love with her. But a couple of nights later I saw her making a fool of herself over a very handsome boy at a Hasty Pudding dance, and I hated her.

MORAN'S MOTHER, Caroline, and her third husband, Amory Benziger, an important Boston attorney, had a townhouse on Dartmouth Street and a country house in Dover. Both places were very elegant. In Dover they had about three hundred acres and kept a flock of geese, a bunch of dogs and three horses, one black, one white, one dappled gray.

"Amo" was very dignified, very distant, very tense in town, but when he was out in the country, surrounded by all his land and his trees and his dogs and his geese and his horses, he would loosen up and be a very good guy.

Caroline—she insisted I call her that—didn't look anything like Moran. She had dark hair, olive skin and hazel eyes. She was very attractive. You could see that she must have been devastating. One day when we were alone she said, "Am I to think of you as a threat, Douglas?"

"I'm not sure I know what you mean," I said.

"Yes, you do."

"Okay, no, you're not to think of me as a threat."

She smiled. "Good. Then we'll get along very well, because I really do rather like you. It's just that, frankly, you're not at all what I have in mind for Moran. You can understand that, can't you?"

"I think so."

"But I know you're very good for her as a *friend*. She talks about you all the time, you know. She thinks you're quite wonderful."

"I think she's wonderful, too, Caroline," I said. "But I want to make it very clear to you why I'm not a threat. Because although I like Moran very much, she is not at all what I have in mind for myself, either. Frankly, most of the time she drives me crazy."

Caroline looked at me as if I had slapped her. "Well, at least you're honest," she said.

"Just like you," I said.

Part Two

❧

DOWN AND OUT
IN CAMBRIDGE

ONE BEAUTIFUL MORNING late in the spring term of 1951 the last few stones of my facade as the resident literary genius of the *Harvard Lampoon* fell down all at once in what remains one of the darkest moments of my life.

That morning Alex Latta and I strolled cheerfully along Mt. Auburn Street toward the Lampoon, totally unprepared for the shock that would greet us when we entered the building. We pushed through the heavy door on Bow Street together and immediately saw that there was a large gathering of the membership in the Public Room. We saw that everyone was gathered in a half-circle around a young man who was sitting on the big oak table at the far side of the room. At first we couldn't make out who it was because he was sitting with his back to the windows and his face was only a blur against the brilliant sunlight behind him. But then we saw that it was Perry Lucas, and that he was laughing and having a marvelous time fielding questions from the admiring throng.

We asked someone near us what was going on, and he said Perry had just heard that he was getting a Houghton Mifflin Fellowship for his novel-in-progress "Head Above Water," which he had been working on in MacLeish's novel course.

This was truly one of those moments when you hope to *God* the alarm will hurry up and go off because you want so badly to wake up and find out this is only a dream. I couldn't believe it. Perry Lucas. Of all people, Perry Lucas. Smiling, eager Perry Lucas, whose writing for the magazine I had always considered corny at best and pretentious at worst. This guy had a Houghton Mifflin Fellowship!

Alex was amazed, too, but he didn't have the stake in it I did, so he could go over and congratulate Perry and join in the adulation, while all I could do was hang back at the edge of the crowd trying not to let my true feelings show. Of course my true feelings were that if Lucas had slipped off the edge of that table right in front of me and broken his neck I wouldn't have minded a bit. But I knew nothing as splendid as that was going to happen. Far from it, I knew that from then until the end of the spring term we were going to hear about nothing around the *Lampoon* but Lucas and his goddam Houghton Mifflin Fellowship.

I didn't think I could stand it. I already felt sick with humiliation, because everyone knew I had spent a lot of time that spring talking to Bob Townsend, a Houghton Mifflin editor, about *my* novel.

I had met Bob, who had been on the *Lampoon* when he was at Harvard, at one of the Thursday night dinners in the fall. Naturally, the minute I had found out he was an editor at Houghton Mifflin I had told him all about my novel, and had shown him the Letter, and he had been genuinely interested, and had invited me to come over to Boston and have lunch with him a few days later.

It had been exciting going to Houghton Mifflin. The offices were in a narrow building that overlooked the Boston Common, and were still very Dickensian in those days. To me the whole atmosphere of the place was thrilling, from the rickety elevator to the framed letter in the third-floor hallway from Winston Churchill, fussily demanding the prompt payment of some back royalties he claimed Houghton Mifflin owed him, to the book-lined reception room where I waited for Bob to come and fetch me.

He showed me around his office, a cluttered room he apparently shared with about six other people and a fine collection of beat-up typewriters. Through the grimy windows there was a view of the upper branches of a dusty tree and the brick wall and grimy windows of the office building across the alley. It all looked so marvelously literary, and I was thrilled when Bob introduced me to several of his colleagues, quite seriously, as a promising new novelist that he hoped to capture for the HM Co. list, and they all smiled and looked at me as if they wanted to be sure they remembered me. In the hallway, as we were leaving, we ran into Jim

Rockwell, who was then the editor-in-chief of Houghton Mifflin. Bob had told me that Rockwell had been on the *Lampoon,* too, and also had gone to St. Mark's. So we chatted for a few minutes about the *Lampoon* and St. Mark's, and Bob also told him that I was working on a novel that he hoped to steal away from the New York publisher who was very much interested in it.

We went to Jake Wirt's for lunch, the first of years of lunches at little restaurants in the neighborhood of Houghton Mifflin. I loved to listen to Bob talk about the inner workings of a publishing house. Hearing for the first time all the details of how a book makes its way from first readings through editorial conferences and sales conferences, and finally into production, was delicious.

Before we parted that day Bob asked me when I was going to let him have a look at my novel, and I said, oh, pretty soon, but I didn't really mean it. I knew he was interested in me, and really wanted to see my book, and was probably prepared to go to bat for me at Houghton Mifflin if he liked it, but I was afraid, because I had no confidence in my novel anymore, and I wanted all of this—Bob's anticipation, the feeling of being courted, the literary lunches—to go on a little longer before I had to live through what I was almost positive would turn out to be another bitter disappointment. So I just said, oh, pretty soon, and we made a date to get together and talk about it some more, and it went on like that for the rest of the spring.

THERE IS NO ENVY like the envy you feel toward someone who is actually living your most precious fantasy. I knew exactly what Perry Lucas's Fellowship meant in concrete terms. Bob had told me all about it. I knew there was an advance of twenty-five hundred dollars, a guaranteed first printing of ten thousand copies, much more publicity and advertising than the average first novelist would ever dream of, plus prepublication cocktail parties both in Boston *and* New York.

Anyway, a few minutes was all I could handle of watching Lucas in his glory, and I slunk back to my room in Lowell House and didn't go near the Lampoon for several days. When I finally did go back there, just as I had expected, all anyone was talking about was Perry Lucas and his Houghton Mifflin Fellowship—but mercifully final exams were soon upon us, and that became the big story.

One afternoon in the lush days when final exams were over and everyone was just hanging around Cambridge waiting for the college to close up—playing tennis, basking in the sun on the banks of the Charles, attending Yard concerts—Alex asked me if I would like to go to the beach with him and Perry Lucas.

I couldn't refuse. I had a ghastly yearning to hear Perry talk about this incredible thing that had happened to him, so I said yes, and we drove to a beach not far from Cambridge in Perry's little coupe, and sitting there on our blanket on the sand I listened to Alex and Perry talk about "Head Above Water." Perry said he was a little worried, because he had a deadline for the final draft that wasn't too far off, so he guessed he would just have to go down to New York (his hometown) and plug in PLOTTO, his imaginary machine for grinding out plots, and SCRIPTO, his imaginary machine for typing up the plots that PLOTTO ground out, and hope that between them they would come up with a smashing finish for his story. But you knew he wasn't really a bit worried, that he was just giving himself a little scare to add some drama to the thing.

I listened to Alex and Perry kidding around about PLOTTO and SCRIPTO, and wished I could kid around, too, but all I could think of was the check for twenty-five hundred dollars that Lucas had coming to him from Houghton Mifflin. I could see so clearly him opening the letter, and the check fluttering out.

We were lounging on a curve of pebble-strewn gray sand that was encroached upon by rows of hideous old brown and gray three- or four-story houses that looked cold and forbidding even then, in late spring. The gunmetal-colored water was still too cold for me to swim in, and there was froth on the waves that looked like the froth in a tub of dishwater. I was thinking, they call this a beach? Then where were the palm trees, the lovely clear blue water, the beautiful fish jumping, the pelicans skimming by in close formation?

THAT NIGHT Alex told me he had decided he was not going to spend another summer in Edgartown, as his parents wanted him to do. He was just so damn tired of Edgartown. "Well, you know what it's like there," he said wearily, implying that it was the most boring place on earth.

Actually, I hadn't the slightest notion of what it was like there. In fact, I didn't even know where Edgartown was.

"Martha's Vineyard," he said. "It's awful. Nothing but little white cottages with picket fences and hydrangeas, and girls in summer dresses, and sailboats, and stuffy people in white flannels and school blazers. Well, I don't want to go to Europe, either—even if I had the money, which I don't. Listen, are you going to be living in the Lampoon again this summer?"

I said yes, I thought so.

"Then I'm going to live here, too. I'll get some sort of a job. We'll have lots of fun."

I felt like saying, "You could go to Edgartown, and yet of your own free will you are choosing to spend the summer here with me in this godforsaken building? You're crazy. But if you really feel you must do it, let *me* go to Edgartown. Just call your parents and tell them to expect me on the next boat."

"Sure, Alex," I said, "we'll have lots of fun."

ã

MORAN SAID goodbye to me as I was moving my belongings out of Lowell House and back into the Lampoon. She was going to Europe on the *United States* with her best friend, Marcia West. Marcia had fallen in love with a gondolier the previous summer, so Venice was their first stop after Paris, where Moran was going to try to determine once and for all how she truly felt about André.

Once again the Lampoon building rang with farewells and promises to meet on a certain day at a certain hour in the American Express office in Paris or London or Rome, last-minute notes were tacked up on the bulletin board in the Public Room, and summer addresses were scrawled in the Common Book.

Then there was silence, and Alex and I were alone. He had said that his feeling was that we should have a two weeks' fling before we began looking for jobs, and he was prepared to finance it with his entire balance at the Harvard Trust Company, which was something like $646.12. So for two weeks it was piling into his Austin-Healey for expeditions to the Cape, movies almost every night, fabulous dinners at Locke-Ober's or Durgin Park or Henri Quatre, visits to Revere Beach to ride the dodgeems and the roller coaster, and then one fine day we found ourselves down to Alex's last $33.20, and we decided it was time to start looking for a job.

By then, of course, all the really good jobs at the Student Employment Office had long since been taken, so each morning on our way to breakfast at Hayes-Bickford's we picked up a copy of the Boston *Herald* and went through the want ads, having a barrel of laughs with the possibilities of applying for jobs as Crane Operators, Fry Cooks, Broiler Men, Diesel Mechanics, Landscape Architects or General Ledger Bookkeepers.

After breakfast we checked in at the Student Employment Office to see if, by chance, something suitable might have turned up overnight, and to horse around with the young lady in charge, Sara Flynne, who liked us, and really looked forward to seeing us each morning, but refused to take us seriously, and therefore gave all the jobs that we would have taken gladly to students she thought needed them much more than we did. So we wandered back to the Lampoon, where we decided that it was really too late in the day to try the Massachusetts State Employment Office, so we agreed to put off the whole job picture until *mañana,* and piled into the Austin-Healey for a trip to Crane's Beach.

But one morning we saw an ad in the *Herald* that absolutely intrigued us. It had been placed by the Raytheon Corporation, and said they were looking for Technical Writers. We had no idea what a Technical Writer was, but since we both considered ourselves Writers, we thought we had half the battle won, so after a good deal of horsing around, with stuff like, did you suppose the rules of dramatic unity applied in technical writing?— we drove to the employment office of the Raytheon Corporation, which turned out to be a grim building on a grim street, where we found a very pretty girl sitting all alone in an almost bare room behind an almost bare desk. When we entered she gave us a radiant smile, as if she had been waiting all her life for us to come through that door.

She asked what "positions" we were applying for, and when we told her she smiled again, and reached into a drawer and produced two very long forms and two very sharp pencils, and then conducted us to a table and told us to take all the time we needed.

After I had read down the form to the place where it wanted to know who my last six employers were, in order, along with *correct* hiring and termination dates, plus *complete* details of reasons for termination, I glanced at Alex and saw that he had a faraway look in his eyes, so without a word having to be spoken we returned our forms, along with our pencils, to the girl behind the desk and thanked her for her trouble. Oh, it was all right, no trouble, she said, and we left her there all alone again, looking as if she no longer had anything to live for.

After our Raytheon experience, we became very discouraged about our prospects of ever finding work, and we began sleeping later and later every morning, the theory being that the longer you stayed in bed the fewer calories you were using up. By then we were down to Alex's last few dollars. What we tried to do was live on cigarets and coffee all day, and then in the evening stroll down to Simeoni's in Central Square, which, miraculously, stood at the intersection of Sidney and Green streets, and where you could get a really first-rate full-course Italian dinner for about a buck and a quarter.

The main thing I worried about was that one of these days Alex would say to hell with this and take off for Edgartown, because I just didn't think I could make it through the rest of the summer without him. I was afraid the loneliness would be unbearable.

ONE SATURDAY afternoon a member of the *Lampoon* who was driving down from Bar Harbor to New York stopped by the building to see how Alex and I were getting along, and while he was visiting with us drank practically the whole bottle of Chianti that was in fact all that stood between Alex and me and starvation. We watched him blithely pouring himself glass after glass of our Chianti while saying how much he envied us the terrific time we must be having compared to his deadly dull summer up in Maine.

That weekend was a sort of watershed. After our friend left we counted up all that was left of Alex's money. It came to something like $1.45. So we had a serious talk, with a minimum of horsing around, and decided that our only course was to pass a bad check on Monday morning, and then, capitalized once more, we would try to think of a way to cover the check before it bounced. The burden of carrying out our plan clearly fell on Alex's shoulders, since I had had trouble with practically every merchant in the Square over checks at one time or another. At first Alex seemed to accept his responsibility in good spirit, saying he still had some checks from his old bank in New York, and they would take at least a week to clear, which would give us time to think of something. After much going back and forth we decided that he should make the check for forty dollars. Anything less wouldn't do us any good, and of course anything above fifty would put him in violation of the federal banking laws.

On Monday morning, with our bad paper in hand, we set out boldly, headed for J. Press, a clothing store on Mt. Auburn Street. While I lingered outside, Alex entered the store. I was dying for a cigaret, since we had run out the night before, but I was confident the door of J. Press would open any moment and Alex would emerge triumphantly with our fresh bankroll. However, five minutes went by, and when I finally went over and looked through the windows, I saw Alex absently fingering some neckties at a sale counter. He appeared to be in a dream state, and I knew immediately what had happened. He had lost his nerve. I went in and grabbed him, and when I got him outside he said he couldn't do it. Not anywhere around the Square at least. He thought we should go over to Boston.

We had no more money for gas, so we took the subway to Boston, and when we stepped off the train at Park Street we had only 11¢ left in all the world, so, in other words, we had reached, as they say, the point of no return.

We went to the Ritz first, but Alex turned around and walked right out again without even trying to cash his check. Then we went across the street to Brooks Brothers, where it was the same story. Then we began wandering the streets aimlessly, looking for a place that Alex said had "the right feel about it."

By this time it was getting into the early afternoon and we were both very hungry, not even having had a cup of coffee so far that day, and we were also both crazy for a smoke.

Alex would stop in front of a store and look in, and I would hold my breath, praying this place would have the right feel about it, but then he would just shake his head and murmur something and we would set off again. After he had done the same thing countless times I wanted to sit down on the curb and give up altogether, but I followed him doggedly, even trying to horse around a little. At last we came to a nondescript liquor store on Washington Street, and the way Alex paused and stared at the place I knew he had finally found a place with the right feel about it. He looked at me and said, "Okay, this is it," and went in. I remained outside, but looking through the window I could see that he had his checkbook out and was talking seriously to the man behind the counter, so I went off a little way and waited and a few minutes later Alex came out of the store and gave me a wink.

I was appalled to see that he was carrying a fifth of whisky in a paper sack, but before I could say anything he told me that the man would only cash the check on the condition that he bought something, so he had bought a bottle of whisky for something like $4.79, plus tax. Anyway, our net profit, after taxes, was around thirty-five dollars, so we went up the street to a hamburger joint and wolfed a couple of cheeseburgers apiece with French fries and Cokes, and we each bought a pack of cigarets.

After that, feeling very happy, we went and sat in the Boston Common for a long time, watching the passing parade, and the ducks, and then went back to the Lampoon and got smashed on the $4.79 fifth of whisky.

ONLY THREE DAYS later, having been exceedingly profligate, as ever, we were broke again, and we both knew it was time to have a serious talk about our situation. I suggested that Alex call his parents in Edgartown and tell them they were going to have to cover his bad check, but he said he couldn't do it.

"Then they're going to be sending the cops after you," I said.

"Well, I'd rather go to jail than have to admit to the Old Man I couldn't get a job on my own this summer," he said. "I didn't tell you this but he pulled some strings and had a summer job at *Time* all lined up for me. I told him thank you very much, but don't you see? I want to find a job myself, not have you do it all for me. Anyway, no, I cannot ask him to cover the check. I have my pride, you know."

"I think this may be one of those moments in your life when you're going to have to forget your pride," I said. "But don't let it get you down. It happens to everyone."

"Just give me a little time, okay?" he said. "I'll think of a way out of this."

I said okay, but I had my doubts. This was around ten o'clock in the morning. We went up to the Bick and spent most of our remaining money on what we called The Last Breakfast, after which Alex said he wanted to go off by himself for a little while. I stood on the sidewalk in front of the Bick and watched him slouch away in the general direction of the river. Then I returned to the building.

ABOUT AN HOUR later Alex came up to the Great Hall, where I was supposedly doing some work on my novel, and said he hated to say it but he was just damn tired of living like this, and he had decided to go to Edgartown after all.

I said I didn't blame him a bit.

"What about you, though?" he said. "Will you be okay?"

"That's not your problem, Alex," I said. "So don't worry about it."

He shrugged. "I'd invite you to come to Edgartown, but you'd just be bored to death out there, believe me."

He went to the telephone and called his parents and told them he was on his way. I helped him carry his stuff down to his car. He said, "I'm going to need the rest of this money for gas and a ticket on the ferry. Okay?"

"Okay," I said.

He sat behind the wheel revving his engine, obviously very anxious to be on his way. "Listen, you're *sure* you'll be all right?"

"Absolutely," I said.

"I'll get the Old Man to send a check to the liquor store," he said.

When he was gone I went back up to the Great Hall and sat down again in the chair at the head of the long table, but before I could tap out one word on the typewriter a vast warm ocean of self-pity swept over me, bringing scalding tears to my eyes and bubbling snot to my nose. When it was finally over, I was left exhausted, weak in the knees and gasping for breath through my mouth, but also, strangely, feeling much better than I had in a long time.

I blew my nose and bathed my eyes with cold water until they weren't so red anymore, and then I hurried to the Student Employment Office in the Yard, where I told Sara that if she didn't find me a job right this minute I was going to starve to death, and that I was willing to take *anything.*

She said, "When you say *anything,* do you really *mean* anything?"

"I sure do," I said.

She looked at me for a moment, and then shrugged and said, "In that case, I may just have something for you."

ॐ

BOSTON PUBLIC HOSPITAL
Boston, Mass.

Dear Sir:

This is just a letter to put down on paper the arrangements we have made about your stay here in the hospital.

In past years several men, some at the college, have come over to help us as volunteers in our experiments. The understanding is that you will come to the hospital to be admitted about August 18 for one month. During that time we will carry out analyses of your urine and stools, you will be on a constant diet during much of the time, and we will study your total metabolic balance. We will give you injections of various substances and solutions to study your total body water, your extracellular fluid, your plasma volume, etc. We will also take samples to measure your blood urea nitrogen, carbon dioxide, chloride, sodium, and potassium, and such other determinations as may be necessary. You will receive several injections of "tracer doses" of radioactive isotopes to study your total body potassium and your total body sodium. During the time you are in the hospital we may give you injections for two or three days of certain hormones to discover the manner in which your body changes and excretes these hormones. We may also carry out a "dummy" diet resembling that of a surgical operation. This will help us in an understanding of the metabolic changes experienced by surgical patients.

While you are in the hospital we will of course provide room and board. We will in addition pay you the sum of one hundred dollars for the month while you are helping us with this study.

Please read this letter and if this describes the agreement as you understand it, sign it and give the carbon copy back to me. We may then both have a record of the plans.

With many thanks.

Very truly yours,

James R. Skoda
Surgeon-in-Chief

ON THE MORNING of August eighteenth I sat on a long bench near the door of the Admitting Room of Boston Public Hospital, waiting to be officially "admitted" to the hospital. I kept looking through the main doors of the hospital at the bright sunshine outside. A couple of times I got up and took my suitcase and went outside with every intention of just keeping right on going. The second time I got about halfway down the driveway toward Huntington Avenue and the trolley cars and freedom, but I came back and sat down again, telling myself there was nothing to be afraid of, they weren't going to turn me into a zombie.

But I couldn't even bear to look at hypodermic needles, and I knew there were going to be a lot of needles, and there was the terrifying thought that something could go wrong. By coincidence the papers around that time were full of stories about an "experimental subject," a convict somewhere, who had died instantly when an embolism (or "air bubble" as the papers always called it), that had been introduced inadvertently into his veins through an i.v. tube had reached his heart.

But what choice did I have? I knew it was either this or a slow death in the Great Hall. And, as ever, I was figuring that there in the hospital with nothing to do all day but let them perform whatever horrors they were going to perform on me (and the little orientation conference I had had with Dr. Skoda notwithstanding, I didn't really know what they were going to be doing to me, because in my heart not really *wanting* to know I had just said yes, yes, yes to everything he had said, without once letting any of it actually penetrate my consciousness), at least I would have lots of free time for work on my novel.

So I went on through with the formality of being admitted to Boston Public, and then a young doctor from Dr. Skoda's "team" escorted me up to my room on the second floor. I was happy to see that it was a very nice private room in a brand-new air-conditioned wing of the hospital, and that I had a big picture window with a view of a beautiful lawn and trees.

The doctor who had brought me up to the room stayed a few minutes to go over with me the most important rule that I was to live by for the next thirty days, which was that, to put it very simply, everything that went in was going to be analyzed and measured and weighed down to the last gram, and everything that came *out* was going to be analyzed and measured and weighed down to the very last gram. Therefore, as of right now I was to start urinating into specimen bottles and defecating into specimen bottles, and I was to write very carefully on the strips of adhesive tape affixed to the bottles the exact date and time of day or night when it happened.

Then he showed me my specimen bottles, which were lined up on top of the small refrigerator that stood near the foot of my bed. He said he knew that defecating into a specimen bottle could be a little tricky, but it was absolutely necessary so he advised me to master "la technique" as soon as possible, okay? And the bottles were all to be kept nice and cool in the refrigerator until the nurses collected them, okay?

Immediately I got a picture of opening the refrigerator and the bright light revealing rows and rows of carefully dated specimen bottles full of my urine and stools.

As if he could read my mind the doctor said not to worry, I would be amazed at how quickly I'd become blasé about the whole thing.

Before he left he told me to stay in my room because the dietician would be along to see me pretty soon.

Alone, I mooched around my room like a tourist in a motel, tried out the bed, which was all right but very high off the floor and contraptionish-looking, of course, and with all the usual hospital room gadgets attached to it, and looked into the bathroom, a broom-closet-sized room with nothing in it but a toilet and washbasin, no shower.

For furniture I had an armchair, a straight-backed chair and a small night table, plus, of course, the refrigerator.

I sat in the armchair and listened to all the hospital sounds that came to me through my closed door—the paging of doctors and the voices and the footsteps of people hurrying by in the hallway. I was anxious to go and explore my new surroundings. Dr. Skoda had said I would have the complete run of the hospital. I could even go and watch operations in the amphitheater if I wanted to.

The dietician was a young woman in a long white coat who swept into my room after a light tap on the door carrying a notebook and a pen and looking at the same time very cheery and businesslike. She said she wanted to settle the question of my menus for breakfast, lunch and dinner for my entire thirty days right now, which (she laughed) wouldn't be as involved as it sounded since I would be eating precisely the same breakfasts, lunches and dinners every day for the entire thirty days.

She said I could order anything I wanted, but to try to think of things I was pretty sure I wouldn't get tired of after the first few days, because I had to eat every last crumb of everything I ordered.

When you're told you can order anything you want, the impulse is to imagine you'd like every meal to be a banquet, but I was restrained by the dietician's warning about having to finish everything, so my choices ended up being fairly routine: orange juice, bacon and eggs, toast and coffee for breakfast, a cup of soup and a tuna salad sandwich and iced tea for lunch, for dinner filet mignon, a baked potato, a vegetable, apple pie with ice cream and coffee.

The dietician said I could also have a snack brought to me around eight o'clock every night, so I ordered a chocolate milkshake. Finally she told me, very cheerfully, that I was to keep any uneaten portions of my meals in my refrigerator, and to remember that every last scrap had to be consumed before *midnight* of each day.

I got another quick flash of opening the refrigerator door and the light coming on and a leftover piece of filet mignon in there among all the specimen bottles, and like the young doctor, the dietician seemed to read my mind and told me not to worry, I'd be amazed how quickly I'd become blasé about it.

Right after she left a medical technician came in and said he had to get some blood from me. When he brought out the syringe and went through the ritual of attaching the needle and then tied the rubber tubing around my arm and started tapping the inside of my forearm looking for a "good one," I got a weird feeling, not just fear, but also dread, as if something was telling me that what I was about to do—letting these people tinker with the delicate balances of my body—was a serious affront to God, and that I would be paid back for it, because when Dr. Skoda and his team got through with me, I would never be the same again.

I was horrified by how much blood the technician took and thought he had made some mistake, and said, "What the hell do you need all *that* for?"

He looked at me and said, "You better get real used to this, you know it?" and stuck a piece of cotton over the little hole and told me to keep my arm cocked for a few minutes, and gathered up his kit and went out, leaving his goddam ugly used syringe on the table for me to stare at.

❧

THE TECHNICIAN had left my door open when he went out. I sat on the side of the bed watching the doctors and nurses go by, and noticed that most of them looked in at me curiously. Some of them smiled, but I thought I knew what they were thinking. That I had to be some kind of a freak. Who else would spend thirty gorgeous summer days of his youth in a hospital as an experimental subject for one hundred dollars?

After a while I took one of the specimen bottles into the bathroom and urinated into it. Then I flushed the toilet, which made me feel like an idiot when I remembered that I didn't have to flush the toilet after I pissed anymore. Hell, I didn't even have to go into the bathroom to piss anymore. I put the lid on the bottle, which was nice and warm. Then I carefully wrote the date and the exact time on the adhesive strip and stuck the warm bottle into the refrigerator.

My new life had officially begun.

I walked down the hallway. At the end there was a nurses' station, where the nurses looked at me but didn't say anything. I knew they were watching me to see what I would do, and to get away from their stares I pushed through some wide swinging doors and found myself in a large ward, in what was obviously an older wing of the hospital. The patients lying on the beds or sitting up were mostly old men and most of them looked very sick. In here there was no air-conditioning and it was hot, even when a stray breeze came through the windows.

The old guys stared at me, too. Who was I anyway? A young guy in chinos and dirty sneakers walking around, what was I doing there?

I could see that outside the ward there was a rather pleasant terrace where some of the men from the ward were sitting around in their bathrobes, some in the shade of a striped awning, others basking in the sun. They had a portable radio playing and were talking when I came out. I sat down a little apart from them and I thought I felt them looking at me just as the ones inside had done, wondering who I was, what I was in for.

The terrace overlooked two tennis courts that were enclosed by the wings of the building. On one of the courts two pretty young nurses were banging a ball back and forth and laughing a lot. I was watching them when the doctor who had brought me up to my room came and sat down beside me.

"How are you doing, Doug?" he said.

"Okay, I guess," I said.

He grinned. "I looked for you in your room and when I didn't see you I thought maybe you'd decided you didn't want to be an experimental subject after all."

"Listen," I said, "is this experiment I'm going to do very dangerous?"

"Of course," he said. "The minute you start messing around with somebody's chemistry it's got to be dangerous. Are you scared?"

"What do you think?" I said.

"I don't blame you," he said. "Why did you get involved in something like this to start with? You need the money that bad?"

"Yes, I do," I said.

"And you couldn't find anything better than this?"

"If I could have I wouldn't be here, would I?" I said.

He looked at me half amused, half pitying. "Well, it's your ass," he said. He pointed off to his left. "Hear that?"

"Hear what?" I said.

I now realized that I had been hearing the faint barking of what sounded like a whole kennelful of dogs somewhere in the distance ever since I had come out on the terrace.

"What about them?" I said.

He shrugged. "They're experimental subjects just like you," he said. "They're in the lab over at the Harvard Medical School. They've been injected with cancer cells and had windows sewn into their stomachs and stuff like that."

"Oh, God," I said.

"Don't worry, we're not going to do anything as drastic as that to you. At least I don't think so."

"Why are you talking like this to me?" I said.

"To try to scare the life out of you," he said. "Listen, this is a very serious experiment. We don't want you to turn green on us and run off when we're right in the middle of it. So I'm saying, if you're going to have second thoughts about doing this, have them now and get out now, before we have a big investment in you."

"I'm not getting out," I said. "I told Dr. Skoda I was going to do it and I'm going to do it."

"Don't say that yet, all right?" he said. "Wait till tomorrow morning. That's when we'll start running tests on you. Before we start you can just say you've changed your mind if you want to. We'll understand. Okay?"

I said okay and the doctor left, and then a nurse came and told me that my lunch had been put in my room.

I went back to my room and there it was, my cup of soup and my tuna salad sandwich and my glass of iced tea, all laid out very attractively on a tray with a real linen napkin and silver dish covers and little silver salt and pepper shakers. I had to force myself to eat, but managed to get it all down so I wouldn't have to keep any of it in the refrigerator.

After that I drew the curtains over my picture window and closed my door and in the cool twilight sprawled on the bed and fell asleep instantly.

But a few minutes later a nurse came in and picked up my tray and right after that another came and took my pulse and my blood pressure and my temperature, and then an intern arrived wanting more blood.

I couldn't believe it. I told him someone else had taken a lot of blood just a little while ago, but he didn't pay any attention to that and went ahead and stabbed me again, and it hurt like hell because I saw too late that to save himself the trouble of finding his own vein the bastard had used the technician's hole.

I added another urine specimen to the one in the refrigerator and then went to sleep again and had bad dreams. But at least it was an escape, and every time I woke up I would turn over and drift off again.

Late in the afternoon a young woman doctor awakened me to say that she had come to do my "work-up," in other words take down my complete medical history. She sat in my armchair and I propped up on the bed and she asked me a million questions and I told her everything, all the way back to Dr. Fahva. Then she listened to my heart and lungs and looked in my eyes and made me walk around on my tiptoes and tapped my knees with the rubber hammer and all the rest of it. Finally she asked me if I wanted her to get a male doctor to do the rectal examination and I said what the hell, so she put on the rubber glove and the Vaseline and stuck her finger up my ass and that was the end of it, and she gathered up her notebooks and her stethoscope and said thank you very much and left.

I suddenly wanted to get out of the hospital and ran downstairs and out the front gate and across Huntington Avenue. There I turned and looked back at the hospital, detesting the sight of it.

≈

WHAT THEY DID to me was come into my room every morning early, about a dozen of them, and gather around my bed with all their clipboards, and one of them would find a vein and stick a needle in it and hook me up to an i.v., and then they would start running through me whatever radioactive isotopes they had decided to run through me that day.

A problem with the morning sessions was that the minute they all came into my room I started getting scared, so it was hard for them to get a vein for the i.v. My veins were hard to find any time, but when it came to the morning sessions they seemed to constrict to the point where it was almost impossible to hit one of them with the point of a needle, no matter how good you were, so there was a lot of pain in it the longer they kept trying and missing.

When they had finally hooked me into the i.v. and the isotopes started entering my veins drop by drop I always felt very cold all over and thought I was either going to get sick or pass out watching for the fatal "air bubble" to come along the tube.

The truth was, I saw a lot of air bubbles come down the tube, but they always assured me it was all right, nothing to worry about. But I didn't trust them, so it didn't make me feel any better. I hated the sight of them. I couldn't bear the way they looked at me. They made me feel like one of the dogs in the cages at the Medical School—subhuman, totally expendable. Even when they tried to seem friendly, I knew it was false. I noticed that they didn't like to look me in the eyes very much, which made me think the only thing they cared about was the experiment itself and if they happened to screw me up for life they would just say well, okay, but look at all the lives we may be able to save through what we have learned from this experiment.

The procedure took about an hour. Then they cut me loose from the i.v. and made their final notes on their clipboards and left me alone. I wasn't allowed to eat or drink anything from six o'clock, when one of them always woke me up to take me down the hall for my morning weigh-in, until the morning session was over. But as soon as they were gone a nurse brought my breakfast tray and collected my specimen bottles and made my bed and straightened up the room. Most of the nurses were friendly, but a few of them resented having to do anything at all for me since I wasn't actually sick, and they didn't mind telling me how they felt, which made me feel rotten. One of them said one day that I thought I was a real hero, didn't I? I told her that was the last thing in the world I felt like.

Later on in the morning somebody from Dr. Skoda's lab came in and gave me an injection. I seldom asked what it was, because if I did they would just say, "Oh, anterior pituitary," or "Oh, seventeen keto-steroid," and what did it mean to me anyway?

For a few days they gave me what they very cheerfully said were "massive" doses of the male hormone testosterone and during that period they often came and stood in my doorway smiling at me and wanting to know what the hell I was doing sitting there like that when I should be out in the hallways chasing the candy-stripers and the student nurses, and a lab girl informed me ecstatically one day that as of now, in terms of sexual drive, their calculations showed that the testosterone shots had put me, in human terms, roughly on the level of a three-year-old stallion.

SOON MY ARMS were covered with needle tracks, which made me self-conscious about being seen in public. So I didn't go far from the hospital. I had borrowed ten dollars against my hundred dollars to buy cigarets with, and I went to the drugstore across the street from the hospital to buy cigarets and look at the magazines, and sometimes I explored the side streets in the immediate vicinity of the hospital, but mostly I did the same thing there that I had done in the Lampoon, wandered aimlessly through the corridors, smoking my head off.

I also spent a lot of time on the terrace that overlooked the tennis courts, and got to know some of the old men from the ward, most of whom were recuperating from some type of surgery. By then I had found out that they were all charity patients who were getting their medical treatment free in exchange for letting the medical students practice on them. Some of them told me they liked it in the hospital, where they had plenty of companionship and were well taken care of, and looked forward unhappily to the time when they would have recovered sufficiently to be sent home—where they would be lonely and not well taken care of. They said they hated to say it but they wished something else would go wrong so they could stay in the hospital even a little longer.

I often attended Grand Rounds, a form of theater in which, one by one, charity patients suffering from unusual complaints would be wheeled up on the dais in the hospital auditorium, before a packed house of medical students, and have their cases discussed by a specialist in that discipline. At first the patients looked ashamed of themselves and guilty, as if they felt that getting hurt or catching a disease was somehow vaguely criminal, but as the thing wore on their expressions turned sullen, their resentment at being made an exhibition of and their natural pride having finally come to the surface.

Sometimes a member of Dr. Skoda's team would tell me there was going to be an operation in the amphitheater and I was welcome to watch if I wanted to. The first operation I watched was an appendectomy performed on a girl of about twenty. Perched right above and looking down through the glass wings above the operating table, I watched the scalpel draw a thin red L-shaped line on her pale white belly. So far so good. But when they began the real butcher-shop business with the retractors, and reached in and started bringing out the lumps of yellow fat and bloody giblets, I had to go.

However, like every other damn thing in that hospital, I got used to it. One night I was watching in the amphitheater when they wheeled in an MTA motorman who had had most of his hand crushed off under the wheels of a trolley car, and I remember not even having to look away when they put him under the anesthetic and started washing away the dirt and gore to get their first look at the horror, and then I knew they were right. I was amazed at how soon you became blasé. I heard them down there on the floor of the operating room talking coolly among themselves and never really getting excited about anything, and it wore off on me. One of the o.r. nurses told me that the only thing that really ever bothered the nurses was having to dispose of a severed arm or leg after an amputation. She said that picking up a limb and having to drop it in the same container where they discarded all the rest of the bloody rummage from the operation was sometimes too much for even the best of them.

EVERY NIGHT just before twelve I opened my refrigerator and got out the chocolate milkshake that I could never drink all at once when it was brought to me around eight o'clock, and finished it off. Then a nurse gave me a sleeping pill, and that was the end of another day.

ɜ&

LATE ONE AFTERNOON when I was roaming the streets in the neighborhood of the hospital and had gone a little farther afield than usual, I saw in the distance ahead of me what looked like a small mountain rising above the rooftops. I kept walking toward it, and when I finally reached it I saw that it was an immense rock that looked as if it had fallen out of the sky and landed there among the houses. I was immediately overcome by an intense desire to climb the rock and after much clawing upward and sliding backward I finally reached the top. It was very peaceful up there, in the wind, under the dark blue afternoon sky, and I could see all around the neighborhood, and the rooftops of the Boston Public Hospital, and the gray walls of the Harvard Medical School, and even, off in the distance, Beacon Hill. I stayed up there, feeling safe and free, until it was almost dark, and then slid back down and returned to the hospital. Not long after I was back in my room one of Dr. Skoda's young doctors came and asked me where I'd gone. He said they'd been looking all over for me. I told him I'd just gone for a long walk, and he said that in the future when I thought I would be gone a long time I must tell someone at the nurses' station roughly how long I thought I would be gone, and, furthermore, I was never to leave the hospital for any length of time without being sure to take a specimen bottle with me. I went back and climbed the rock several times after that and never took a specimen bottle with me or gave a damn whether I lost any of my precious body fluids through sweating, and years later when I saw the famous picture on the cover of *Life* of the sullen face of the rhesus monkey that had escaped from an experimental laboratory, I thought that was how I must have looked to the people in the houses all around, crouching up there.

WEARING A LONG-SLEEVED shirt to hide my needle tracks, I rode a trolley car into the Park Street station and took the subway from there to Harvard Square. I found Mt. Auburn Street deserted, and also the Lampoon. In the mail there were three postcards from Moran, one from Paris and one from Venice and one from Rome. They all said that she was having a good time, and hoped I was okay. I had thought it would make me feel good to be back among those familiar surroundings, but I had only been there a little while when the heat, the silence, the dirt, and the loneliness and the eeriness of the place made me want to get out of there and go back to my cool clean room at the hospital. I had said I would draw the cover for the Freshman Number, so I picked up some drawing paper and drawing pens and a bottle of india ink. I considered putting a note in the Common Book saying where I was, but decided against it. I really didn't want anyone to know what had happened to me. Returning to the hospital, I found myself beginning to understand how the old men in the charity ward felt about not wanting to leave. Without realizing it I had become attached to my room in the hospital, and to the regularity and stability of my life there. I was even becoming so used to the humiliation and degradation of being an experimental subject that it didn't bother me so much anymore. At any rate, I thought my existence there was much better than what I would have to look forward to when I was released, because I knew that with my mediocre grades from the spring term there wasn't the slightest chance that I would be able to get another student loan from Harvard, and so, short of some miracle, my fate would be to go back once again to the Ibis Room, and the very thought of it was unbearably depressing.

I WAS LYING on my bed reading a paperback copy of *The Man With the Golden Arm* that one of the nurses had given me when I heard a tap on my door. I said, "Come in," and looked toward the door expecting to see a nurse, or a medical technician wanting more blood, but it was Alex.

He cautiously entered my room, which was dark except for the area under my reading lamp because I had drawn the curtains to keep out the glare of the afternoon sun.

"How did you find me?" I said.

"Sara," he said. "I kept calling the Lampoon and never getting an answer, so I thought I'd better come up here and see what had happened to you. You hadn't left any messages or anything at the Lampoon. The only thing I could think of was to call Sara and ask her if she knew anything about you, and she told me about this. Douglas, I cannot believe that you would have let yourself become a goddam guinea pig. It's the worst thing I've ever heard of."

"Oh, it's not so bad," I said.

He stared at me. "Not so bad?" He came closer and saw my arms. "My God, you poor bastard," he said. "What are they doing to you?"

"It's not as bad as it looks, believe me," I said.

"Oh, sure, I believe you. All they want to do is turn you into a cabbage, right? What's so bad about that? Listen, I'm getting you out of here *now*. Where are your clothes? My car is right outside, and I'm taking you back to the Vineyard with me."

"Alex, take it easy," I said. "I can't leave here. I signed up to do this experiment and I have to go through with it."

"How long does it go on?"

"Thirty days all together."

"And how long have you been here as of now?"

"Eighteen."

"And how much are they paying you for this?"

"A hundred bucks."

He shook his head. "A hundred bucks, and they could be screwing you up for the rest of your life. Well, I blame myself for this. I knew I should never have left you alone in Cambridge."

We talked for a little while, but I could see how he hated being there and I told him to go back to Edgartown and not worry about me, I would be okay.

As he was going, he said, "I really mean it, Douglas. This is the worst thing I ever heard of."

ON MY LAST DAY in the hospital I paid Ken a visit. He was in the room next to mine, and I had always looked in on him at least once a day. He was sitting in his armchair, wearing his bathrobe. The room was dark because he always kept the curtains drawn. He said sunlight hurt his eyes terribly. He was an experimental subject in a deprivation study. I asked him if he was all right.

"I'm dying," he said.

"No, you're not."

"Yes, I am. I can feel myself slipping away."

"They won't let you die, Ken."

"I don't believe it. Death was here again. This is the truth. He knocked on the door, and I said come in, and the door opened and there He was. He looked at me for a minute, and then He said He'd be back after a while. So I'm just waiting for Him now. When you knocked I thought it was Him."

"You're hallucinating. I promise you they won't let you die."

But, actually, in that pale light he did look about half dead. His eyes were hollow, his cheeks sunken, and there was a peculiar greenish cast to his skin.

It was amazing how much he had changed since he had first come to the hospital. In the beginning, for the first week or so anyway, he had been very cocky, saying he could do this standing on his head. It was simply a question of mind over matter. Stuff like that. He had been so confident he had even come into my room and watched me eat my meals, telling me he could will himself not to let it bother him a bit. Then he would challenge me to a game of chess and beat me just to show me what great mental shape he was in.

He had come to the hospital for four weeks at one hundred dollars a week, four times what I was getting. But then his experiment was much more dangerous than mine. It had to do with the almost total deprivation of certain essential vitamins and minerals. He got no real food at all. They would hand him chalky-looking mixtures in tall glasses that he was expected to drink right down, and which after a while made him sick just to look at—plus, perhaps, a small bowl with some lettuce in it, with a few radishes thrown in, or a couple of weird gray crackers that he said tasted like cement. Once a day they put him on an i.v. and gave him glucose, and they were constantly at him, running tests.

At first we had gone for walks together. But it wasn't long before he became so weak that it was difficult for him to walk at all, and then he had reached the point where he could barely make it from his bed over to his armchair. He would ask me to take him out on the terrace, so I would prop him up and we would go crabwise down the hall, through the ward and out onto the terrace, where he would have to sit with his eyes closed because of the sunlight, but where at least he felt happier than he did cooped up in his room.

Looking at him, I remembered that I had once considered volunteering for deprivation myself. The thought of making a hundred dollars a week had been a powerful incentive. I had even talked to Dr. Mulhausen, the man who was conducting the experiment, about volunteering, and he had been delighted, because by then I had developed a reputation as a very reliable subject, and he needed at least six more good subjects to complete his study.

When I had told Ken that I was thinking of volunteering, he had said, "You fucking moron. You can stand there and look at what they've done to me and say a thing like that?"

"I need the money," I had said.

"Then do it!" he had yelled. "And I hope your balls fall off! And I hope you lose all your fucking marbles! And I hope your bones turn to shit! And I hope all your hair falls out! And I hope you go blind in one eye and fucking deaf in the other!"

"I'm leaving today," I said.

It made no impression on him. I knew all he had on his mind was Death. Anyway, I said goodbye to him, and then I went down to the cashier's office and collected the eighty dollars I had coming to me after the total of twenty dollars I had asked for in advance was deducted. Then, lugging my suitcase, I walked down the long driveway and waited on the island in the middle of Huntington Avenue for the trolley that would take me to Park Street. Standing there I looked back at the hospital and remembered that my excuse for having gone through all that was that I would have some time to work on my novel, when, it turned out, I hadn't written one word of it the whole time.

ᢞ

JOHN UPDIKE had been elected to the *Lampoon* in the spring of 1951, along with Prince Sadruddin Aga Khan, the half brother of Aly Khan and son of the old Aga Khan, the spiritual leader of the millions of Muslims of the Ismaili sect and one of the richest men in the world. Updike brought to the *Lampoon* a terrific sense of humor, a marvelous whinny of a laugh, short stories, cartoons and the most beautiful light verse that had ever been printed in the magazine. "Sadri" brought enormous charm, boundless enthusiasm, a poignant desire to be accepted just for himself, and a bright red 1936 Daimler-Benz SS "Swallow."

In the fall of 1951 Sadri moved from the Yard into a suite of rooms in Eliot House he shared with Stephen Joyce and Paul Matisse, presenting John Finley, the Master of Eliot House, with the glorious chance to ask the now-celebrated rhetorical question, "Where but in Eliot House would you find the grandson of Joyce, the grandson of Matisse and the son of God rooming together?"

THERE WAS a very awkward situation that fall. I was still technically the president of the *Lampoon,* but I wasn't in college. Finally, it was decided that I should remain president, and the place on the masthead where the president's name usually appeared would simply be left blank.

Although I tried very hard not to show it, I was really not deeply interested in the *Lampoon* any longer. My twenty-fifth birthday was approaching and I had begun to feel more out of place in the building than ever before. In a desperate attempt to raise some money to get out of Cambridge, I delivered my novel to Bob Townsend one rainy day that fall, and then, fearing the worst, waited for his reaction. It took him but a week to send the manuscript back to the Lampoon, along with a note saying that while he did think I had some talent he was very disappointed in "Welcome Stamp Collectors," which he was sorry to say he had found hopelessly confused and overworked, and his advice would be to give it up altogether and start something brand-new—but of course remember that this was only his opinion, and obviously the editor in New York who had liked it so much before might like it just as much when she saw it again.

I became physically sick when I read those words, and for a couple of days I could barely speak to anyone. As soon as I felt a little better I went to the Student Employment Office. Sara wasn't there any longer, but the new young lady said there was an opening for a busboy at the Statler Hotel, or was that beneath my dignity? I told her nothing was beneath my dignity now, and she made an appointment for me to have an interview with the manager of the Café Rouge at three o'clock that afternoon.

The manager of the Café Rouge was a very pleasant woman who seemed genuinely glad to see me, and charmed at the thought that I might like to work there. I told her I would like to start right away and she said that made her happy. She took me and showed me around "the room," which was attractive, and said I could start the next day. My hours would be from three o'clock in the afternoon until eleven o'clock at night, and I would work six days a week at $1.25 an hour, with a free dinner each night at eight o'clock in the employees' cafeteria up on the sixth floor.

I WAS HAPPY at the Café Rouge. It was really an immensely civilized place. By the time I came on at three o'clock the lunchtime rush hour was well over with, and there would only be a few customers scattered around the room, mostly women shoppers, hotel guests and personnel from the various airline ticket offices in the building, having coffee or tea, perhaps with one of the restaurant's marvelous desserts, or an aperitif. The women slipped off their shoes, one at a time, and dangled them on the tips of their toes, and everyone smoked a lot and talked in hushed voices and serious voices, as if they were telling secrets from the bottom of their hearts.

Around six the low sun suffused the room with a lovely golden light, and it was then that our trio appeared, piano, drums, bass. After much whispering among themselves, and sometimes even arguing in bitter undertones, and shifting chairs around, and tuning up, and riffling through their charts, they began playing, and their arrangements were so muted and dreamy and seductive that it was hard to keep your mind on what you were doing, and all of us, waitresses, busboys, even the bartender, seemed to drift around at our work as if we were in love.

At dusk we drew the curtains over the windows that looked out on Park Street, shutting out the evening, the traffic, the people going by, and from then on the restaurant became very crowded, and gradually the voices and the clatter and the clinking of dishes and glasses and silverware drowned out the music, except for a stray bar or two that might find you somewhere in the room and took you back to the earlier mood and for a moment got you feeling bewitched again.

My uniform was very simple, white duck pants and white duck jacket with a red collar. In the Café Rouge the waitresses set their own tables and cleared them too, so a busboy's main concern was keeping his waitress's station fully supplied at all times with plates and glasses and silverware, filling the water glasses on the tables, emptying the ashtrays, and making sure that the rug in his area was kept immaculate by the constant running back and forth of his very handsome little solid brass carpetsweeper.

The waitress I worked with was a pretty Irish girl named Kristen, who had only been in the country about a year and still had an accent that was a little difficult to understand at times but very nice to listen to anyway. She was amazingly sweet-tempered, unlike most of the other waitresses, and we got along very well together. She didn't mind that I had a tendency to forget where I was about half the time, or my bad habit of disappearing into the kitchen to sneak a cigaret while observing "Sully," the head dishwasher, a three-hundred-and-fifty-pounder, who sweated rivers in the heat from the dishwashing machine, but didn't let that stop him from continuously stuffing his mouth with the half-eaten steaks and chops and crepes suzette he found on the plates that came back from the dining room before he sent them through his machine, or from lording it over his helper, a frighteningly pale kid who worshiped him, and assisted him with his "racket," which was scraping the partly used pats of butter from the butter dishes and packing them into Dixie cups—perhaps as much as ten pounds a night—to resell at a discount to a restaurant in his neighborhood that was owned by his wife's uncle.

As SOON as I received my first week's roughly fifty-three dollars take-home pay, I checked out of the Lampoon building and into a clean, warm dollar-a-night room at the Central Square YMCA. I dropped in at the Lampoon every day, before going to work, but there were always fewer and fewer people around the building from "my time."

I saved my money carefully, because every day I felt more strongly that I wanted to get out of Cambridge and go back to Florida. I decided that I would stay out my full term as president, and as soon after that I felt I had enough money saved to buy a bus or train ticket to Miami, with enough left over to last me while I looked for a job down there, I would go.

At the same time something else was happening to me. I was gradually allowing myself to face the fact that it looked now as if I never would have a novel published. In one way it was a tremendous relief. At least I didn't have to feel guilty any longer for every moment I spent away from my typewriter. But of course there was the nagging question, then what was going to become of me? Aside from drawing, I had no other talent, and I really didn't have enough interest in drawing to want to make a career of it, in advertising or some field like that. I kept thinking that once I got back down to Miami I would have plenty of time to decide what to do with myself for the rest of my life, and tried to let it go at that.

BEFORE SHE LEFT for Christmas vacation, I told Moran I wouldn't be in Cambridge when she came back. She asked me if she would ever see me again and I said I didn't think so. The tears began. I said of course I would see her again, I was crazy about her, wasn't I?

"But what about your novel?" she said.

"There is no novel anymore, Moran," I said, and told her what Townsend had written me about "Welcome Stamp Collectors."

"But what about that woman in New York? Aren't you going to send it to her and see what she says about it now?"

"She wouldn't like it the way it is now either," I said. "Look, I've ruined it, and the fact is, I'm just going to have to find something else to do with my life besides pretending to be a novelist."

"Well, what do you think you'll do?"

"I have no idea."

"Well, promise me you'll write as soon as you get to Miami, and tell me where you are, and I'll come down and see you at Easter vacation."

"Okay," I said.

I QUIT my job at the Café Rouge, and on a snowy morning went over to the Greyhound station, off Park Square, and I left Boston, thinking that this time it really was for the last time.

≥⍺

WHEN I ARRIVED in Miami, I went directly from the Greyhound station on N.E. Second Avenue to the YMCA, which was across the street. I had decided that before I even told anyone I was in town I would get a job. It was very hot in Miami, and for two days I trudged around in the heat, first going to Florida Power & Light to see if they had any openings on their line gangs, and being told no, not at the moment, try us again in a couple of weeks, and then to the IBEW local to find out if there was any work available with the subcontractors. They also said there was nothing at the moment, maybe in a few weeks.

I couldn't wait a few weeks. I was sitting out on the front porch of the Y in the cool of the evening, trying to think what to do next, when a middle-aged man came over and asked me for a match. I gave him my matches and he lit up, and then sat down next to me, groaning as he did.

"Damn near broke my back," he said. "I was carrying a hundred-pound sack of potatoes when my foot hit a slick on the deck where the jackass of a messboy had spilled half a bottle of Wesson oil and I came down like an elephant. They had to charter one of Chalk's planes to fly me back from Nassau, and now the doctor here says I have to go to the Marine Hospital in Savannah to get my spine checked out. Well, at least I'll be getting paid for the whole time I'm laid up."

"You were on a ship?" I said.

"A yacht," he said. "I'm the chef on the *Southwind*. A very fine vessel. The owner is a real gentleman, of the old school. He only uses the boat three or four months out of the year, not like some of these *nouveau riche* Johnny-come-lately bastards that think they have to be aboard the whole winter season down here and the whole summer season up north, and then charter the goddam thing out the rest of the time, or they ain't getting their money's worth. No, Mr. Glendon comes from very old money. His father's yacht, the first *Southwind*, was three hundred and ten foot long, and had forty-seven men in the crew full-time. She was in a class with the Morgan and Vanderbilt yachts, you understand."

"How big is this *Southwind?*" I asked.

"A hundred and fifty-two foot," he said. "And there ain't but twelve in the crew. Still, it's a damn good ship, and we have a very quiet, peaceful life compared to most of the rest of the yachts that are around today."

"Are there any more really big yachts left now?" I said.

"Damn few. Just the *Elpetal,* Woolworth's yacht, and the *Sea Cloud,* and Mrs. Dodge's yacht, the *Delphine.* A hundred feet is considered big nowadays, and a crew of six or seven is considered a big crew. It's trying to raise a crew that's the big problem. It's hard to get a good man to go to sea on a yacht anymore for the kind of money they pay, even though everything you earn is found, because they give you all your uniforms and your room and board free, plus sometimes even beer and cigarets. A sailor on a yacht can save practically every penny he earns, but even so, it's hard to find good men."

"How would you go about finding a job on a yacht, if you wanted one?" I said. "Just go down to the docks and ask around?"

"Are you looking for work?"

"I sure am."

"Do you know anything about boats?"

"Not much."

He shrugged. "Well, sometimes that don't make any difference. Listen, see that store across the street? In the Leamington Hotel? The Acton Uniform Company? That's where you go when you're looking for a job on a yacht in Miami. See Harry Cohen. Tell him Tommy Albury sent you. That's me. Harry and I go back a long way, and if you say I sent you I know he'll try to help you out."

"I really appreciate this," I said, and introduced myself.

"Don't mention it, Doug." he said. "That's how I got my start in yachting, too, forty years ago. Somebody steered me to a ship chandler. Well, I have to go upstairs and lay down now. I probably won't see you tomorrow. I have to catch a train for Savannah first thing in the morning. But good luck, and maybe I'll see you around the docks one of these days."

THE NEXT MORNING around ten I entered the Acton Uniform Company, "Yachting Uniforms & Accessories," a small, quiet, very orderly shop with racks of uniforms lining the walls and showcases full of yachting caps and all kinds of yachting insignia. Sitting behind a desk at the rear of the shop, a dark, sort of tough-looking guy was talking on the telephone. He looked up at me when I entered and the bell over the door jangled, and keeping right on talking into the telephone, crooked a finger, beckoning me to approach him.

When I had come close, he put his hand over the mouthpiece and said, "Are you a deckhand?"

Without a moment's hesitation, I said, "Yes."

He nodded and said into the phone, "John, let me get back to you. Somebody just came in. Maybe we're in luck."

He hung up and looked at me quizzically. "Have I ever seen you before?"

"No, I just got into town a couple of days ago," I said. "I was talking to Tommy Albury last night, and told him I was looking for a job, and he said to come and see you and tell you that he'd sent me."

"Tommy Albury? Yeah, the poor son of a bitch. Damn near broke his back over in Nassau. Supposed to be going to Savannah today, isn't he?"

I nodded. "He left early this morning."

"Okay, what's your name?"

I told him and he wrote it down on a file card. "And what's your experience, Doug? Sail? Power? Both?"

"Most of my experience has been on sailboats," I said.

"Give me some names," he said.

"Names of boats?"

"Yeah, names of boats."

I couldn't go on with it. "Mr. Cohen—" I began.

"Harry."

"Harry, I've got to tell you the truth. I've never sailed as a professional."

He stared at me and slowly closed his eyes. "Oh, Christ," he said.

"I owned a sailboat once, that's all."

He opened his eyes again, hopefully. "How big?"

"Twelve feet."

"Oh, Jesus," he said, and picked up the phone and quickly dialed a number. "This is Harry Cohen. Page Captain Wicks on the *Bellerophon* for me, will you?"

He looked at me disgustedly. "You've really fouled me up, you know that? What did you have to lie for?"

"Because I really need a job."

"John?" he said into the phone. "Listen, I was wrong. I thought this man here was an experienced sailor. He isn't. He's just a guy off the street looking for a job. Hang onto him? Okay, what time will you be here?"

Harry hung up and said, "Doug, go and have a cup of coffee. Wicks will be here in about half an hour. He says if you look okay he'll sign you on the *Bellerophon.*"

"He doesn't mind that I don't have any professional experience?"

Harry shrugged. "Look, he's in a spot. There are no experienced men on the beach right now, but he can't make this cruise with only one deckhand."

"Where's he going?"

"Bimini. Leaves tomorrow morning."

As I started to go, Harry said, "Wait a minute. I think I ought to warn you. Wicks is a mean little bastard. He'll make your life miserable for you if you let him. Frankly, I always have a hard time getting anybody to sail with him. You still want to do it?"

"I told you," I said. "I really need a job."

CAPTAIN JOHN WICKS was a red-faced little man, about five-two, wearing black pants, shiny black shoes, a black necktie, and a white short-sleeved shirt with black shoulderboards bearing the four gold stripes of a captain. He had a thick mane of silvery hair, and a silvery carefully trimmed little brush of a mustache. He looked me up and down contemptuously.

"You a drinker?" he said.

"No, I'm not a drinker," I said.

He walked slowly around me. "You ever set foot on a boat in your whole goddam life?"

"Well, I owned a sailboat once," I said.

"What kind of a sailboat?" He didn't seem to know how to speak except in a snarl.

"A Nassau dinghy."

"Christ Almighty," he said. He glanced at Harry and then said, "This is a real beauty you're giving me. Fit him out with two sets of uniforms and a pair of Topsiders."

He looked back at me. "Do you think you could find your way to the City Yacht Basin? Or do I have to draw a map for you?"

' "I've lived in Miami since 1938," I said. "I know where the Yacht Basin is."

He gave me a fierce look from beneath his bushy white eyebrows. "Well, then as soon as you've got your uniforms come down to Pier A and look for the *Bellerophon,* and when you come aboard I want you to report to me first thing. Understand?"

"Yes, sir," I said.

He liked that a little better. "Write down your name and Social Security number," he said. "I've got to go over to the post office and clear you with Customs."

"What did I tell you?" Harry said, when Captain Wicks had gone. "Regular little prick, isn't he?"

"I've seen worse," I said. "By the way, what do you think this job pays?"

"I don't think, I *know.* All these deckhand jobs pay exactly the same. Two and a quarter a month."

He took my measurements and issued me two sets of khaki uniforms and a black necktie, plus a white web belt with a brass buckle, a pair of white Topsiders and a khaki baseball cap with a long bill. "That's the half-assed uniform they wear on that bucket," he said. "Instead of real sailor whites."

He tied the uniforms up into a neat package and handed it to me, and said, "Well, you're in the navy now."

"Thanks a lot, Harry," I said. "I really appreciate this."

"Let's see if you can still say that when you get back from this cruise."

爱

I stood on Pier A looking at the *Bellerophon* from a slight distance. She was a beautiful ship, about a hundred feet long, with a graceful white hull and a fantail stern, and a deckhouse of varnished mahogany and highly polished brass that gleamed like gold in the afternoon sunlight. At the forward end of the boatdeck was the wheelhouse, also varnished mahogany, then the launches resting in their chocks, a stout white funnel with crossed yachting pennants painted on it, and above it all a short mast with pretty flags fluttering in the stiff wind.

I had spent a lot of time on Saturdays in my youth hanging around the

City of Miami Yacht Basin, particularly the commercial pier, Pier Five. That was where the party boats departed from early in the mornings and returned to in the evenings, loaded with fish from the Gulfstream. Then the broad-sterned cruisers, with their powerful propellers churning the water, backed into the slips, and there was great excitement as the captain and his mate began heaving their catch onto the dock. The biggest crowds gathered near the boats that had come in flying pennants from their outriggers with the symbols of sailfish or marlin, and they gaped envyingly at the grinning, sunburned tourist from White Plains or Caldwell who had caught the big billfish hanging from a block and tackle in the stern, and gathered around cheerfully while he had his picture taken with his trophy. Then the boat crews began cleaning their fish, tossing the heads and tails to the flocks of pelicans that scooted in circles like paper boats in the water all around them, their tails flicking, their bills wide open, their webbed feet paddling furiously as they jockeyed for the best positions.

I had never paid much attention to the yachts that were tied up along Piers A, B and C, because there wasn't anything much to see—just sailors in white uniforms standing gangway watch, and looking bored to tears.

I saw a man sitting on a deck box at the head of the gangway of the *Bellerophon*. He was dressed in the same khaki uniform that Harry Cohen had issued me, so I assumed he was the other deckhand. There was no one else in sight. As I approached the gangway the man looked at me, and said, "Come on aboard."

Lugging my suitcase I walked up the gangway, with its brass stanchions and white ropes, and I sensed that I was entering a world that was going to be unlike any I had ever known before.

"Are you the new deckhand?" the man said.

"Yes," I said, and introduced myself.

"I'm Jim Slattery," he said, shaking my hand.

"Captain Wicks said I was supposed to report to him as soon as I came on board," I said. "Do you know where he is?"

"Probably in the fart-sack," Jim said. "He usually takes his beauty rest around this time of day. Maybe you ought to leave him alone until he wakes up."

"No, I think I'd better go and report to him," I said.

Jim smiled, shaking his head. "He's already got you nervous, right, Doug?"

He had curly black hair and blue eyes that stared at you unnervingly, as if there was something about you he found sort of amusing. He would have been good-looking if it hadn't been for a terrible scar that started at the left corner of his mouth and ran all the way back to just below his ear.

I shrugged. "Maybe so."

"Go up that companionway there to the boatdeck, and then go forward to the wheelhouse. His cabin is right aft of the wheelhouse. Knock on the door and see if you can raise him. You can leave your tack right here."

I climbed the ladder to the boatdeck, feeling the yacht swaying gently under me from the wake of a boat that had passed close off her bow. Up on the boatdeck I stood for a moment looking around and listening to the flags popping in the wind, and then I made my way forward to the wheelhouse with a certain amount of trepidation, hoping that Captain Wicks would be in a better mood than before. There was no one in the wheelhouse, so I paused again to look at the brass compass, the chart table, the big brass-bound spoked wheel, the brass engine room telegraphs, all the little cubbyholes where the signal flags were kept and the radar scanner, and the thing I noticed most of all was that the wheelhouse, like all the rest of the yacht that I had seen so far, was astonishingly spic and span.

There was a door on the port side of the aft bulkhead of the wheelhouse. I hesitated and then knocked softly.

I heard Captain Wicks yell, "Who is it?" and I yelled back my name, and then I thought I heard him yell, "Come in!" and opened the door, and saw Captain Wicks sitting on the side of his bunk in his underwear. He stared at me as if I'd lost my mind. "Get out of here!" he howled. "Get out! Get out, you damn fool! Get out!"

I closed the door and it flew open immediately and Captain Wicks stuck his head out and shouted, "Stand right there!" and slammed the door in my face.

I waited and in about ten minutes Captain Wicks opened the door again and came out glaring at me, a cigar between his teeth, and dressed as before in his shiny black shoes, black pants, black tie and white shirt with shoulderboards. "Why did you open that door?" he demanded.

"I thought I heard you tell me to come in," I said.

"Well, you should get your ears looked into," he said. "I told you to *wait a minute*. What took you so long to get here, anyway?"

"I had to go back to the Y and pack up my stuff, and then I had to buy a few things I'm going to need."

He looked at me very doubtfully. "You're not going to get seasick on me crossing the Gulfstream, are you?"

"No, sir," I said.

"Okay, here's all I have to say to you. You don't know anything, so just try to stay out of everybody's way around here. I've only signed you on for this cruise to help wash down and polish brass. Do you understand that?"

"Yes, sir," I said.

"All right, go down to the fo'c'sle and tell the messboy to show you your berth, and make it up right away, and then put on your uniform and relieve Slattery on the gangway watch."

"I heard him yelling at you all the way down here," Slattery said. "What did you do, for God's sake, goose him?"

"I opened his door by mistake and caught him in his underwear."

Jim laughed. "Hell, you're lucky he didn't have you keel-hauled."

DESCENDING THE LADDER to the fo'c'sle, I went down into a crowded space where everything was arranged to conform to the interior shape of the bow of the yacht. In other words, the space was not only V-shaped going fore and aft but V-shaped from top to bottom, so that when you stood on the deck at the bottom there was barely room to move around at all, while above you, there was all the room in the world, and the total effect was rather like standing in the bottom of a teacup.

On either side there were two pipe berths, upper and lower, the lower ones pulled up and held back close to the bulkheads with chains and hooks, so people could sit on the benches on either side of the messtable in between. High up, under the overhead, there were three portholes on either side. Forward there were lockers, and the door to the head, and aft there was a narrow hallway, with a small cabin on either side, that led aft to the galley.

Slouched on one of the benches a kid of about nineteen, wearing a long white apron, was listening to the loud music on the beat-up radio that stood near him on the messtable. He had straight blond hair, pimples, a pug nose, bad teeth and a small pointed chin, and he was smoking a cigaret and chewing bubble gum at the same time. On the bench across from him a middle-aged man with gray hair slicked straight back, a very pale face and cheeks shaved so close they shone, wearing beautifully pressed black pants, gleaming black shoes and an immaculate white mess jacket with gold buttons was reading the Miami *Herald*. He was smoking too, and the air was thick with smoke because the ventilation was poor.

The kid and the man looked at me, and the kid said, "Are you the new guy?"

"What do I look like?" I said.

"Like something the fuckin' cat drug in," he said. "What's your name?"

I told him, and asked him his, and he said, "Jack, and that's Alfred over there. Only don't call him Alf or Fred. You have to call him Alfred or he throws a fit, don't you, Alf?"

"Nice to meet you, Doug," Alfred said, with a fairly pronounced English accent. "I'm the second steward, that little bleeder there is the messboy. Jack, go get the man his bedding, and turn off that damn radio."

"Yes, sir," Jack said mockingly, and then to me, "Don't be fooled by his limey accent. He's Liverpool Irish. I got that very reliably from the steward on the *Mercury*."

"Do what you're told," Alfred said, and reached over and turned off the radio himself.

"Yes, sir, yes, sir," Jack said, saluting. "Whatever you say, sir."

"He's not really so bad," Alfred said, when Jack had left the fo'c'sle. "They just should have drowned him at birth and done us all a favor. Doug, if I were you I'd take that upper berth on the starboard side. You'll get a nice breeze up there, and you're out of everybody's way."

"Okay," I said.

Alfred lit one cigaret from another, looking at me. "The skipper said you've never been on a yacht before. Is that true?"

"It's true," I said. "This is my first one."

"Well, it probably won't be your last. You can get addicted to this life. We all say we want to get out of it, but we go on, from one yacht to another, year after year. A fo'c'sle gets to be a home, you know. I've been on yachts and merchant vessels since I was thirteen, so I'm a prime example. But it's not too bad a life, believe me, once you get used to it, and learn how to make things easy on yourself. Where are you from?"

"I'm from Miami," I said.

"You don't sound much like Miami."

"I've lived here since '38," I said. "But I've spent a lot of time up north."

"What made you decide to go yachting?"

"I was talking to a man named Tommy Albury last night. Do you know him?"

"Everybody knows Tommy Albury. In fact, everybody on the yachts knows everybody else on the yachts. Tommy was the chef on the *Southwind.* Before that he was the chef on the *Isis,* the *Blue Heaven,* the *Red Witch* and Christ only knows how many others. I thought he was going to Savannah."

"He left this morning. Anyway, I was talking to him last evening up at the YMCA. I told him I was looking for a job and he said to go and see Harry Cohen, so here I am."

"Let me give you a couple of words of advice," Alfred said. "If you want to get along on a yacht, all you have to do is treat the owner like God, the captain like Horatio Nelson, and never let anybody catch you smoking a cigaret anywhere but in the fo'c'sle or on the forward deck. Everything else is secondary."

Jack came back, popping his gum, and handed me a bunch of sheets, blankets and towels. "There's all your shit," he said. "You can have that locker there on the left up front, and you can take the upper bunk on the starboard side or the lower on the port side. Which do you want?"

I told him, and he said, "Whichever, but make it up right now, because I've got to start setting the table for chow."

"At three-thirty, for Christ's sake?" I said.

"On the yachts breakfast is at seven, lunch at twelve and dinner at four," Jack said. "Oh, and by the way, Alf, Jerry wants to see you up in the main salon toot sweet."

"Why didn't you tell me that in the first place?" Alfred said, quickly ducking out his cigaret.

"Because I didn't feel like it," Jack said.

"You bloody little twit," Alfred said angrily, and hurried up the ladder.

"Who's Jerry?" I said.

"The first steward. Also a pain in the ass."

"How many are in the crew on this yacht?"

"Well, there's Herman, the engineer, Joe, the cook, the skipper, Jerry, Alf, Slattery, me and you. Nine. Sometimes the owner's chauffeur comes along with us, like if we're going to Nassau and he's going to want to hire a car over there, but you can't really count him as one of the crew, because all he ever does when he's on board is sit around and read the *Daily Racing Form.*"

"Who owns this yacht, anyway?" I said.

"Mr. Walter Mitcham."

"Who is he?"

"A rich guy, what do you think?" Jack said. "He had something to do with Roosevelt. I think he was an ambassador to somewhere. Ask Jerry, he knows all about him."

"Is he on board now?"

"Yeah, he's on board now." He leered. "Him and Penelope, this blond who's supposed to be his secretary."

"That's all?"

"Who else does he need? Listen, he's about sixty and she's about twenty, and I mean *beautiful*. They don't even come up for air but about twice a day."

I MADE UP my bunk, which wasn't the easiest thing I'd ever done, and then put on my uniform. "How do I look?" I said to Jack, who was busy setting the messtable.

"Like some jerk that works in a gas station. That's the trouble with this boat. You ought to see how the sailors have to dress up on a *real* yacht. Whites, bellbottoms, sailor hats, black neckerchiefs—just like the U.S. Navy."

A man in a chef's hat came and stood in the doorway. "You the new man?" he asked. He was sweating so much the cigaret stuck in the corner of his mouth was all soaked and had gone out although he didn't seem to realize it. He was very thin and looked mean as hell.

I said I was, and he said, "Well, just stay out of my way and we'll get along all right," and then said, "Jack, ring the fucking bell and let's get this over with."

"Let me give you a little inside information, Doug," Jack said when Joe went back to the galley. "Ninety-seven percent of all the cooks on yachts are drunks, and ninety-nine percent are crazy."

"How many yachts have you been on?" I asked.

"This is my fourth," he said. "And the worst. Listen, on the *Fox* they even gave you free beer and cigarets. On the *Escapade* they gave you free beer and cigarets, plus free razor blades and toothpaste and shaving cream. Between you and me, when we get back from this cruise I'm going to see my pal, the steward on the *Stella Polaris*. He says I can come over there any time I want to, they'd love to have me. That's the kind of reputation I have in this business."

196

❧

I WOKE UP in the middle of the night and didn't know where I was. Then it all came back to me, and I lay awake, listening to the ripples slapping against the hull, the hawser ropes creaking, and the heavy breathing and snores of Jack, in the bunk right below me, and Jim Slattery in the one across from me on the port side, and feeling the *Bellerophon* alternately straining against her lines and then nudging back against the pilings.

A pipe berth is exactly what it says, a frame made out of sections of pipe with a piece of canvas stretched in between to support a mattress. Mine was hinged to the bulkhead on the outboard side and on the other suspended by chains about three feet long that were hooked into eyebolts in the overhead. Above me there was a network of water pipes and electrical conduits, as well as the heavy crossbeams that supported the teakwood planking of the foredeck. When I sat up on my bunk I had to hunch over, but when I was lying in it I had the snug feeling of being in a cocoon. This feeling was enhanced by the fact that the frame was raised slightly higher on the inboard side than the outboard side, so that there was no danger of falling out, I imagined, even in a rough sea.

The wind had shifted to the northeast toward evening, and a cold wind sailed through my portholes, but of course that only made me go deeper into my cocoon. I thought of what Alfred had said, about how a fo'c'sle could become a home, and how everybody in yachting says they want to get out of it but they just keep going from one yacht to another year after year, and I wondered if that could happen to me, and decided that for someone who after a while had even found the Boston Public Hospital not too bad, the possibility wasn't so farfetched.

I fell asleep again thinking that, actually, tomorrow would be the first time in my life I would ever have been outside of the United States of America.

A BRIGHT LIGHT was shining in my eyes, and Jack lifted up the side of my bunk and let it come down hard on the chains. "Come on, look alive," he said. I looked out the porthole and saw that it was still dark outside.

"Will you move it?" Jack said. "I've got to get this goddam table set."

I could smell coffee and bacon frying, and I swung down from my bunk and went up to the head and took a quick shower and shaved, bumping into Slattery, who was doing the same thing. The space was so small we had to look out so we didn't hit the other guy's elbow and make him cut himself. Then we put on our uniforms and went up on deck, and saw the sky beginning to lighten in the east.

"That's the trouble with going on a cruise," Slattery said, already dragging deep on a cigaret. His first words so far, except for assorted grunts in the fo'c'sle. "They always seem to think they have to get you up two hours before dawn, and then they never can get their ass in gear before eleven. You watch and see if I'm not right."

Breakfast was the same sort of mind-boggling boardinghouse-style feed that dinner the night before had been—when the messtable had been laden with sizzling platters of sirloin steaks broiled rare, medium and well, three different kinds of potatoes, mashed, hash brown and steak fries, great bowls of fresh peas, fresh corn and fresh squash, two golden loaves of bread fresh out of the oven, tons of real butter, and for dessert peach pie fresh out of the oven buried under a mountain of heavenly whipped cream that Jack came around and slapped on out of a big silver mixing bowl.

For breakfast there were platters of eggs fried sunnyside up, over easy, over medium and over well, and scrambled soft, medium and well, home fries, steaming stacks of pancakes, with genuine maple syrup, bacon, fried ham and sausage, all there to be washed down with gallons of marvelous coffee.

The thing I had noticed at dinner was that practically everybody found something to complain about. The engineer remarked peevishly that none of the steaks that were supposed to be rare were quite rare enough. The first steward bitched about the corn-on-the-cob, saying it certainly wasn't as sweet as it might have been, somebody whined about the gravy, and the captain said he was getting goddam tired of pie all the time, and how about some rice pudding heavy on the raisins for a change? The chef, standing in the doorway drenched with sweat, muttered darkly under his breath and went back to the galley to start getting ready to cook for "the people."

It was the same at breakfast. Everybody was dissatisfied with something, the eggs, or the toast, or the pancakes, or the sausage, and it reminded me of Harvard, where the food in the dining halls had really been very good, but everybody had always found something to gripe about.

After breakfast, when I could barely move, I had time for one cigaret, and then Wicks said, "Slattery, show this guy how to wash down, and then show him how to polish brass. You've got about an hour and a half to get the whole job done."

I began to see why the yacht looked so clean—because she was washed down with hoses every morning of her life from stem to stern, and then every last drop of water was removed from the varnish-work with shammies, and then came the polishing of the brass, which was hard, because most of the brass would have tarnished overnight from the fall of dew.

We raised the flags at eight o'clock, the yacht club pennant at the bow, the owner's house flag at the top of the mast and the American yachting ensign at the stern, and Slattery showed me the small navy blue flag called the "Owner Absent" flag, which had to be run up to the yardarm every time the owner so much as stepped off the gangway, and dropped the instant he came back on board again.

ANYWAY, SLATTERY was wrong, we got under way at nine o'clock sharp, right after Mitcham and Penelope finished their breakfast. Then the big diesel engines kicked over and Slattery and I were very busy bringing in the gangway and pulling the lines aboard as the men on the dock released them from the pilings, and soon we had passed all the way through Government Cut and left the sea buoy behind us, and Miami Beach was disappearing below the horizon off our stern. It was a fine morning, with the seas calm and the wind cool and gentle. When we passed by the party boats fishing along the weed line at the edge of the Gulfstream we waved to them and they waved back, and I thought we must have looked very pretty to them.

ॐ

BIMINI LOOKED MYSTERIOUS. The long unbroken line of the dazzling white beach, the palm trees, the green waves rolling in, not a single person or even a rooftop to be seen anywhere. It was all so much like a Winslow Homer.

Wicks kept sounding the ship's horn, as we stood a couple of hundred yards offshore rolling badly in the heavy groundswell. He wanted a native of the island to come out and pilot us through the narrow channel at the south end. But nothing happened, and it was getting pretty late in the afternoon. If we were still out there when it started getting dark we would be in a lot of trouble, Slattery said.

Mitcham and Penelope were having drinks on the fantail and he wasn't the least bit pleased with the delay. He may have been close to sixty, as Alfred had said, but he was in fantastic shape. He was built like a fullback, with massive legs and powerful shoulders and a washboard stomach. He vaguely resembled Broderick Crawford. Penelope was small, boyish, with ash-blond hair, a beautiful tan, a beautiful little ass, beautiful legs and a beautiful smile. The unusual thing about her was that she didn't talk much. She paid very close attention when Mitcham talked, but as far as I could see seldom seemed to say one word herself.

Mitcham came up to the bridge and told Wicks he wanted him to take the *Bellerophon* through the channel without a pilot if we didn't raise somebody within the next half hour, but the captain flatly refused. "You did it last time," Mitcham said. "Why can't you do it now?"

"We went in on a flood tide last time," Wicks said. "The tide is ebbing now, and we'd only have deep water in the dead center of the channel, and even there it would only be about eight feet, and I won't risk tearing out the bottom on the coral rock, or even bending a propeller, when we aren't carrying a spare."

You could see that Mitcham didn't like to be defied, particularly when Penelope was standing right there beside him. "I'm telling you again, Captain," he said, "if we don't raise somebody from the island within the next half hour, I want you to pilot us through the channel on your own."

"I'm very sorry, but I won't do that, Mr. Mitcham," Wicks said, and turned away and went back into the wheelhouse, and began blowing the horn again, knowing he had left the owner in a bad mood but obviously not caring too much.

Then Slattery, looking through Wicks's binoculars, spotted a small sailboat with two Bahamians on board a half mile to the north of us, running along swiftly before the wind, up close to the beach, and clearly making for the channel. Wicks headed the *Bellerophon* toward them, and when we came up to them it was another Winslow Homer scene, with the small boat rising high on the crests of the waves, showing its red-painted, barnacle-encrusted bottom right down to the keel, and then sliding deep into a trough, its patched, torn, mildewed sail luffing violently in the hard wind, the two blacks, a man and a boy of about twelve, standing in the cockpit, the man holding up the green turtle they had captured and yelling did we want to buy him, the blue sky and white clouds, the whitecapped green water, the beach, the island in the background.

Wicks yelled at them that we didn't want a turtle, we wanted a pilot to take us into the harbor, and the man yelled, "How much you payin', Captain?" grinning. "Ten dollars!" Wicks yelled. "Twenty!" the man yelled, knowing he had him, and Wicks yelled okay, and signaled him to come in close enough so we could take him aboard, and while Slattery and I fended the sailboat with boathooks, the man reached out and grabbed a stanchion and swung himself over the railing of the *Bellerophon* and landed on the deck as light as a cat. He was wearing nothing but a pair of faded red shorts and a thin gold bracelet on his left wrist. Smiling, he said, "You have nothing to fear now. Raymond knows that channel better than any mon on the island, and he'll take you through there with perfect ease."

He waved to the boy in the sailboat, motioning him to continue on to the island, and then he went up to the bridge, and with a following sea and the wind behind us we went south about a mile and then came back north, heading for the channel, and I could see Alice Town strung out along the lee shore of North Bimini. We did go through the channel between South Bimini and North Bimini with perfect ease, and Wicks worked the *Bellerophon* alongside a T-wharf in the center of Alice Town, where a small gathering awaited, including a constable, on a bike, glorious in his British colonial police uniform, blue trousers with a wide red stripe, pipe-clayed web belt, khaki shirt, highly polished brass insignia and a pipe-clayed pith helmet with a brass spike on the top.

At that time there couldn't have been more than a hundred people living on the entire island of North Bimini, about half in Alice Town at the south end and half in Brown Town, up at the north end. As far as I could see nobody at all could have lived on South Bimini, which appeared to be completely covered with mangrove.

Alice Town consisted of a post office; three little one-room bars where you could go and drink warm bottles of Beck's or Lloyd's beer, or Guinness ale or stout, standing under a bare light bulb; a bakery where they made heavenly fresh bread and rolls that you could smell all over town; a grocery store where there was nothing on the almost empty shelves but bags of flour and rice and grits, cans of peas and pork and beans and corned beef, and butter from New Zealand in tins and tubes that you squeezed like toothpaste; a "marine biology laboratory" that was run by a man named Michael Lerner, where there was nothing to see except a few harmless-looking little sharks and turtles kept penned up for no apparent reason, except, perhaps, to give the people who wandered out onto the catwalks over the pens something to look at; a dinky hotel called the Mid-Ocean Sporting Club that was supposed to be a hang-out of Hemingway's; a bunch of small frame houses with rusting tin roofs set up on concrete blocks.

The main street was a narrow, sand-swept macadam strip that ran from the ramp down near the south end of the island where the Grumman Mallards from Chalk's Flying Service ("The Oldest International Airline in the World") in Miami, having landed on the smooth bay between the two Biminis, came with a withering blast from their props waddling dripping up out of the water each evening around six, bringing mail, and bonefishermen loaded down with tackle and headed for the Mid-Ocean Sporting Club, through Alice Town and then, following the shoreline, all the way on up to Brown Town.

There was another road, but it was really only a path, that ran along the crest of the low ridge that formed a spine going from end to end along the western side of the island. This path had a wall made of crumbling coral rock on the ocean side that was in some places covered with purple bougainvillea, and it was a place where you could get away from everything, because people seldom used it, preferring the macadam road, and you could sit up there on the wall and look down on the empty beach and dangerous-looking sea, where nobody ever swam for fear of being swept away by the undertow and never seen again, and imagine that you were absolutely alone in the world.

There was only one car on the island, a jeep that belonged to the Mid-Ocean Sporting Club, but there were many bikes, and you always heard their bells jingling.

The water out there was so extraordinarily clear that you could read the label on a beer bottle somebody had tossed over the side twelve feet down. The bottom was pure yellow sand that was constantly swept clean by the incoming and outgoing tides. As someone who had never seen water anything like as clear as that, I could hang over the bow rail of the *Bellerophon* for a long time watching brilliantly colored tropical fish circling around the pilings of the dock, stingrays gliding by, schools of mullet being chased by fierce jacks, lethal barracudas lying motionless in the shadow of the dock, like three-foot silver pencils, ready to strike at anything that moved, hair-raisingly ugly and evil-looking moray eels swaying like cobras down at the base of the pilings, also ready to strike at anything that moved, an occasional big shark just passing through, red snappers, yellowtails, mango snappers, sheepsheads, grouper, and two or three species of fish I had never seen before.

All the people on the island were so friendly that it seemed it never would have occurred to them to pass you by without some sort of pleasant greeting, and the atmosphere reminded me of my other island, Fort Myers Beach, as it had been when we had first come there, before it had let itself get caught up in the twentieth century. Not only did everyone know everyone else, but they all seemed to have either affection or great tolerance for each other, and you wondered how much work the constable really would have to do in a year, apart from telling a drunk to go home and sleep it off now and then. How could there be a robbery when there would be nowhere to hide? And what was there to steal anyway? The people were very poor. For instance, you wondered how long the ones with bicycles had had to save up to buy them. The entire economy of the island depended, as far as I could see, on bonefishing, big game fishing and the Mid-Ocean Sporting Club. And yet the natives didn't act like very poor people. There was nothing mean, or resentful, or bitter or hangdog about them. In fact, they had a princely way about them, because they were inherently dignified and good-natured, and could laugh so easily.

Also, like Fort Myers Beach, when darkness came, silence came, and there was the same intensification of the feeling of isolation from the rest of the world. There was a small generator in the town that provided electricity for the hotel, and the bare light bulbs in the bars, but in the houses it was kerosene lamps, and since there was no shore current available to hook into, as we had had at the dock in Miami, the *Bellerophon*'s generator had to run all the time to keep the lights burning and all the food in the refrigerators from going bad.

When it got dark the town calypso band came out on the dock and played and sang for Mitcham and Penelope, who sat on the fantail with all the lights off, drinking highballs and smoking.

The men had husky voices, like black velvet, and they sang:

Brown skin gal, stay home and mind babee,
Brown skin gal, stay home and mind babee,
I'm going away on a sailing boat,
And if I don't come back,
Stay home and mind babee.

and

Bimini, sweet Bimini,
The biggest fish that ever was caught,
Was caught in Bimini.

and

Mama don't want no peas, no rice, no coconut oil,
Mama don't want no peas, no rice, no coconut oil,
Mama don't want no peas, no rice, no coconut oil
All she wants is brandy handy and champagne.

and all the rest of the island songs, and when they were finished Mitcham and Penelope clapped, and he gave them some money, although it was obvious that they would have done it even if he hadn't wanted to pay them, just because they loved to perform for an audience.

THE BEST PART was that you could see the Milky Way so clearly out there. You could lie down beside the spooky, pitch-black waves and look up, and without the loom of city lights to ruin it, see the same sky the Babylonians looked at.

❧

MITCHAM WAS a bonefish fanatic, like practically everyone else who came over to Bimini from the mainland. He went out early every morning in a flat-bottomed skiff with an elderly black man called "Bonefish Sam," who was supposed to be the finest bonefish guide in the entire Bahamas Islands, to the distant warm, shallow flats where the bonefish, which are also known as banana fish or ladyfish, and can go as much as three and a half feet and around eighteen pounds, fed on shrimp and crabs and worms. Bonefish are useless for eating because of all the tiny bones that give them their name, but they are prized as one of the fightingest small game fish in the world. Penelope usually went along, and they wouldn't come back until late in the afternoon, because Mitcham was very serious. He had informed Wicks that he was going for a record bonefish, and he didn't care how long it took him to catch it.

That left the crew of the *Bellerophon* without much to do all day, at least in term of coping with the owner, but Wicks, nevertheless, thought up plenty of work for Slattery and me, like chipping rusty places on the stanchions and daubing them with bright yellow zinc chromate and then painting them over white again, or he told us to borrow a float from the dockmaster and paint the places on the hull where rust was beginning to bleed through, and where the paint had been marred by rubbing against pilings, and scrub away the hairy green slime and barnacles from along the waterline with Ajax, and when we were through with all that he set us to scrubbing down the teakwood on the main deck with Ajax and bronze wool, to restore the natural creamy luster of the wood, which gradually turned pale gray from being washed down with fresh water all the time—and if not any of that he had us sanding down and varnishing the covering boards and the rails and the deckhouse.

The work was hard, but we didn't exactly kill ourselves, and Wicks realized (although it clearly burned him up) that it was pointless to try to make us kill ourselves because Slattery had been in yachting long enough to have learned every trick in the books of how to make a job last.

To give us a pleasant respite from our labors, there were our coffee breaks, at ten o'clock in the morning and three in the afternoon, when the chef always outdid himself with lavishing upon us feather-light, marvelously tender, ambrosial, rushed-warm-fresh-from-the-oven coffee cakes, or cinnamon buns, or three or four different kinds of danishes. Naturally, there were always complaints. The coffee cakes were always much too sweet for some and not nearly sweet enough for others, or, why never any prune danishes? Or, why never any pineapple danishes? Or, why never any cherry danishes? Or, why never enough goddam cinnamon in the goddam cinnamon buns? Or, why always too much goddam cinnamon in the goddam cinnamon buns? Or, you should have seen coffee time on the *Sea Cloud,* my friends.

I began to understand why, as Alfred had told me, life on the yachts could be very seductive. It was a life lived in a clean, orderly, secure, fairly predictable, disciplined environment, in which everyone knew his place in the hierarchy, and for the most part accepted it, and, also for the most part, took pride in doing his job well, a life of sailing to the most romantic ports at home and abroad, of lying at the very best yacht clubs, eating like a king, always having a snug bunk to come home to, and getting pretty well paid for it, and I thought it was so true, as Alfred said another time, that the only people who can ever really enjoy yachting are the crews of the yachts, because they are the only ones who never have to worry for a second about the enormous, on-going, relentless, never-ending, confiscatory expense of keeping a first-class yacht in commission.

ONE OF THE BEST parts about the life, at least as far as I was concerned, was sitting around up on the forward deck in the evening after the day's work was done. Usually several members of the crew gathered up there to relax, and you could sit on a deck box and lean back against the rail and smoke, and talk if you felt like it, or just listen to the others, and the only light would come from the open fo'c'sle hatch and the only sounds except for our voices would be the faint throbbing of the generator and the fish jumping.

One night, when we happened to be alone on the forward deck, Slattery said to me out of a blue sky, "When did you give up hope?"

"What makes you think I've given up hope?" I said.

"Oh, I can always tell," he said. "It takes one to know one. Myself, I gave up hope in 1946. That was when I had to face the fact it didn't look like it was going to be too easy for a guy with a hole in the head to make it in civilian life. The SS damn near blew my head off when my tank took a direct hit from an 88 in the Ardennes offensive, and after that I spent a year and a half in four different hospitals while they tried to put my head together again with stainless-steel plates. But they just didn't do too good a job of it, so when I went back to NYU on the GI Bill to try to get the degrees in psychology I'd been working on before I joined the Army, I couldn't do the work because with this *Loch im Kopf* I couldn't read for any length of time without my vision blurring and giving me terrific headaches, so I finally said to hell with it, and just started hanging around, living on my disability checks, until one night, in a bar, I met this yacht sailor, who said if I wanted a little change, he'd give me the names of some people in City Island, so I went out there the next day and got a job on a yacht called *Dilemma*. And four years later, here I am. Now what about you?"

"I wanted to be writer," I said. "It just didn't happen."

"Why not?"

"Well, you have to have more than the desire. You also have to have the talent, so after I'd tried very hard for a long time to write a novel and it didn't work out, I gave up."

Jim nodded. "I knew it. Well, I hope this is just a little diversion for you. I hope you don't intend to make a career of this."

"Being a yacht sailor? Why not? It's not so bad."

"No, if you don't mind being a flunky for the rest of your life, just a swab in some jerk's private navy. Listen, I'm in this because I don't have any choice in the matter. But you should get out before it's too late."

"But I don't really have any choice either," I said. "All I ever did was write. I never learned how to do anything else."

"Then may God have mercy on your soul, because you'll probably be a yacht sailor for the rest of your natural life."

❧

MITCHAM NEVER caught his record bonefish. One evening, very down-cast, Penelope took the seaplane back to Miami, and Mitcham didn't even go and see her off but just sat on the fantail looking shattered, and the next evening Mrs. Mitcham and her sister and husband, a chiropractor, arrived on the seaplane. After that Mitcham turned sullen and didn't go out to the flats with "Bonefish Sam" anymore, and one morning he ordered Wicks to take the *Bellerophon* back to Miami, and I was just as glad because Bimini was getting very boring.

Moran never came down to Miami to see me at Easter vacation as she had said she would. She wrote me that she had decided to go to Bermuda for Rugby Week with her mother instead, and I was just as glad because I had begun to have an intense yearning to leave all my past behind, which filled me with a warm and deliciously satisfying feeling of martyrdom that was the very next best thing to imagining how much everyone you knew was going to regret not having been much nicer to you when they found out you had taken all those Seconals and had just lain down and gone to sleep forever.

I didn't even have much to do with Steve and Michelle. I went to see them a couple of times, but she was all involved with her baby, and Steve was goo-gooing almost as bad as she was. I visited Wes now and then. He was living in the same place, but told me he had gotten discouraged about his novel when he had sent it to Jean Luft and she had sent it back with a polite note saying that she didn't feel it was suitable for their list at this time, but good luck if you decide to submit it elsewhere, etc., etc. Through a "connection" he had gotten a job as chief of security at the Roney Plaza Hotel on Miami Beach, and seemed, in general, pretty happy.

IN MIAMI the *Bellerophon* was suddenly crowded with a flurry of guests coming and going, and there were cocktail parties and dinner parties almost every night that kept Alfred and Jerry and the chef working overtime, and we often went on little "day trips" up to Delray and Boca Raton and Palm Beach that were an enormous pain for the whole crew because, actually, they were more trouble than a real cruise to some-where. It was easy to tell that most of the guests were Mrs. Mitcham's friends, because Mr. Mitcham looked as if he secretly wished they would all go back where they came from. But they kept coming and going for the rest of the season. Then everybody left except Mitcham, and Penelope returned, and Mitcham told Wicks to take on full tanks of fuel and water and plenty of provisions, and one morning we headed south along the Inland Waterway to Key West, and from there sailed the sixty miles west across shallow water, where the rounded coral rock formations that Wicks called "niggerheads" were a constant menace, and very large ham-merhead sharks in schools seemed to be everywhere, to the Dry Tortugas, where we anchored in the small harbor under the immense, threatening red brick walls of Fort Jefferson, the bizarre apparition visible for miles around that stood on Garden Key, an island in the middle of nowhere.

The group of islands known as the Dry Tortugas were discovered by Ponce de León in 1513, and later became a base for pirates. In 1846 the United States built Fort Jefferson, which has the distinction of being the largest all-masonry fort in the Western hemisphere, but never quite finished it because in the meantime it had been rendered obsolete by the perfection of the rifled naval gun, whose shells could easily penetrate masonry walls. But after the Civil War the fort had another incarnation as a federal prison, and became famous as the prison where Dr. Samuel Alexander Mudd was locked up when he was sentenced to life imprisonment for setting John Wilkes Booth's broken leg on April 15, 1865.

At that time the moat surrounding the fort was stocked with man-eating sharks, which gave it the romantic name "Shark Island," and a reputation as a prison from which no man could ever hope to escape.

There was not one living soul at Fort Jefferson when we arrived there except a U.S. Park Service caretaker, who lived in a small house near the main gate of the fort with a dog and a short-wave radio. This man apparently had the lighthouse keeper's mentality, which made him impervious to the crushing solitude. When we came ashore he gave us pamphlets that related the history of the fort, which had become a National Monument in 1935, and told us a ghost story about how a little bouquet of flowers always appeared mysteriously every year on the same day on the grave of one of the soldiers who had died in the cholera epidemic that had almost wiped out the entire garrison of the fort in 1868—and *would* have wiped it out entirely if it had not been for Dr. Mudd, who was let out of his cell to treat the sick, and saved many lives, for which heroic service he was pardoned by President Johnson in 1869.

But after you had walked all around the vast walls of the fort, and had stared at the empty horizon, and kicked the huge cannon that were scattered all over the ramparts, pointing every which way, as if they had been dropped out of the sky like burnt match sticks, and had seen Dr. Mudd's awful little cell, and looked down into the dry moat where the man-eating sharks must have circled endlessly, and observed the thousands of sooty terns, whose principal breeding ground happens to be Garden Key, you felt that you had had all of the Dry Tortugas you needed, and were quite ready to leave.

Unfortunately, Mitcham didn't feel that way at all. We had towed a twenty-four-foot Prowler behind us all the way from Miami, and had picked up a guide in Key West, and Mitcham and Penelope and the guide went fishing every day, while we stayed there in that little harbor, under the oppressive walls of the fort, and slowly died of boredom. Bimini, of course, had been a paradise compared to this, and with so much time on our hands I kept thinking about what Slattery had said about us being nothing but swabs in some jerk's private navy. It was as if it was taken for granted by the owners of yachts that you had no life of your own, particularly when you were on a cruise and literally had to be available twenty-four hours a day.

"I figured it out once," Slattery said. "At two hundred and twenty-five dollars a month, we make seven-fifty a day. But if you break that down on the basis of a twenty-four hour day, it comes out to thirty-one cents an hour. Not bad, eh?"

THE FISHING PARTY didn't usually return to the *Bellerophon* until after dark, and then Slattery and I had to climb down into the cockpit of the Prowler and clean the day's catch of grouper, dolphin, redfish, snapper and yellowtail, which often was well over a hundred pounds, because in those days down in the Dry Tortugas you could scarcely throw a hook over the side without some kind of fish hitting it a moment later. We rigged up a light bulb over the stern and ran a hose out through the engine room porthole, and as we worked under the glare of the dancing yellow light bulb above us, washing, scaling, gutting and fileting the fish, and tossing the heads and tails and guts over the stern, the bloody water began to roil as dozens of fish swarmed around the stern in a feeding frenzy, striking at a head or tail or a mouthful of guts and getting out fast, and then circling back immediately to strike again. Pretty soon the sharks moved in, and then all you would see was their gray fins knifing back and forth through the light until the last head and tail and bag of guts had disappeared, and then it would all be very quiet again, as if none of it had ever happened.

When we had cleaned all the fish, we delivered them to the chef, who wrapped them in pink butcher's paper and slapped them into the freezer. Slattery told me he had heard from Alfred that the chef already was planning to sell most of the fish to a friend of his who owned a seafood restaurant in Miami, and give Wicks and Jerry a cut, and Mitcham need never be the wiser. "On the yachts practically everybody's got a racket going for them," Slattery said. "The first steward is usually taking down ten percent on every buck's worth of provisions that comes up the gangway, which he maybe splits sixty–forty with the chef. The captain will be getting back anywhere from ten to fifteen percent on every gallon of diesel fuel that comes on board, plus quiet little deals with the dockmasters and the shipyards. You haul out a boat like the *Bellerophon* for even a minor thing like getting her bottom painted and you're looking at a bill for ten or fifteen thousand dollars, and if there's any major work to be done it could be anywhere from thirty to fifty thousand, so the shipyards all want the contract, and you know who gets it, don't you? The guy who's willing to be very, very nice to El Capitano."

After Mitcham and Penelope had finished their dinner, and while they were having their brandy back on the fantail, Jerry set up a projector and a small screen in the main salon, to show one of the movies Mitcham had rented in Miami and brought along on this cruise. The crew was invited to watch the movies, but the rule was, of course, that you couldn't smoke, and since there weren't enough chairs most of us had to sit on the floor, while Mitcham and Penelope lounged regally in their overstuffed arm-chairs, puffing on cigars and cigarets respectively, and sipping highballs or champagne.

As for the movies, it was always the same. The first thing on the reel was always a "short subject," usually an "Our Gang Comedy" or a "Pete Smith Specialty," and then the main feature, which was almost always a black and white B picture from the middle or late '40s, starring people like Sonny Tufts, The Andrews Sisters, Turhan Bey, Eddie Bracken, Billy de Wolfe, Dan Duryea, Faye Emerson, Sabu, Oscar Levant, Dick Haymes, June Havoc, Dane Clark, Farley Granger, Gig Young, Martha Vickers and Harry James, and with a title like *Hold That Blonde,* and *They Made Me a Killer, The Very Thought of You, Rainbow Island* and *Feudin', Fussin' and A-Fightin'.*

Mitcham loved every one of them. He laughed out loud at every dopey joke, and then glanced around at the crew to see if we were with him all the way, which you sort of had the feeling he was saying you had damn well better be.

But the movies were the only thing we had to look forward to all day, so as bad as they usually were, and as humiliating as it was to have to sit cross-legged on the floor in that mahogany-paneled, lushly Oriental-carpeted, moldy-smelling main salon, which itself looked like a set from a twenties picture, all of us went every time, and in the flickering half-light from the screen laughed along with Mitcham, lying there in that little harbor miles and miles from civilization, under the walls of a building that was full of terrible history, in a darkness that was lit up only by stars and about half a moon.

WE WERE ONLY supposed to have been in the Dry Tortugas for ten days, but on the ninth day a northeaster came up, and in the morning we found the harbor full of shrimp boats, lashed together side by side, and some of them so close to us that Wicks told Slattery and me to put fenders and fender boards over the sides to keep the shrimpers from blackening the *Bellerophon*'s hull with the old tires they used as fenders. The gale lasted for three days, and in that whole time you could barely go to sleep at night from the noise the shrimpers made with their ship-to-shore radios crackling at full volume all the time and their continuous drunken yelling, and by the fourth day Mitcham was in a very bad mood and even though the sea outside the harbor still looked very "dusty," as they say, he ordered Wicks to take the *Bellerophon* to Key West. So Wicks and Slattery and I went up on the boatdeck and damn near got blown overboard lowering the port and starboard launches down to the level of the main deck and hanging "puddin' booms"—long wooden booms with big fat cylindrical canvas-covered fenders called "puddin's" in the middle—to cushion the launches against the sides of the yacht after we had lashed them in close to the hull. The purpose of this maneuver was to lower the center of gravity, which was very important under the circumstances because yachts of the *Bellerophon*'s class were alarmingly top-heavy and in heavy seas had been known to capsize.

Around eight A.M., to the ringing of bells and the blowing of horns and the cheers of the crews of the shrimp boats, we left the harbor and with our bow right in the teeth of the wind headed for Key West, where we arrived late in the afternoon covered with salt spray from stem to stern but aside from that in perfect condition. Mitcham promptly chartered a plane, and he and Penelope said goodbye to us there, probably so he wouldn't have to be present when, after all that, Wicks told us, back at Pier A a couple of days later, the whole crew was being let go.

All along, Wicks had been saying that when we got back to Miami we would fit out at Miami Ship for a few weeks and then go up the Intracoastal Waterway to City Island, and from there to the Indian Harbor Yacht Club in Greenwich, where we would spend the summer cruising on Long Island Sound. But about an hour after we tied up in

Miami he picked up a cable from Mitcham at the dockmaster's office saying that he wanted Wicks to take the *Bellerophon* up the Miami River to Merrill-Stevens and put her under the shed for the summer, and that he, Wicks, was the only member of the crew who would be retained on the payroll.

"Well, that's yachting for you," Slattery said.

THE TROUBLE WAS that this was the end of May and most of the yachts that were going north had already left or were just about to leave. The chef and Alfred and Jerry the engineer and even the messboy went to Acton and got jobs on yachts heading for Long Island Sound without any problem, but there was no big demand for sailors.

Harry said to us, "I got nothing for you guys but an eighty-five-footer that's going over to Nassau next week. You want it?"

"Nassau?" Jim said. He sounded intrigued, and looked at me. "What do you say?"

"Listen, this ain't exactly the *Bellerophon*," Harry said. "I want you guys to know that. But if you need the money real bad, well, I'd say, go ahead, take it."

"What do you mean, it ain't exactly the *Bellerophon?*" Jim said.

"What do you think I mean?" Harry said. "You've been around. You well damn well what I mean. I mean I wouldn't exactly call this a first-class yacht. I mean if you don't need the money real bad, forget it."

"What do you think?" Jim said to me.

"I think we should go to City Island," I said.

"Well, we could go take a look anyway, couldn't we?"

"I don't want to," I said.

"Oh, come on."

"I think we ought to be calling that guy in the paper who wants somebody to drive his car up to Jackson Heights for him," I said.

"We can still do that later, if this doesn't work out. Come on."

"I don't like the way it sounds," I said.

"Listen, what harm can it do to go and take a look?"

I gave up.

"Her name is the *Life o' Riley*," Harry said. "She's what they call a Twentieth Century, a type of yacht that was originally designed as a commuter for businessmen who lived out on Long Island and worked on

Wall Street. She's been out of commission for about two years now, so Christ only knows what kind of shape she's in now. And another thing, my friends, the fo'c'sle on the *Bellerophon* was Buckingham Palace compared to the crew's quarters on this boat." He handed me a slip of paper with an address scribbled on it. "That's where she lays."

৯

FROM THE MOMENT I first laid eyes on Captain Eric Hanlon all I wanted to do was wait for a chance to take Slattery aside and say, "Let's get out of here right now. I wouldn't go to Miami Beach with this guy, much less Nassau." But Jim didn't seem to notice a thing. Not even the fact that Hanlon was so drunk he could barely stand up.

As for his ship, the *Life o' Riley,* Harry Cohen was absolutely correct, she sure wasn't the *Bellerophon.* We had found her lying by a dock in a grimy backwater shipyard far up the Miami River, a very sorry sight, with her paint and varnish all bubbled up and flaking away, her brass tarnished and her decks in terrible shape. I knew Wicks would have gone apoplectic if someone had told him this yacht was about to go on a cruise.

Hanlon had finally emerged from the engine room after we had walked around the deck for about ten minutes calling his name, and had stood before us on the afterdeck, swaying slightly and trying his best to get us in focus. I knew that in reality he was probably only about forty-five or fifty, but he could have passed for sixty-five any day. He had an unusually narrow face and a thin-lipped little mouth that always seemed to be trying to form an O, and the whites of his eyes were both dirty yellow and bloodshot. He wore frayed dungarees, deck shoes with holes in the toes and a filthy white T-shirt. He kept ducking his forehead into the shoulders of his T-shirt to try to soak up the sweat, but only succeeded in blackening his face much worse than it already was.

Slattery told him that Harry Cohen had sent us, and he said, "Yeah, he called a little while ago. You're off the *Bellerophon,* right? How's that old bastard Wicks?"

"He's okay," Jim said. "He's going to be spending a restful summer under the shed at Merrill-Stevens. Everybody else got fired."

"Hey, you don't have to tell me anything about Wicks," Hanlon said. "I know him from way back. He always comes up smelling like a rose. Did

Harry tell you I'm taking the boss's boy over to Nassau next week?"

"He just said you're going to Nassau," Jim said.

"Yeah, well, the boss's boy is getting married the day after tomorrow, and I'm taking him and his bride over to Nassau for their honeymoon. That is, if I can get a new main shaft put in the starboard side engine between now and then. I took over this construction a month and a half ago and the only goddam thing I've been able to do so far is work on the engines. Then I took her out for a shakedown yesterday and she started shaking like a bastard, and it turns out the portside main shaft is bent like a pretzel. So I'm hauling out at Miami Ship on Monday. When do you guys want to come to work? You can start right now as far as I'm concerned, but all we'll be able to do is clean her up a little before we go to Nassau, and take care of all the major stripping and painting when we get back. Don't worry though. These people don't know what a yacht is supposed to look like anyway. They're shitkickers. The boss told me that before he bought this yacht he'd never set foot on a boat before in his entire life. Can you believe he didn't even have her *surveyed?* The son of a bitch just sat down and wrote the broker out a check for the full amount, no questions asked. He's got a lot of money, from developing real estate and raising cattle up around Lantana. He told me he's got a hundred and eighty thousand acres of land and twenty-five thousand head of cattle up there. Name's Julius Mayfield. The boy's name is Arthur. They both came on board wearing these high-heeled cowboy boots. I told them to take off the boots or they could drive this construction over to Nassau themselves. They're two real shitkickers. Julius and Arthur. They look just alike, except the old man wears a white cowboy hat and the boy's is pearly gray. So tell me, when do you want to come to work? Like I say, you can start right now as far as I'm concerned."

"Well, skipper, myself, I'm going up to City Island," I said.

Hanlon gaped at me. "Then what the hell are you wasting my time for?" He glared at Slattery. "What about you? You just messing around with me, too?"

"No, I want to sign up with you," Jim said.

"Yeah, but I need two sailors," Hanlon said. "This here is too much boat for one man."

"Well, hold on a minute," Jim said. "Let me talk it over with Doug." He turned to me and said, "Come on," and we went back down the gangway and ambled over to a shed where a couple of guys were doing some welding. We sat down on an old engine block in the shade and both lit up cigarets.

"Jim, I'll tell you right now I'm not going anywhere with that guy."

"Why not?"

"You know damn well why not."

Jim nodded. "Yeah, I admit he doesn't look so good. But maybe he's not drunk *all* the time."

"I don't like him anyway," I said.

"You don't have to like him. You didn't like Wicks, did you?"

"No, but I respected him. I don't respect Hanlon and I don't respect his boat either. Look at that goddam thing, will you? She looks like she'd break up and go down with all hands about halfway across the Gulfstream."

"Well, I'm going to sign up with him anyway," Jim said.

"Okay, if that's what you want," I said. "But I'm going to New York."

"I'd just like to go over to Nassau. I haven't been there yet. Wouldn't you like to go to Nassau?"

"Not that bad," I said.

"This is your final word on the subject?"

"Yes, it's my final word on the subject, except to say that I wish you'd just forget about this and come to New York with me. We could take that guy's car and be up there in twenty-four hours with both of us driving."

"No, I'm staying here," Jim said.

We sat there until we'd finished our cigarets and then went back aboard the *Life o' Riley*. We found Hanlon crapped out on the afterdeck on a pile of rolled-up rugs that looked as if they came from the main salon. He had a cigaret in one hand and a cold can of beer in the other. Jim told him he was signing up, but I was going to New York.

"Okay, I'll just have to call Harry and tell him to get me another guy," he said. "Now the first thing I want you to do is go below and try on some of those whites you'll find in the starboard locker. See if any of them fit you, so I'll know if I have to order any more from Acton. And you don't have to be any too particular about the fit, if you know what I mean. These shitkickers don't know any more about what a yacht sailor is supposed to look like than a monkey knows about Sunday, but I like my sailors to wear whites anyway."

I went down to the fo'c'sle with Jim. It was cramped, dingy, poorly ventilated and poorly lighted, and had such a sour smell that you had a feeling nothing on earth would ever be able to make it smell good again. But none of that seemed to bother Jim. He looked around and said cheerfully, "Don't worry, I'll have this place squared away in no time."

He started pulling whites out of the locker and trying them on and I watched him for a while and then said I'd better be going.

We shook hands, and he said, "Don't look so worried. I'll be okay, believe me."

"I believe you," I said, "but it just seems to me you're too nice a guy to be working on a broken-down boat with a drunk for a skipper and shitkicker for an owner, and to top it all off you have to wear whites."

"Yeah, well, the truth is, when you have a hole in the head your tendency is to take as few chances as possible. You don't want too many adventures. You hope that when you go to bed at night you'll be in exactly the same bed when you wake up in the morning."

"I know," I said. "And who knows, maybe you'll find happiness on the good old *Life o' Riley.*"

He grinned. "Maybe I will. Listen, one thing, when you get to New York go to the Seamen's Church Institute. It's down on State Street, right across from Battery Park. You can get a cheap room there, and also cheap food. All you have to do is tell them you're a seaman and they'll let you stay there."

"Thanks for telling me," I said. "Look, we'll probably see each other around down here next winter."

"Sure we will," he said.

I left him trying on the whites under the dim overhead light and took the bus back into town. I called the man with the car, but he said he'd already made arrangements with someone else. Anxious to get going I went to the Seaboard Coastline station up near the Dade County Courthouse and bought a ticket to New York on the East Coast Champion, which was leaving at six o'clock that evening.

❧

THE SEAMEN'S CHURCH INSTITUTE of New York was one of the most depressing places I had ever seen. Down on the first floor there was a cavernous, echoing, smoky hall where seamen sat around all day, staring into space, wandering around aimlessly, smoking, talking in loud voices.

They were presumably waiting to hear about openings on the merchant ships in New York harbor, whose names, arrival dates, departure dates and destinations were written on a huge blackboard at one end of the hall. Most of them looked like lost souls, and I thought it must have been because after so many years of going to sea they could never be really at home anywhere except in a fo'c'sle. Intermittently all day a voice on a p.a. microphone called out the names of ships and announced what jobs were open on them: able seaman, cook, second mate, third engineer, etc. Few of the men seemed to pay much attention. Occasionally one of them would get up and go over to the rostrum where the man with the microphone stood, and speak to him for a while and then leave, or, more likely, just come back and sit down again.

You paid a dollar a night for a narrow room upstairs with wire mesh on the window, which I assumed was there to keep the constituents from getting any funny ideas about flinging themselves onto the skylight below. The bathroom was down the hall, a steamy place that always smelled overpoweringly of disinfectant, and the men you ran into there were often very pale and their arms and legs and the backs of their hands and faces raw from wine sores. At night you were awakened by unearthly howls. Maybe bad dreams. Maybe something else. You never knew. You didn't keep your suitcase in your room. They warned you about that when they gave you your key. They said go and have your suitcase or your seabag or whatever you've got locked up in the baggage room. The baggage room was a huge wire cage presided over by hard-looking guys who handed you your check and then told you not to keep coming back wanting to go into your seabag or suitcase all the time because that could get to be a pain in the ass, know what I mean? So I stuffed a change of clothes into my flight bag along with my toothbrush and shaving kit. My money, which was all in cash, but only amounted to a couple of hundred dollars after the extravagance of the train ticket, was a constant source of anxiety. Finally, I put most of it in an envelope and asked the desk to keep it in the safe for me.

There was a cafeteria in the building where the food was not bad and very cheap, so I ate all my meals there. At night they showed free movies in the auditorium, and I usually went. Every morning I told myself this was the day I was going to go to City Island and see about getting a job on a yacht, but instead of actually doing it I sat on a bench in Battery Park and watched the ships pass, or took a ride on the Staten Island ferry, or prowled through the streets in the neighborhood of the Seamen's Church

Institute. On the morning of my sixth day in New York I called Moran's number, and asked if she was there. The maid said no, she was in Paris, did I want to speak to Mrs. Phillips? I said that wouldn't be necessary and hung up. Then I called Alex Latta's number, but hung up before anyone answered because I suddenly couldn't imagine what I would say to him if he was there.

I started walking, and went as far as Fulton Street before I stopped, and in that moment I knew the truth. I hadn't come all this way to get a job on a yacht. I had come all this way because in my heart I was yearning to "go home"—back to Cambridge, back to the Lampoon building.

I quickly returned to the Seamen's Church Institute and got my money from the safe and then retrieved my suitcase from the baggage room. On my way back up the narrow winding iron stairway an old seadog grinned at me with his yellow teeth and said, "You got a ship, lad?" and stuck out his palm. "If you want good luck, toss down a couple of sixpence from the yardarm." Confused, I dug in my pocket and gave him all my change.

I took a taxi to Grand Central and caught the next train to Boston, and soon I was gliding along on the coastline route I had seen so many times before, and listening to the conductor call out all the stops I knew so well. "Westerly! Westerly!"

IT WAS EARLY evening when I emerged from the subway kiosk in Harvard Square, and then lugging my suitcase I walked down Linden Street in the dusk. When I reached the foot of Linden Street I stopped, standing there by Claverly Hall, and looked across the street at the Lampoon building, and an ominous feeling came over me. I didn't know what it was. Just that something was wrong. I kept looking at the building. There wasn't a single light on in the whole place, and for some reason that put me off, and I thought of going back up to the Bick and having something to eat before I entered the building, just to kill a little time. But finally I went on across the street. I still had my key to the building, and as I had so many hundreds, or thousands of times before, I stuck it in the lock and turned it and pushed open the heavy door and entered the building, and right away all the familiar smells and sensations hit me. Of course even in the darkness I knew exactly where to find the light switch, but the instant the light came on and I found myself standing in the narrow Delft-tile-lined hallway, the ominous feeling returned, but now I knew what it was. It was the feeling that I shouldn't have come back, that I didn't belong in this place anymore.

I put down my suitcase in the Public Room and stood looking at the bulletin board, stupidly reading the notes that had been tacked up there at the end of the spring term. Most of them were signed with initials I had never seen before. Obviously new members who had been elected that spring. I went into the Business Office and looked around there, and then into the Narthex and the Sanctum. Turning on lights as I went I continued to the President's Room, and then ran up the stairs to the Great Hall, and soon I had the whole building lit up, except for the Ibis Room. When I climbed the winding stairway and found myself once again in the Ibis Room, I sat down on the old couch and the bad memories of all the nights I had spent there closed in on me, and I thought, "What if someone finds me here?" Then I began to hear voices. I heard Latta and Arlen and Bink Young and all the rest of my old friends talking and laughing, and when I went over to the balcony and looked down at the Great Hall for a moment I could see them all so clearly sitting at the long table, in the light from the flickering candles in the chandeliers above them, a Thursday night dinner, everyone slightly drunk and in high spirits, the air swirling with smoke, and then there was just the silence again.

I went up to the Bick and had the ham and egg special, and stayed there for a long time drinking coffee, and then went back to the Lampoon building, and sat in the President's Room not doing anything except trying to think what to do next. Then I heard the front door open and my heart began pounding, and in the next moment Elmer Green was standing in the doorway of the President's Room smiling at me, his glasses shining.

"Hello, Elmer," I said.

"Haven't seen you in a long time, sir," he said. "Come back for a little visit?"

"Yes, that's right," I said. "Just a little visit."

"Well, it's nice to see you back," he said. He started to go, but then hesitated. "Are you going to be sleeping upstairs again?" he said.

"Yes, I think I will," I said. "But not for long. Not for long."

He stood looking at me, and the feeling I had had before with him, of his pitying me, came back, and made my cheeks burn.

"Well, good night," he said, and left the room, and then I heard him going down the iron steps to the basement.

That night I slept on the couch in the President's Room, unable to go back up to the Ibis Room. The next morning, right after breakfast, I went to the Student Employment Office in the Yard and asked the young woman if she had anything for me. She said there was nothing at all at the moment, but told me to give her my phone number and she would call me if anything came in. I gave her the number of the *Lampoon* and left, thinking it was the same as always. I was always just a little too late. I spent the better part of the next two days hanging around the building, half waiting for the phone to ring, half knowing perfectly well it wouldn't. Not one soul, except Elmer, came into the building in that whole time and the loneliness was almost unbearable, and I began thinking that the only thing I could do was go back down to New York and try to get a job on a yacht.

But on the third day the phone did ring, and it was the young woman at the Student Employment Office, who said that she had an opening at the American Sugar Company that I was welcome to if I thought I wouldn't mind throwing bags of sugar around all summer, because that was what the job was. I said I wouldn't mind at all, and got the address and took two subway trains and got off at the Andrews Street Station and a few minutes later found myself in the personnel office of the American Sugar Company with a few other guys, waiting for a physical examination. Most of the others were college football players looking for a job where they could stay in shape over the summer, and although I thought I was in pretty good shape after working on the yacht, I was afraid I might not have much of a chance in that kind of company. But the doctor told me I looked fine to him and sent me to the personnel manager, who told me I was on the afternoon shift, and that I was to report the next day at three o'clock ready to go to work, the pay was sixty dollars a week.

When I got back to the Lampoon building I felt much better about my situation, and I took my stuff up to the Ibis Room and then went to the Harvard Coop and bought a couple of sheets, telling myself to hell with it, I'll stay in the building all summer and save my money, and then in the fall before they all come back I'll move out and get a room in one of the rooming houses on Linden Street or DeWolfe Street, and maybe see if I can't get a job in Boston in advertising or commercial art.

⁊

ON MY FIRST DAY at the "Sugar House," as they all called it, I was put to work on the loading dock, which had open bays on one side for loading trucks and on the other side for loading freight cars. It was a very noisy place where everyone had to yell to be heard over the roar of the diesel engines of the trucks, the putt-putt-putting of the little fork-lifts that scooted all over the place carrying pallets loaded with hundred-pound bags of sugar on their forks or pulling iron carts loaded with hundred-pound bags of sugar behind them, plus the rattling and screeching of the main conveyor belt that brought the bags of sugar down from the refinery.

For the first couple of days I helped load trucks and freight cars, and the thing that worried me was how hard it was for me to manhandle the hundred-pound bags. I noticed that everyone else seemed to be able to carry them around without any trouble at all—even skinny guys who I didn't think were nearly as strong as I was. While I was almost dying, they were hefting the bags as if they weighed fifty pounds instead of a hundred, and when, on my third day, the foreman told me he wanted me to join the crew on the main conveyor belt, I felt like quitting while I was still ahead. I had watched the conveyer belt and had dreaded the possibility of having to work there because it never stopped moving except on the occasions when a bag of sugar that had somehow been ripped open came down, and then one of the crew pushed a button that stopped the belt and yelled "Broken sugar! Broken sugar!"—at which point a dozen urchins appeared out of nowhere with brown paper sacks and kitchen scoops and shoveled all the sugar they could into the sacks before they were chased away, presumably home to mother, who could use all the free sugar she could get. Two men stood on the platforms on either side of the conveyer belt and lifted the hundred-pound bags as they came along and dropped them onto the iron carts that were lined up alongside the platforms. When I took my turn on the platform I could only go for a few minutes before I was exhausted and had to ask somebody to take over for me. The other guys looked at me, and asked me if I was all right. I said, "Well, I'm just not used to this, I guess. But I'll be all right in a minute."

"You're purple in the face, you know that?" one of them said.

"*Purple* in the face?"

"Yeah, I'm not kidding. You're not going to have a heart attack or anythink, are you?"

"No, I'll be okay," I said.

"Listen," he said, "you know what your problem is?"

"What is it?"

"Your problem is, you don't know how to make the weight of the bag work for you. In other words, you don't have any rhythm. You've got to have rhythm or you can't work at the Sugar House, because that's the only way you can handle this kind of work. Want me to show you what I mean?"

"I sure do," I said.

"Okay, now watch," he said, and he grabbed hold of a bag and jerked it into the air and all in one easy motion swiveled and dropped it onto the iron cart. "You see what I did?" he said. "I never had the weight of the damn thing for more than a split second. The rest of it was all just plain rhythm."

I watched him do it again, and then tried it myself, and I was amazed to see that he was absolutely right. You couldn't *lift* the bags. You had to use the momentum you created when you first took hold of them to make them sail around the way he did. By the end of my first shift I was really beginning to get the hang of it, and not too long after that I was flinging the hundred-pound bags around as easily as everyone else. In fact, it wasn't too long before I learned the trick of picking up a bag and flipping it in mid-air as I dropped it onto the cart below. And I became one of the few men in the whole place who actually liked working on the main conveyer belt. Most of them hated it, but I liked it because it was such a simple-minded job that you didn't even have to think about what you were doing, but could just let your mind wander freely, whereas down on the floor you always had to stay alert and try to look busy.

We were relieved on the belt for about ten minutes every half hour, when you could go out and sit in the doorway of one of the freight cars and have a cigaret, assured that no one would bother you. At six o'clock the belt shut down and we had half an hour to eat our dinner. I went across the railroad tracks to a diner where they had very good food, and then in the dusk went back to the Sugar House and jumped up on the platform and was ready to go when the belt started up again. Once or twice the foreman came by and asked me if I didn't want to do something else for a change, but I told him very politely no thanks, I liked this.

Usually I came to work a little early and after I got changed in the locker room upstairs I went and sat on the fire escape outside the locker room and looked at the guys down below who were working around the immense open tank where the raw sugar was stored after it was taken off the ships. Once in a while one of them would piss into the brown sugar and it would get a laugh from his buddies, and maybe from some of the sailors on the freighters that had come in from Cuba and were tied up right alongside the Sugar House. The sailors sold very good rum and brandy for only a few dollars a bottle. They passed the bottles out through a porthole amidships and took the money and said, *"Muchas gracias, amigo."*

One of the men on the conveyer belt had a radio and we listened to the Red Sox games, both home and away. Bitching about the Red Sox was our principal subject of conversation, but we also discussed the war in Korea, Communism, religion, women and cars. After dark the Sugar House was eerie because the lights were dim and the whole place was suddenly full of dark corners. About eight o'clock a little truck came and sold us hot coffee, and from then until ten-thirty when the quitting-time bell rang and we all went up to the locker room to shower and dress and get the hell out of there, we were all pretty quiet and didn't kid around very much.

Basically, I was happy working at American Sugar, just as I had been happy at the Café Rouge, and yet there was always the gnawing feeling that I wished I could be doing something in which I could use whatever talent I had. One night I got up my spit and retrieved the manuscript of "Welcome Stamp Collectors" from the place where I had hidden it before I had left Cambridge the last time, and took it into the President's Room and settled down with a full pack of cigarets and the notion of trying to give it an absolutely objective reading, and that was exactly what happened. I was finally at such a distance from the story that I could see very clearly that Bob Townsend had been right about it being hopelessly confused and overworked. Feeling deeply discouraged I put the manuscript back in its place, resolving to leave it there forever.

I continued working at American Sugar until late in August, when, one morning, two members of the *Lampoon,* Jerry Fannon and Peter St. Coeur, appeared in the building and after they had expressed their total astonishment at finding me there, started telling me about all the problems they were having with the book for their Hasty Pudding show, which was supposed to go into rehearsal about a month from then. They said what the bloody thing needed was a play doctor and how marvelous it was that I, who was their only hope of salvation, happened to be right here when they needed me most. In other words, they were asking me to come back out to Dover with them, where they were working at Peter's house, and collaborate with them on the script, and without a moment's hesitation I said yes, and went over to the Sugar House and told the foreman I was all through.

&

OF COURSE I KNEW what I was doing was absurd. Even more absurd than when I had let myself be talked into continuing as president of the *Lampoon* when I wasn't even in college. Now, here I was not only not even in college but letting myself be talked into working my ass off on a project from which there was no possibility whatsoever of any gain for me personally, when I knew very well that I should have kept my job at American Sugar, where at least I was making sixty dollars a week, every week.

But the thought of working on a musical was really exciting, particularly when I knew that nowadays Hasty Pudding shows were produced and directed and choreographed by professionals who were brought in from New York, and the whole idea of having this experience was simply irresistible.

Jerry and Peter were both in the class of '53. That made them considerably younger than I was, which bothered me, although it didn't them. Also I had never really been friends with either of them. In fact, I had always found Peter a little annoying. For one thing, he was the only person I had ever known who wore a handkerchief tucked in his sleeve. For another, he was an incorrigible exhibitionist who had a way of getting very pouty when he felt people weren't paying enough attention to him. He was handsome in a fiery-cheeked, black-haired, lazy-eyed sort of way, and much chased after by Radcliffe girls. But on the minus side, for some reason when he got the slightest bit excited sweat popped out all over him and poured down his face in torrents and he had to mop up furiously with the famous handkerchief from up his sleeve. He was on the literary board of the magazine and in my time had regularly contributed stories that no one had ever thought funny except him, and then had gotten into terrible huffs when they had been rejected.

As for Jerry, he was small, cynical, slightly depressive and capable of violent temper tantrums. Most of all he liked to walk around with his little round paunch sticking out and his thumbs hooked in his belt loops and make scathing remarks either in his Donald Duck voice or his fake stutter. But he was a very talented writer of light verse and had made some brilliant contributions to the *Lampoon*. I was glad that he was writing all the lyrics for the show as well as collaborating on the book.

They had gone to Groton together, where I had heard they had been close friends from the first form straight through the sixth, and the relationship had continued at Harvard, where they roomed together in Adams House. It seemed to me they complemented each other very well, one the dashing Student Prince and the other his dark and brooding sidekick.

In Dover, I found that Jerry and Peter had taken over the entire living room of Peter's house, which was large and elegant and had vast grounds and beautiful trees and flower gardens and a free-form swimming pool, and even a river flowing gently by.

Peter's mother, Ellen, who had lost her husband, the director of about ten corporations and principal stockholder in most of them, in a plane crash, was still fairly young and very good-looking and had plenty of men hanging around all the time, but you always had the feeling that her son was the only man she really loved. She was *intensely* proud of him for having won the competition that had led to the selection of his and Jerry's script as the one that would be produced by the Hasty Pudding that fall, even though she had never read it herself and hadn't the vaguest notion of what it was about, but I knew that even if she had known how dumb it was, and it was very, very dumb, just as every Pudding show that was ever written was very, very dumb, Peter still would have been her little genius.

The first thing they did was run through the music for me, which Peter played on the Steinway that had been rolled by the servants into the living room from the music room specially for him, with Jerry singing along with the lyrics from the songs he had finished so far. I thought the lyrics and the music were pretty good. Anyway, they were certainly way ahead of the book, which took place Out West and, suffice it to say, involved cowboys and Indians, a saloon called the Golden Horseshoe and a madam with a heart of gold called Sally Highway, Esq.

"We were going along just fine," Peter said, "and then somehow we lost our way."

"And we want you to guide us back to the light," Jerry said. "P-p-p-p-please!"

Peter turned on him fiercely. "What did I tell you about that goddam *stuttering!*"

"S-s-s-s-sorry," Jerry said humbly.

"If you want to know the truth," Peter said to me, *"that's* why we lost our way! It's the *continual* fucking *stuttering* and *quacking* that goes on around here! You can't imagine what it's been *like* for me! He's driving me *mad,* I tell you!"

"Oh, don't be so *dramatic,"* Jerry said in his Donald Duck imitation.

Peter jumped on top of Jerry and began strangling him. "I can't *take* it anymore! Hear me? I can't *take* it anymore! I can't *take* it anymore! If you stutter or quack one more fucking time I'm going to lock you up in the basement and I won't let you out for fifteen years!"

"Oh, for Christ's sake," I said. "C-c-c-c-can't you g-g-g-g-guys be *s-s-s-s-s-serious?"*

"He's absolutely right," Peter said. "We're going to be very serious from now on, aren't we, Jerry?"

"What for?" Jerry said. "He's only been here one day and already he's *Hitler.* I thought this was going to be so much *fun.* You can tell him for me that if he doesn't stop being a regular little *Hitler* I'm going up to my room and I won't come down again until Sunday afternoon."

"Douglas, if you don't stop acting like a regular little Hitler, Jerry is going up to his room and he won't come down again until Sunday afternoon," Peter said.

"Okay, I won't be a regular little Hitler anymore," I said.

"Promise?" Jerry said.

"Promise."

"All right then, we can get on with it."

"First of all, we've got to try to figure out exactly where it was that you began to lose your way," I said.

"But if we knew that we wouldn't need you!" Peter yelled. "Look, you're supposed to be the play doctor, and you're supposed to put the patient on your little examining table and bring the roses back to its cheeks, while we do what we're supposed to be doing, which is playing tennis! Come on, Jerry, let's leave the doctor alone now, so he can work his wonderful magic on our poor pale script."

After I had read the script through four more times I thought I had a pretty good idea of how it could be saved without too much rewriting, and when I told Peter and Jerry my ideas they said, okay, that sounded good, so why didn't I start blocking out my changes right away, but I told them that even though they might accuse me again of being a regular little Hitler, we were going to block out the changes together. That brought on a storm of quacks and stutters, but in the end they settled down with me at the long oak table in the living room and we began working on the revisions that I had thought were necessary.

OUR WORKING CONDITIONS were heaven on earth. Peter and Jerry and I got up early every morning and went over to the Dedham Hunt Club and played three or four sets of doubles. Then we came back to the house and had a dip in the pool, then lunch on the terrace, and then to work in the living room, where there were unlimited cigarets, mixed nuts, chocolate-covered thin mints, plus every afternoon at four o'clock sharp a full English tea brought to us on silver trays, complete with cucumber sandwiches, scones, homemade strawberry jam and marmalade, petit fours and a fragrant, steaming pot of Darjeeling. Around six o'clock a maid brought us a great wheel of cheddar cheese and crackers, and Ellen joined us for cocktails. Dinner was invariably a magnificent affair, with superb wine that Peter would have selected personally from their very extensive cellar, followed by Havana cigars and cognac or anything else your heart desired.

Once we got going on the revisions we made very good progress, and it wasn't too long before we had a script that we could actually hand to the director and the actors and they would be able to begin working on the scenes. Of course we all knew that once the rehearsals began the script would undoubtedly have to go through many more revisions, but we made it our objective to go in with the strongest first draft possible.

The closer it came to the time when we would be going back to Cambridge the more I could hardly wait. The thought of seeing our script gradually come to life on a stage was intoxicating.

❧

ONE DAY just before we went back to Cambridge, I borrowed Peter's car and drove down the road to Moran's mother's house, which was only about half a mile away. She was very surprised to see me.

"Moran told me you were working on a boat down in Florida," she said.

"I was."

"Then what are you doing in Dover?"

When I told her she looked very upset. "Then this means you're going to be in Cambridge this fall?"

"I'm afraid so."

"I don't want to sound cruel," she said, "but I thought we were finally rid of you."

"Well, not quite yet."

"I want to tell you something. When Moran first went to Radcliffe she said she was going to try for a summa. Now she doesn't even think she can get a magna, and will probably have to settle for a cum, if that."

"And you blame me, don't you?"

"Yes, I do."

"I'm sorry you feel that way."

"I'm going to ask you to do something for me."

"What is it?"

"I'm going to ask you to promise me you'll leave Moran alone this fall."

"I don't think you have much to worry about," I said. "She's going to be working very hard, and I'm going to be in the rehearsals all the time."

"What if I wrote you a check for a thousand dollars and asked you not to go to Cambridge at all?"

"I'd love to have the money, but I really have to be there for the rehearsals."

"Two thousand?"

"Are you serious?"

"Yes."

"Well, as I say, I'd love to have the money, but I just have to be there for the rehearsals."

"All right, then I'm going to ask you once more to promise me you'll leave Moran alone this fall."

"I promise."

She was astonished. "And I can trust you to keep your word?"

"Absolutely."

&

"WELL, I'M all done," Moran said. "How about you?"

"Yeah, I guess so," I said.

She went and got her cigarets and then came back and crawled in beside me in Peter's bed again.

"I still think you should have taken the money," she said.

"I'll have one of those," I said.

"I don't think she should have tried to bribe you that way, so I think it would have been perfectly ethical for you to have taken the money."

"Can I have one of those?"

She lit a cigaret and passed it to me. "She thinks you're crazy, you know. She thinks there must be a mix-up in your chromosomes or something. In fact, I think she thinks I could catch it from you. If she's asked me once she's asked me a million times if you've ever let on that there was any insanity in your family."

"Well, if you think it will make her feel any better you can tell her that I was rejected by the army three different times for neurotic symptoms."

"What does that *mean* exactly?"

"It means *they* thought I was crazy."

"Boy, wouldn't she love to hear that?"

"You know, I was supposed to have been at the rehearsal an hour ago."

"I think she really thinks you're going to hypnotize me and force me to marry you."

I got out of bed and put on my pants.

"I keep thinking that if she could have seen all the unsavory types I was having affairs with this summer in Europe, then she would really have had something to worry about. But it's just you. You know why? Because she knows that you were the first man I was ever *really* in love with. So she thinks you have a strange power over me."

"I'm sorry, but I've got to go," I said.

"Wait for me. You can't leave me here alone."

She got out of bed and started putting on her clothes very quickly.

"And she's right, you know. I still think about you all the time, and worry about you all the time."

We parted outside the Hasty Pudding.

"I've been meaning to tell you," she said. "You don't look too good."

❧

"I TOLD my mother I think I'm still in love with you.

"You know what she said?

"She said she wished something would happen to you.

"I said I think something *is* happening to you.

"I told her how awful you look.

"I told her I think you're going to pieces.

"I told her you say nothing seems to bother you anymore.

"You don't care what anyone thinks of you anymore.

"Or how you look.

"Or what you say.

"And how you said it actually feels pretty good.

"I told her you're living in the Ibis Room again.

"She didn't know what that meant.

"So I described it.

"She said she just prays every night that something will happen to you.

"I said I just told you.

"Something is happening to him.

"I think he's going to pieces.

"I said half the time you don't even shave anymore.

"I said you shake like a leaf.

"I said you never eat anything anymore.

"You live on cigarets and coffee.

"I said you ought to see his eyes.

"She said she doesn't want you to *die.*

"'Do you think he's going to *die?*'

"I said I don't know.

"She said, well, she doesn't want you to die.

"That isn't what she means.

"I said, well, what do you mean?

"She said she wishes you would just *disappear.*

"*Disappear?* I said.

"'Yes, *disappear,*' she said.

"'One day you'd go looking for him and everyone would tell you he had simply vanished.

"'And you would never hear another word out of him again.

"'And you could get your life back to normal.'"

&

"I SWEAR to God I think this guy is dying," Harold Clemence, the producer, said.

Jerry came over and pretended to take my pulse.

"It's just an *act!*" he sputtered in his Donald Duck quack, showering me with spit. "This man is as sound as a dollar!"

"I don't believe it," Harold said.

He was about thirty-five but could have passed for fifty easy. He had a very deep voice, one slightly drooping eyelid, a passion for cigars that smelled like rope burning and were continually sending long trails of white ashes tumbling down the front of his vest, very deep acne scars on his neck, an apparently perpetual head cold, a fondness for mauve-colored glasses, and a way of seeming to be wearing his overcoat all the time and of never being without a briefcase of very worn, battered and cracked imitation leather with a broken clasp from which masses of papers kept spilling at the worst possible moments.

"You don't know him," Peter said. "We've seen him look *much* worse than this millions of times and he never died. Anyway, we've told him he can't die until the script is finished."

"Will you just shut up now, all of you, *please?*" Donn Haskell, the director, said.

Donn sat down on the other side of me. He was a pale, fragile, very nervous little thing with a colossal ego that you had to keep circling around all the time.

"You really shouldn't talk to us like that, Donn," Jerry said. "We have feelings too, you know."

Donn ignored him. "Now I'm going to tell you why I've called this meeting," he said. "And I'm going to tell you in a very few words. We are going to have to take the *entire* third act apart and put it back together stone by stone."

"You're not serious, are you?" Peter said.

"I'm very serious."

"With the opening in less than two weeks?" Peter said.

232

"Let me put it this way," Donn said. "Either we do it or I'm walking out on this production. There is *nothing* in the third act that works right. Not one single solitary fucking *thing,* and I refuse to try to cope with this material one day longer. You have your choice. Rewrite the entire third act the way I want it rewritten or start looking for a new director."

Peter looked at me.

"I don't think you should make this guy do any more rewriting," Harold said.

"It's not as simple as that," Peter said. "He has to. I don't have the time."

"Me either," Jerry said.

"Anyway, you don't understand, Harold," Peter said. "See, he *loves* to rewrite."

"That's right," Jerry said. "You just wind him up and push the rewrite button and he starts rewriting."

"Okay," Donn said. "Let's go."

 ❧

"MY GOD, if this doesn't take me back a thousand years," Alex said.

I forced my eyes open and looked at him.

"Hello, Alex," I said.

He shook his head bewilderedly.

"To think that I could come up those stairs and find you back in the Ibis Room again."

"What are you doing here?"

"I've come to save you. From what I hear you're very much in need of saving, and since nobody else seems to be doing much of a job of it, I'm taking over, as of now."

He came and looked at me closer.

"Yes, it's absolutely true. Everybody who has seen you has told me you look awful, and you do. Look, it's going on noon. I'm going back downstairs, and here's what I want you to do. I want you to get up out of that pathetic bed and go down and wash your pathetic face and brush your pathetic teeth and shave and put on some clothes, and I'll take you somewhere very nice for lunch, and then we'll talk about what comes next."

In the restaurant, he said, "First, I heard you were writing the Pudding show with Jerry and Peter and I couldn't believe it. Then, last week, I was at the Harvard Club and Willie Magder said, 'Alex, you won't believe this,' and told me you were back living in the Ibis Room again, and I knew it was time for me to do something. So here I am, and I'm telling you right now I will not leave this town until I've accomplished my mission, which as I've said, is to save you. First, this question. Are you ready to be saved?"

"Yes."

"Good, because I'm going to do it whether you want it or not, but it will certainly make everything so much easier if you're going to cooperate. Next, I assume you're broke? Of course. Obviously. Or you wouldn't be living in that stinking Ibis Room. Okay, I've brought along rather a lot of money for you, in cash. And don't say you won't take it."

"I'll take it."

"Bravo. I thought you might feel you had to be difficult about it. Next, I want very much for you to get out of Cambridge. Otherwise, I'm afraid this place will quite literally be the death of you. What do you say? Will you do it?"

"Yes."

"Marvelous. Where will you go?"

"To Florida."

"Just what I was hoping you'd say. Now, you know what I wish? That you go down there and get warm and get your health back, and then, in the spring, come back up to New York and let me introduce you to some of the people at *Life,* and I can almost promise you that if you don't throw up on the carpet or anything like that, they'll give you a job."

He leaned toward me.

"You'd *love* it. Listen, I'm having more fun there than I've ever had before. You can't imagine how exciting it is. They're always sending you off with a photographer and an unlimited expense account to cover an earthquake or Korea or to interview someone who says he's God. And the *women.* I tell you, the goddam place is full of beautiful, bright, immensely passionate young women who think that all *Life* reporters are irresistibly sexy."

I shook my head. "Alex, when I go down there this time, I'm never coming back."

"You don't mean that."

"Yes, I do."

"What in God's name would you *do* down there?"

"The same thing I did last time. Sign on a yacht. It wasn't so bad."

"But a total dead end."

"Yes, I suppose so."

"You say this now, but you'll change your mind."

"No, I won't."

"You know what I'm doing? I'm discounting everything you're saying now because I think you're a little delirious. Next you're going to be telling me you'll never try to write another novel just because things turned out badly for your last one."

"Yes, that is what I will tell you," I said. "Alex, I believe now that writing a novel is something some people can do and others can't, and that I am simply one of those who can't."

"You know, I think you really mean it."

"I really do," I said. "I feel that I had my chance. I tried very hard for a very long time and nothing came of it, and I can tell you now that there is no power on earth that could ever make me try again."

He stared at me for a minute. "Well, you know, honestly, I can't say I blame you a bit."

&

"WHEN YOU told me that," Moran said, "I was positive my heart would break.

"But then I thought about it.

"And I realized that of course you're right.

"When we say goodbye now I should accept that this is the end of it for us.

"And what I was saying, that I *know* the phone will ring some day and it will be you, that's just trying to save myself from feeling any pain when I watch you go.

"I've accepted it.

"I know I will never see you again.

"So kiss me."

Part Three

ಶಿ

LOVE IN CANNES

WHEN THE *Coloratura* was lying in Cannes, which was most of the time, it was my job to go every morning around eleven o'clock to the office of M. Glémot, the ship chandler, on the Quai St-Pierre, to pick up the ship's mail. On my way back to the *Coloratura,* which was moored on the Jetée Albert-Edouard, I never failed to linger for a while on the terrace of a bar called Les Allées, which was located in the long avenues of plane trees at the foot of the harbor which were known as Les Allées de la Liberté, to have a café au lait, smoke a cigaret, check the *Cannes-Nice Soir* to see if my number had come up in the lottery, and shoot the bull with some of the business girls from the Rue d'Antibes, who would just be coming back to life around that time of day.

It was very pleasant on the terrace, sitting at one of the round white tables with the red and blue Cinzano ashtrays on them, in the deep shade of the plane trees. The whole terrace would recently have been hosed off and would still be wet and cool, and the air was sweet with all the fragrances from the stalls in the flower market.

It was while I was lounging there one morning in May that I saw Christine Rimbaud for the first time. She went past fairly close to me, just on the other side of the hedge that enclosed the terrace, and I noticed a couple of things about her immediately. The first was that she was very

237

pretty, with short brown hair, greenish eyes and freckles on her nose. The second was that she was loaded down with a big wooden paint box, a camp stool, a collapsible easel, and had a canvas tucked under one arm.

She was wearing espadrilles and blue shorts and a bright yellow sweater, so it was easy for me to follow her with my eyes as she crossed the street and passed by the pavilion where they sold tickets for the excursion boats that went to the Lérins islands, Ste-Marguerite and St-Honorat, but then I lost sight of her when she disappeared among the fishing boats that were hauled up out of the water on the Allées beach.

The next morning I saw her pass by again, carrying all the same paraphernalia, and the morning after that, too, but this time, fortunately, Louisette, the woman who ran the bar, and who seemed to know practically every living soul around the Cannes waterfront, was sitting at my table having coffee with me, and I asked her if by any chance she knew who that was.

Louisette squinted in the direction I had indicated and then nodded. "Her name is Christine Rimbaud."

"Yes?"

"She's just come down here, from Paris."

Louisette could be very difficult when she felt like it.

"Keep going," I said.

She shrugged. "Do you know the bar called La Potinière, in the Rue des Serbes?"

"I've gone past it a couple of time," I said. "I've never gone in. I've often wondered what that means, La Potinière."

"It means The Gossip-Shop," Louisette said. "Anyway, it's owned by Hélène Gassin, who is Christine's aunt on her mother's side. Christine is going to be working there this summer. Well, you know what I mean when I say 'working.'"

She waggled her hand.

"She's very good-looking," I said.

"Also very stuck-up. Just like everybody from Paris."

"How old is she? Do you know?"

"She just turned eighteen."

"That a very nice age," I said, smiling.

Louisette just gave me a look, so I finished my coffee and gathered my mail and stood up. "Well, I've got to be getting back to the ship," I said.

"I don't believe you," Louisette said. "I think you're going over there and talk to that girl."

"Well, maybe for a minute or two," I said.

"Take my advice," she said. "Look out for her. Those girls from Paris can be dangerous."

I smiled. "All right, I'll be careful," I said.

I found that Christine had set up her easel between two fishing boats down near the water's edge. She was sitting on her camp stool staring at her picture very thoughtfully, her left thumb stuck in the hole in her palette, while she chewed on the tip of one of her paintbrushes.

As I approached she glanced at me.

"Hello," I said.

She shrugged, and took a long time to do it, but finally said hello.

I looked at her picture. It was supposed to be a view of the yachts on the Jetée side of the harbor, but it was really an awful mess. For one thing, she didn't seem to know the first thing about the laws of perspective, and for another she didn't know how to use color, because the whole picture was about to go to mud.

"Not bad," I said.

"You don't have to say that," she said. "I know it's not very good."

"Yes, well, actually, there are a couple of things that need fixing up a little," I said.

She looked at the name on the front of my shirt. "What would you know about it? What are you? A sailor on one of those yachts?"

"Yes, I'm on the American yacht," I said.

"Well, what would you know about painting a picture then? I'll bet the only kind of painting you know anything about is painting the side of a boat."

"No, you're wrong," I said. "I know quite a lot about picture painting, too."

She said, "You know, I think you're just trying to pick me up."

I smiled. "Yes, well, actually, that, too."

"What's your name?"

"Douglas."

"Dooglas."

"That's close enough," I said.

"No, say it again for me."

"Douglas."

"Dooglas."

"Very good," I said.

"Dooglas."

"Perfect."

She looked very pleased with herself. "Dooglas," she said again.

"You don't have to tell me your name," I said. "I already know it. Christine."

She looked surprised. "Who told you my name?"

"Louisette."

"Louisette? Oh, yes, I know who you mean. She's a friend of my aunt's. What else did she say about me?"

"That you're from Paris. That you're going to be working at La Potinière this summer."

She nodded. "You speak French rather well."

"Well, I've been here in Cannes almost a year now."

"I can tell," she said. "You even have a Cannoise accent."

"What would you expect? A Parisian accent?"

She laughed. "I'm only teasing. Where in America did you come from? New York?"

"No. Miami."

"Where is that? I've never heard of it."

"What cities in the United States have you heard of?"

"New York, Washington, Chicago and San Francisco."

"Well, that's pretty good," I said.

"Tell me honestly, do you really know anything about how to paint a picture?"

"Christine," I said, "I've painted a lot of pictures. Oh, I grant you I may not be Rembrandt van Rijn, but I do know something about the subject."

"And you can help me with this picture?"

"Yes."

"Well, will you show me right now what you think I should do with it?"

"I'm sorry, but I can't do it right now. I've got to be getting back to the yacht. How about tomorrow?"

"All right," she said. "Tomorrow."

"You'll be here at about the same time?"

"Yes."

I started to go and then came back. "Just tell me one thing. Why did you decide to take up oil painting?"

"I used to paint with watercolors all the time," she said. "Then I found all these things at my aunt's house. They belonged to her son André, who got tired of them. Well, I've always wanted to try painting with oils. I've always thought it looked so *easy*. Now I'm beginning to see that it really isn't."

"No, it really isn't," I said. "Well, tomorrow. Same time."

"Yes, tomorrow. Same time."

Hurrying back to the *Coloratura* with my letters, I knew I had fallen madly in love.

ॐ

THAT NIGHT I had the gangway watch, but I persuaded one of the other sailors to stand by for me a little while, and I went along the Croisette to the Rue des Serbes. On one side of the street was the Majestic Hotel. On the other, about halfway up the block, was the narrow side door of La Potinière. I walked past the door quickly, and glanced inside. This was not at all like the bars down by the waterfront. Here there were thick carpets on the floor and candles on the tables, and the men wore suits and the women evening gowns, and the whole room had a very misty and romantic look to it.

I hadn't seen Christine the first time I went past the door, so I went on a ways up the block and then turned back and went by the door again, and this time I did catch a glimpse of her. She was wearing a peach-colored evening gown, and was carrying a tray with a bottle of wine and some glasses on it through the door on the far side of the room, which gave onto a large courtyard where there were some shops and a couple of restaurants, and in the center of it an open-air dance floor where an orchestra was playing and people were dancing.

I started to go back to the ship, but when I came to the Croisette I turned in the other direction and went on up the block until I came to the passageway that led into the courtyard, and there I stayed in the shadows on the other side of the dance floor from La Potinière, and watched Christine. She looked very slender and beautiful in her evening gown, and also very much at ease in that milieu. I noticed the way the men sitting at the tables outside La Potinière looked at her when she went past, or paused to take an order. They obviously thought she was beautiful, too.

La Potinière did rather a large business, and there were two other young girls working there besides Christine Rimbaud, but she was by far the best-looking, and the only one who wore an evening gown.

I stayed there in the chilly night long enough to smoke three cigarets in a row, and in that time I saw two different men make passes at Christine. One was young and slick-looking and the other was older, silver-haired, well-dressed, and obviously very suave. She stopped and sat down with each of them for a minute, smiling, and flirting a little.

On my way back to the *Coloratura* I thought, my God, this is awful. I barely know her and here I am doing *this*.

ॐ

I WAS VERY happy in Cannes. In the first place it was the most beautiful town I had ever seen. Every day you could look at the long lovely crescent of the littoral of the Golfe de la Napoule curving gloriously up past the great hotels along the Boulevard de la Croisette, the Majestic, the Carlton and the Martinez, to the Pointe de la Croisette and the glistening white casino at Palm Beach. And the harbor itself was charming, and always exciting, with some of the largest and most elegant yachts in the world constantly coming and going. Then there were the hills that enclosed the town, kept dark green, and often obscured, by swiftly flying rain clouds, and way past them, very far in the distance, the faint blue, snow-capped peaks of the Pre-Alps.

Also, the *Coloratura* was a particularly fine yacht, and I had considered myself very lucky when I had signed aboard her in Miami, and even luckier when, soon after, Captain Marryat had announced that we were going to be spending that summer cruising in the Mediterranean. The *Coloratura* was one hundred and seventy-three feet on the waterline and had a dark blue steel hull with the lean, swift, eager lines of a destroyer, and two immense chrome-plated Enterprise engines that could drive her along at close to the speed of a destroyer. Wherever we went in the Mediterranean she was always one of the most impressive yachts in every harbor we entered, and she was by far the most impressive yacht that stayed regularly in Cannes.

The owner was George Apollodorus, a Greek-American who was the owner of a fleet of oil tankers that was ranked third largest in the world, after those of Niarchos and Onassis. He was a pleasant man who was very solicitous of his crew, and when, at the end of that first summer, he had informed Captain Marryat that he had decided to station the *Coloratura* in

Cannes permanently, to be used as a sort of floating European headquarters for his fleet of tankers, the same way Niarchos did with his two-hundred-foot, three-masted, black-hulled staysail schooner *Creole,* but would happily pay first-class passage back to the States for anyone who wanted to go, only one man out of the total of seventeen in the crew had taken him up on it, and he was just the third steward, a bitter little man nobody had liked anyway, so we weren't sorry to see him go. And he wasn't replaced.

As a matter of fact, I thought I would just as soon stay there in Cannes for the rest of my life. I felt as much at home there as I ever had anyplace. I had made quite a few friends in the town. Perhaps not really close friends, but people like Louisette, who were always glad to see me, and that was good enough for me. Another thing was that, since the *Coloratura* had been in Cannes for almost a year, the crew of the yacht, like the crews of all the yachts that stayed in Cannes permanently, were accepted as part of the local establishment. This meant, among other things, that we were charged the same prices that the Cannoise charged each other, which was an important concession, because, in general, there were three different prices for everything on the Riviera. The highest price was that charged the sailors of the Sixth Fleet, which was three or four times more than that charged anyone else. The rationalization was that the sailors could afford it, and wouldn't know the difference anyway because they were drunk all the time. On top of that, the owners of the bars around the waterfront felt that they had the right to overcharge as a form of insurance against all the damage they knew would be done once the inevitable fist-fights among the sailors got started. The second price was for tourists of all nationalities, including the French, and the third price, the rock-bottom one, was, of course, the *prix Cannoise.*

Also, in terms of what was being paid the French and English and Italian sailors on the other yachts, we on the *Coloratura* were practically stinking rich. The sailors on other yachts got their room and board, plus a salary that didn't amount to a tenth of ours—which, actually, was just the usual American yacht sailor's two hundred and twenty-five dollars a month. Still, there was a rumor on the Jetée Albert-Edouard that the sailors on the *Coloratura* were making only a few dollars less a month than the captain of the *Creole,* who happened to have been a U-boat commander in the war, and now had forty-two men in his crew. So, of course, we were the envy of all the other sailors in Cannes, who knew that we not only made this princely wage but also ate like princes and were provided with all the American cigarets we could smoke, which were provided by Mr. Apollodorus, free of charge.

But the thing that made me happiest of all, that made me feel like singing all the time, was the fact that at the end of the month Fred Appel, the first mate, was going to quit and go home, at which time the second mate, Bill Wimmers, was going to become the first mate, and, Captain Marryat had promised me, I was going to become the second mate. He had made this decision, he had told me, because he felt I was the only man in the crew whom he could trust, all the others being, in his view, too unreliable either because they drank too much or were simply too damn stupid.

The prospect that I soon would not only get to swagger around Cannes in officers' whites and shoulderboards but would also be making more than twice the money I was as a common sailor was intoxicating. Every morning when I woke up I thought right away, now it's one day closer.

ॐ

THERE WERE ONLY two good things to be said about standing the night watch on the *Coloratura*, which was basically an incredibly boring thing to have to do. The first was that you always got the next day off, since you would have had to stay awake all night. Of course the trouble with that was that you were always so tired the next day that you couldn't do anything but sleep anyway, or mope around all day yawning.

The only other good thing was that you had an opportunity to observe the whole cycle of an evening and night in the harbor, from around six o'clock when you went on watch until seven the next morning when you dragged yourself below for breakfast.

At first you had plenty of company, because the Jetée Albert-Edouard was crowded with tourists of all nationalities who thronged out there to look eagerly at the yachts, which lay squeezed in side by side as they did in the ports all around the Mediterranean, which, unlike the marinas in the United States, were very old and had been intended to accommodate small fishing boats and not hundred-foot yachts. If you stood out on the quai, at the foot of your gangway, in your uniform, there were always lots of people who would stop and ask you all kinds of questions about the yacht. Of course it was because she was American that she fascinated them. They were used to seeing the French and German and Italian and British flags, but the American flag was unusual. And some of those people would be Swedish or German or French or English or Irish girls, who would give you their names and the names of the hotels where they were staying and tell you they wouldn't mind going down to Juan-les-Pins with you tomorrow night.

The crowds along the Jetée brought with them an atmosphere of intense excitement and anticipation, as if they always expected at any moment to see someone very famous lolling on the fantail of one of the yachts. *Brigitte Bardot! Yves Montand! Johnny Ray!* So they hurried along with their sunburned faces, their wild eyes and their cameras always at the ready, always prepared for the precious instant when they might hear someone cry, *"Simone Signoret!"* or *"Greta Garbo!"* Of course they often did see famous people. The Duke and Duchess of Windsor were on an Italian yacht called the *Hidalgo* that lay right next to the *Coloratura* for a long time, and we had to put up with her strident voice all day long giving orders to the stewards. Mostly it was about menus and flower arrangements, and as if to get away from it all the duke retreated to the stern of the yacht, obviously hoping to be able to smoke his pipe in peace. But he would always soon be chased back into the main salon by the tourists on the Jetée, who would scramble for a place on the quai close to the stern of the *Hidalgo* the minute they caught sight of him, and *applaud* him for everything he did, even if it was just a little thing like tossing a match over the side.

And King Farouk was there, too, on his yacht, but he was seldom seen, and all you really ever heard of him was how he sent his emissaries to places like the Trois Cloches and the Blue Bar and Palm Beach to find beautiful young girls for him.

Just before the sun went down behind the low hill across the harbor from the Jetée, Mont Chevalier, or the Souquet, as they called it in Cannes, where the small houses of the old town were packed close together like so many brightly painted child's building blocks on the slopes, the light suddenly turned very hard, and all the shadows were very deep and had such sharp edges that when you looked at people's faces it appeared as if their features were cut out of stone. And then, when the sun did go down behind the Tour du Souquet on the crown of the hill, the light softened again, but the sky quickly lost its translucence and darkened very fast, and it began turning cold immediately.

Then the last boatloads of excursionists were returning from Ste-

Marguerite and St-Honorat, with much shouting and blowing of horns, and the powerful old varnished Chris-Craft speedboats with names like *Mr. Quick* and *Sultan* came chugging back into the harbor from a long day of towing waterskiers or making full-speed runs down to Eden Roc, and the yachts that had been out for a casual day's cruising up and down the coast returned, too, and the whole harbor was an enormous confusion of yelling and laughter and throbbing boats' engines, and added to this was the insistent honking of horns as cars bringing guests to the yachts' dinner parties and cocktail parties and "galas" tried to make their way through the crowds on the Jetée.

There were loud shouts as the owners of the yachts welcomed their guests, and the stewards had to run around faster and faster to make sure that everyone was kept supplied with cocktails and hors d'oeuvres, and, of course, sometimes, dope.

Soon the members of the crew of the *Coloratura* who were in the mood to go ashore that evening began coming down the gangway, all dressed up, and hurried off along the Jetée. By then it was getting cold and dark, and the crowds were thinning out, and the owners of the yachts led their guests indoors.

Occasionally Mr. Apollodorus and his guests dined at one or another of the better restaurants in Cannes, but usually they had an immense dinner on board the *Coloratura,* because, as Mr. Apollodorus was so fond of saying, the *Coloratura* was by far the best restaurant in town. And he was probably right, since the chef on the *Coloratura* had been chef on the *Sea Cloud* for seven years, and the cuisine must have been about on a level with a two- or three-star restaurant.

After dinner Mr. Apollodorus and his guests always went ashore, to a night club, or to Palm Beach. He usually had at least a dozen guests on board, and sometimes as many as twenty. They were for the most part very good-looking young women and sleek and rather arrogant older men. They spoke in a Babel of languages, and it seemed as if they all could go from one language to another as smoothly as a sports car shifting gears.

After they were gone, the man on watch could relax, and go back up on the stern of the *Coloratura* and huddle in his peajacket under the dim light in the doghouse where we kept the cushions for the chairs on the afterdeck and read a book or a magazine, or stroll up and down the quai and visit with the sailors on the other yachts, or go up on the seawall that ran the whole length of the Jetée Albert-Edouard and just lean on the iron railing and watch the waves breaking on the rocks below and stare at the lights along the Boulevard de la Croisette and the lights of the houses up on the hills to the north of town, or he could just go on observing the course of a night in the harbor.

It happened that at this time one of the strangest yachts in the world was moored in the harbor. She was called *La Moineau*, and what made her so strange was that she was, in fact, a C4-class freighter, in other words a Liberty ship left over from World War II that had been haphazardly converted to a whole new life as a "yacht." She flew the flag of the Dominican Republic and her owner, Rául Morro, was a very rich old man who was said to be very closely connected to Rafael Leonidas Trujillo. The story was that many years before he had come to Cannes one summer on his yacht, and that one night he had been approached in the street by a beautiful young flower girl who was known to everyone on the Riviera as La Moineau, The Sparrow. She had a lovely, touching voice and sang as she walked the streets selling her flowers, and Rául Morro had been so captivated by her that he had married her, and taken her back to the Dominican Republic with him. But every summer she had insisted that they return to Cannes on his yachts, which ever after had been named *La Moineau,* and had kept getting larger and larger, until finally Morro had bought the Liberty ship and converted her, not at all successfully, because although they may have painted her white and made a few minor changes in her superstructure, she remained unmistakably a Liberty ship.

Anyway, this *Moineau* was a monstrous thing that seemed to take up half the harbor, and her steep sides towered high above every other ship. All day long there was more clamor from her than from the rest of the yachts in the harbor combined, and most of it came from her captain, a sort of small-time Captain Bligh, who kept after his crew unceasingly day and night with a megaphone, yelling at them, "Get to work, you miserable bastards! What do you think you are, for God's sake, *caballeros?*"

As for Rául Morro, he was a semi-tragic figure, who wandered around the deck all day—always, for some reason, swaddled in heavy gray sweaters and with a white towel wrapped tightly around his throat. On his head he wore a floppy white panama hat with a black band. Sometimes, if you looked up there, you would see him looking at you, much the way the Duke of Windsor had done now and then. It was as if they were thinking how much they would rather be you than them.

Every night La Moineau herself, who, however beautiful she may have been when she was a girl, had by now grown round as a potato, sat at a desk up there on the stern of the ship, under a bare light bulb that swung back and forth in the wind. She wore a uniform that would have been worthy of a Ruritanian field marshal, a huge peaked cap that glittered with ornamentation, and a cream-colored tunic that was looped and spangled with tons of gold braid and gorgeous military decorations, and one by one her petitioners, people who had come from near and far and every night formed a long line on the Jetée Albert-Edouard, climbed up the narrow steep gangway to tell their sad stories to La Moineau, who, it was said, bestowed money on them almost without exception. Sometimes it was a lot of money. Other times just a few hundred or thousand francs. When she had seen as many of them as she wanted to see for that night, a velvet cord would be placed across the foot of the gangway by a crewman, who would say he was sorry, and that La Moineau hoped they would all come back again tomorrow night.

After that La Moineau would stand up and smile and wave to the people on the quai, and they would applaud her until she disappeared into her quarters amidships. Then the petitioners dispersed, and the Jetée quickly became deserted and very quiet, until the parties on the yachts began breaking up and there were many noisy farewells as the guests came down the gangway and got back into their cars. Most of them had only Citroens and Renaults and Simcas, but several had Cadillacs and Buicks. It seemed that all the rich people in Europe at that time aspired to owning a huge American car, even if they did burn up gasoline at such an alarming rate.

By midnight it was very cold. It was around then that the sailors from the *Coloratura* began straggling back to the ship. Sometimes they stopped and kept the man on watch company for a few minutes, but what they had on their minds most of all at that time was the "black pan" they knew was waiting for them in the big oven down in the galley. The name black pan originally came from the big ships, the freighters and tankers, where the black pan was leftover food that was kept warm for the "black gangs," meaning the engine room crews, when they came off watch in the middle of the night. Of course on the *Coloratura* the leftovers in the black pan could be anything from filet mignons to crown roasts of lamb, and that wasn't all, because the chef saw to it that there were a couple of layer cakes available as well, and a steaming kettle of Dutch cocoa along with the usual pot of coffee.

After the owner and his guests returned to the ship, usually around one o'clock, the real night watch began. After that there were no longer very many distractions, and there was no one else to talk to, because none of the other yachts in Cannes had a night watch. The problems with trying to stay awake were insurmountable. One technique I developed was to rest my elbow on the arm of the chair where I was sitting and then cup my chin in the palm of my hand. If I began to fall asleep my elbow slipped off the arm of the chair and I was awake again in an instant, and got up and paced around for a while, or went below and had another cup of coffee.

And sometimes I would go out to the end of the Jetée and stare at the lights of the cruise ships standing offshore, like the *Excalibur* of the American Export Line, or the *Andrea Doria* of the Italian Line, or, if not one of them perhaps a destroyer or a cruiser or one of the aircraft carriers, *Franklin Delano Roosevelt* or the *Coral Sea* from the Sixth Fleet.

But sometimes interesting things did happen in the night. For example, there was the time a pair of Italian drivers arrived on the Jetée with a great roar around three o'clock in the morning and rushed up the gangway to shout at me very excitedly that here was Mr. Apollodorus's new Jaguar. Although they spoke to me in Italian and I could barely understand them, I did make out that they had broken some kind of speed record in driving from Genoa to Cannes, and they insisted that I go down and fetch Mr. Apollodorus so he could congratulate them personally. I had to tell them that it was out of the question, and I thought they were going to burst into tears. Then they called me what I assumed were pretty bad names and slouched disconsolately off along the Jetée after having thrown the keys to the car down on the table before me, and having made some gestures involving flicking their thumbnails against their teeth and clenching their fists and driving them in an upward motion while slapping their palms against their biceps.

And often there were scenes at unlikely hours on the yachts as people came on deck and either made love under the stars, or had bitter quarrels that always seemed to end very abruptly with slamming doors, or with pitiful wails that could be heard all over the harbor.

At dawn the tradespeople began delivering bread and fruit and fresh vegetables to the *Coloratura*. The bread was still warm and smelled heavenly, like the bread in Bimini, and the tomatoes all came individually wrapped in tissue paper and had both a smell and a flavor that you never found anywhere in America. Then the girls from the laundry arrived with our freshly washed and pressed uniforms and Mr. Apollodorus's shirts, and soon after that a man in a rowboat came to the bow of the yacht and waited there while the man on watch brought up the garbage from the galley and lowered it all over the side with a rope to the man, and the beautiful child who was his daughter. And then they sat down there, rocking gently, and sorted it very meticulously, bones, bottles, bits of flesh, rags, everything, before they went on to the bow of the next yacht, where they did the same pathetic thing all over again.

Finally it was seven o'clock. The sun had risen and it was beginning to warm up a little. The night watch, barely able to keep his eyes open, went below and had breakfast, and then fell into his bunk, hoping to be able to sleep in spite of all the noise he knew he would have to endure as the ship came to life and another day in the port of Cannes began.

୫

THE NEXT MORNING I found Christine in the same place on the Allées beach as the day before, and even in almost the same pose, sitting there on her camp stool staring thoughtfully at her picture.

"You look terrible, Dooglas," she said when she caught sight of me.

"I should," I said. "I was awake all night."

"What do you mean you were awake all night?"

"I had the night watch on the yacht."

"And they make you stay awake all *night?*"

"Unfortunately, yes."

"Well, you shouldn't have bothered to come here then. You should be in your bed sound asleep."

"I tried to sleep. Sometimes it just doesn't work. But that's not what I'm here to talk about anyway. I'm here to talk about your picture."

She shook her head glumly. "I'm afraid I'm beginning to see this whole subject in a very different light."

"What do you mean?"

"Well, I'm beginning to think that I should face the fact that I'm not any good at painting with oils now, and probably never will be, no matter how many lessons you give me."

"But you haven't even given me a chance yet," I said.

She shrugged. "And another thing. I came here to have fun this summer. I thought oil painting was going to be fun, but now I begin to think it's nothing but a lot of hard work, with maximum frustration."

"Yes, but it can be fun, too, if you just don't take it too seriously."

"I'm sorry, but I'm just beginning not to believe that."

"Well, may I just talk to you about this picture for a few minutes, and then see what you think?"

"All right," she said.

"First of all, you have to start out with a good strong drawing underneath it all. So what I thought I'd do first of all, with your permission, is go back to the basic drawing and work on that."

I picked up her palette and brushes and began working on the picture, scraping away several of the thick layers of paint she had slapped on the canvas, and trying to explain to her what I was doing as I went along. She sat very patiently on her camp stool for about twenty minutes, and then she began fidgeting and squirming and I knew I was losing her.

"I can see that you were truthful," she said. "You do know a lot about painting, but I still believe what I said before, that it looks like nothing except hard work and maximum frustration."

"And you came to Cannes this summer to have fun."

She grinned. *"Yes!"*

"Well, I guess you're right, actually," I said. "Painting can be a bore unless you're in the right mood for it. Listen, I have an idea. What would you say if I invited you to have lunch with me?"

"Where would you take me, Dooglas?"

"How about Au Fin Bec? If we get there early enough we can get a table outside."

"I'd like that," she said. "But what will we do with all my paints and everything?"

"We'll go and ask Louisette to take care of them for us."

"Yes," Christine said. "And I can call my aunt from there and tell her I won't be home for lunch."

While Christine was calling her aunt, Louisette said to me, "Don't you remember what I told you about girls from Paris?"

"I remember," I said, "but I'm just not paying any attention."

Au Fin Bec was a small but very fine restaurant on the Quai St-Pierre. We were lucky and got a table outdoors, overlooking the harbor. Christine was by far the prettiest girl there, and all the men looked at her appraisingly, even the waiters. She loved it. After lunch I ordered another bottle of wine.

"Well, you're not in a big hurry to go back to La Potinière, are you, Christine?" I said.

"Oh, no," she said. "We can stay here all afternoon if you want to."

I said, "You know, I think you're so beautiful."

"Do you?"

"I think you must be one of the most beautiful women in Cannes this summer."

She smiled. "You should see me in my evening gown."

"I already have."

"You *have?*"

"Yes, last night."

"But you said you had the night watch last night."

"I did, but I got someone to take it for me for a little while, and I went and gazed at you, from a distance."

"Why didn't you come and speak to me?"

"I don't know. I guess I just didn't want to disturb you."

She smiled again. "You wouldn't have disturbed me," she said. "I would have liked seeing you. In fact, I've told my aunt about you, and she wants to meet you."

"Really?" I said. "What did you tell her about me?"

"Oh, that I think you're very nice, and that you work on the American yacht, and that you're an artist."

"Well, I'd like to meet her, too," I said.

Christine took another of my Pall Malls, and I lit it for her.

"I love American cigarets," she said. "You could come to La Potinière tonight if you felt like it, you know."

"All right, I will," I said.

She sipped her wine, staring at me. "Tell me something," she said. "You don't happen to be rich, do you?"

"Me?" I said, laughing. "No, I'm not rich."

"You don't have a rich father somewhere?"

"No, believe me. Why do you ask that?"

"You don't have a title of any kind?"

"No, no, no!"

She shrugged. "Well, I like you anyway."

"I hope so," I said. "Because the fact is, I fell in love with you at first sight."

She smiled. "I know you're just saying that."

I shook my head. "No, it's true. I fell in love with you the first time I saw you go past the terrace at Les Allées."

She kept smiling. "Does this happen to you all the time?"

"No."

"I really do like you," she said. "Since that's the case, I think I'd better make a confession."

My heart sank. "Oh, my God," I said. "Are you *married?*"

"No," she said. "But when I told you that I'd come to Cannes this summer to have fun, I wasn't really telling the truth. The truth is, I came here this summer for one reason and one reason only. Which is to meet a very rich man. You see, this is the third summer I've come here, and each summer I've told myself that the first summer after I got out of school I would come back down here and seriously make an effort to meet a very rich man. Preferably a baron or a viscount or something like that. Anyway, someone with a title, because I would *love* to have a title to go along with all the money. Well, this is my first summer after I got out of school, and here I am. So, what do you have to say now?"

"I'd say you came to the right place."

"You're not shocked to hear me say something like that?"

"No. You know I have no right to be shocked, Christine."

"Well, what if I tell you *this?* That I don't care how *old* he is either. I mean, if he were young and handsome it would be very nice of course. But even if he were *old, old, old* it would still be all right. Now, you're still not shocked?"

"No," I said. "Actually, I don't blame you. And I think the chances are excellent that you're going to find just what you want."

"Listen, you're *positive* you're not rich?"

"I'm positive."

"Well," she said, "I've heard of people taking jobs like that just for the fun of it, even though actually they're rich. How can I be *sure* that isn't the case with you?"

"Because I promise you I'm telling the truth."

She shrugged again. "Well, I mean it, I still like you anyway. It's just that you understand, don't you, that we can't be anything but friends?"

What could I say to that? I said, "Yes, Christine, I understand."

Christine smiled. "Good," she said. "Now let's go and play some baby-foot down at the Carlton beach."

She was very good at baby-foot, the miniature soccer game you play by kicking the little soccer balls back and forth with the little feet, and beat me seven games to three. Then we strolled back up the Croisette to La Potinière, where Christine introduced me to her aunt Hélène, a very pleasant, cheerful and direct woman in her mid-forties.

"Hélène," Christine said, "this is my new friend Dooglas."

"Christine has told me all about you," Hélène said. "That you're a sailor on the American yacht that's moored on the Jetée, and that you're also an artist. And she told me she rather likes you. I'm glad. She's never had a boyfriend when she was here in Cannes and I don't think that's right. I think every girl should have a boyfriend. It keeps them out of trouble."

"I've told him about my ambition," Christine said.

"And what do you think of her ambition, Dooglas?" Hélène said.

"Well, I think she has a right to it," I said.

"But do you think she'll get what she wants?"

"I think she has an excellent chance," I said. "I've already told her that."

"My only regret is that I didn't get here in time for the film festival," Christine said. "I was all ready to jump on the train, and then my dog got sick. So I finally arrived here two days after it was all over. I was hoping that some big, important American producer would see me and sign me up to make a movie, and I *know* it would have happened if I had just been here."

Hélène smiled, and then said to me, "You look as if you're about to fall asleep."

"He had to stay awake all night," Christine said. "He had the night watch on his yacht."

I went ahead and yawned.

"Come on," Christine said. "I'll go back to the Jetée with you. I want to see this yacht of yours up close."

On the way, she said, "I'm glad my aunt likes you. She sometimes doesn't like people for one reason or another, and once she's made up her mind about it, then there's no changing it."

When we reached the Jetée she said, "I had a good time today."

"So did I," I said.

When we came to the *Coloratura*'s gangway, Christine stood and gazed at the yacht rapturously. "It's really magnificent," she said. "The man who owns this yacht must be *very* rich."

"Yes, he is," I said.

"What's his name?"

"George Apollodorus."

"A Greek?"

"Yes."

"What's his business?"

"Oil tankers."

"Oh, yes, of course," Christine said. She kept staring at the *Coloratura* for a little while longer, and then said, "Now I want you to go and get some sleep, and then come back to La Potinière tonight."

વ

"Do you know what's going to happen to me if I don't meet a rich man this summer, Dooglas?"

"What's going to happen to you?"

"I'll end up getting a job in a little shop somewhere, if I'm very lucky."

We were dancing. As usual all the men on the dance floor were looking at Christine. Even the ones who were dancing with good-looking women themselves looked at her.

This time her evening gown was pale blue satin. She told me she had made all her evening gowns herself.

"I'm just a poor girl from Clichy," she said. "No one in my family has any money. My father is a policeman, and you know as well as I do that you can't get rich being a policeman."

She sighed deeply and we went back and sat down at a table just outside the main door of La Potinière. The two other girls, Colette and Elena, were doing all the work, while Christine just sat and talked to me. Hélène came out and asked me if I would help her uncrate a case of wine, and even when I was doing that Christine came right along with me and talked to me the whole time.

I stayed until closing time, helping out whenever I was needed, and when we parted, Hélène and Christine for their house in the Place du 18-Juin, Christine said, "Be sure and come back again tomorrow night, Dooglas," and gave me a big kiss.

Hélène smiled and said, "Yes, be sure and come back again tomorrow night, Dooglas."

The next morning at Les Allées Louisette said, "You look dazed."

"It's nothing," I said. "It's just that I've fallen in love with Christine Rimbaud."

"What about her? Is she in love with you?"

"I don't know. Maybe. But there's a problem."

"What is it? You know you can tell me anything."

"Well, she came down here this summer because she wanted to meet a rich man, preferably with a title, and get married."

"Oh, yes, I know all about that," Louisette said. "Is there anybody in Cannes who doesn't?"

"I'm afraid all I'm doing is distracting her."

"She's so stuck-up, isn't she. Didn't I tell you?"

"I think she has a right to be. I think she's one of the most beautiful girls I've ever seen in my life."

"That's because you're in love with her. Listen, my friend, Cannes in the summer is always full of beautiful women. You've seen that. Christine doesn't realize it, but she is only one among the many."

I shrugged. "Anyway, the last thing I want to do is spoil her big chance, because if she doesn't meet a rich man she says she'll end up having a job in a little shop somewhere, if she's lucky."

Louisette leaned over and pulled my nose. "I've always thought you were a little crazy. Now I'm sure of it."

When I got back to the ship the boatswain said Captain Marryat wanted to see me up in his stateroom.

Captain Marryat was about forty-five, a superlative seaman who had come to yachting as a change from commanding oil tankers for Texaco. He was basically a rather stiff, quiet, brooding man, but there were fires smoldering within him that could burst into flames very quickly when there was sufficient provocation. He was tall and slender, had black hair that he always kept trimmed very short, and looked impressive when he stood on the bridge or in the wheelhouse in his immaculate white uniforms, staring out at the world through horn-rimmed glasses. The only thing that detracted from the perfection of his image was that he was a chain-smoker of Camel cigarets, and you almost never saw him without a Camel stuck in his mouth.

When I knocked on the door of his stateroom aft of the wheelhouse, he said, "Come in," and when I entered I found him sitting at his table trying to decipher the instructions that had come with the Leica camera he had bought on the black market.

"I can't figure this goddam thing out to save my neck," he said. "Here I've spent five hundred dollars on a camera that is nothing more than a piece of junk to me if I can't figure out how to operate it. Can you read any German?"

"A little," I said.

"Well, sit down over there and see if you can read any of this."

I took the manual he handed me and sat down and tried to read it, but the vocabulary was much too technical for me. "I'm sorry, skipper," I said. "This is way beyond me."

"Look at this one then," he said, passing me another manual. "This one is in French."

I tried to read it, but again the vocabulary was too technical for me.

"How about Spanish?" he said, passing me another one.

I looked at it and then said, "I'm afraid they're all too technical for me."

"Hell," he said. "Who ever would have thought the goddam thing would come without an English-language manual? I hate to say it but it sure as hell serves me right for buying an expensive camera like this from a pack of thieves who I knew damn well would promptly disappear off the face of the earth. But that isn't what I wanted to see you about. There are two things. The first is that Fred Appel has asked me for permission to sign off the yacht a couple of weeks earlier than scheduled, because of some sort of legal business that has come up at home that he'd like to take care of right away—and I said okay. Which means that you'll be taking over as second mate sooner that expected. In fact, on Monday morning."

I was elated. "That's very good news," I said.

He lit another Camel, adding to the already dense smoke in the stateroom.

"Here's the other thing," he said. "We're going on a cruise next week. Most of the usual places. Monte Carlo. Portofino. Capri. Maybe Naples this time, because some of the party want to go to Pompeii and Herculaneum. Then the boss says he may want to swing down to Sicily. To Taormina, specifically. He's interested in seeing a Greco-Roman amphitheater that's near there. So we'll probably be gone two or three weeks, and this brings up a question of your uniforms. How long has it been now since we sent your measurements to Harry Cohen?"

"About three weeks," I said.

Captain Marryat sighed impatiently. "And he was told to rush them by airmail to Ferrand in Nice, wasn't he? Well, I called Ferrand yesterday and he said they haven't come in yet. This really disturbs me. Acton is usually *very* reliable."

The one other thing that worked against his image of perfection was that, like Captain Wicks, he fretted a great deal over the small proprieties of yachting.

"The point is, I guess Fred'shting.

"The point is, I guess Fred's uniforms would probably fit you well enough. You seem to be roughly the same size. But, dammit, if you're going to be an officer on the *Coloratura,* I want you to *look* like an officer on the *Coloratura* and not as if you're wearing somebody's hand-me-downs. So this is what I'm thinking. Surely, Glémot can find us a seamstress in Cannes who could alter Fred's uniforms so they'll fit you properly in case your new uniforms never do get here in time for this cruise. What do you think?"

"I'm sure he could find someone," I said.

"Why don't you get right on it then?"

"Yes, sir," I said.

He frowned. "Do you think his hats will fit you all right?"

"I think so."

"Well, try one on anyway."

"Yes, sir."

I turned to go.

"Oh, yes," he said. "One further thing. We'll have to hire a sailor from here in Cannes to take your place, much as I dislike the idea of hiring a foreigner. Do you know if there is anybody in Cannes who would be good enough for the *Coloratura?*"

"Let me give it some thought, skipper," I said. "I think there may be one or two men who might be all right."

"Frenchmen?"

"One is a Frenchmen. The other is an Australian."

"Okay," he said. "I'm leaving the decision entirely up to you."

Before I went to see Glémot I stopped by Fred Appel's stateroom, which of course would soon be my stateroom, and found him lying on his bunk in his underwear looking pretty glum. He had a bottle of Mr. Apollodorus's Black Label handy on top of the chest of drawers next to him and a tumbler with three fingers of scotch in the bottom in one hand and a long green cigar in the other.

I knew he was only somewhere between fifty and fifty-five, but he looked a lot older because he had a face like a bloodhound and a bad back that kept him bent over in agony about half the time.

"I know what you're going to say, Doug," he said. "The skipper already told me. You can go ahead and take my uniforms any time you want."

"I'm also supposed to try on your hats," I said.

"Okay. There's one right there."

I put on his officer's hat and looked in the mirror over the washbasin and thought I looked pretty good.

"You know, now that I'm going I sure wish I wasn't," he said.

I didn't say anything, but I was thinking that if the son of a bitch decided to change his mind now I would strangle him.

"And I wouldn't either, except my wife is threatening to sell our house in Miami and move out to some kind of spiritualist community in California if I don't come back right away. On top of that she's being sued by some asshole who says she ran over his foot in the Piggly-Wiggly parking lot."

He took a big drag on his cigar. "You know, she has the nerve to say I had no right to make this cruise in the first place, and definitely didn't have any right to stay on here for a whole year. Frankly, I don't know what she's complaining about. All she does is yell at me when I'm home anyway. Listen, I send her two-thirds of my paycheck every month, and you know what she does with it? I'll tell you. After she makes the mortgage payment and saves out something for groceries, all the rest goes to bingo. The woman is a goddam bingo *fanatic!* She knows where every game in town is at any moment of the day or night, and when I was home that was all she ever did. Go to the bingo halls. Her and her girlfriend Madge. Right after supper they'd grab their purses and off they'd go— which would have been okay with me if she'd *won* once in a while. But that's the other thing. She has never, to the best of my knowledge, won more than fifteen dollars on any given night in all the years she's been going to those blasted halls, and *that* was only two or three times."

He reached over and opened the top drawer of his chest of drawers and took out a cedar box. "Here, have one," he said. "The boss gave me these as a going-away present. They're real honest to God Havana cigars. Goddam things cost about three dollars apiece."

I took a cigar and ran it under my nose. "I'll keep this for later," I said.

He looked at me slyly. "Want to see what else he gave me?"

He reached back into the drawer and pulled out an envelope, and removed a check from it, and said, "Read what that says."

The check was for a thousand dollars. Fred took it back from me and stuck it into the envelope again with a wink. "He said this was just a little something to show me how much he appreciated my faithful service this past year."

"Well, he's a real nice guy," I said.

"He sure is, a bottle of Black Label, a box of hand-made Havana cigars and a check for a grand. That's more than I ever got on any other of these fucking buckets. The most I ever got before was usually a limp handshake and some bastard wishing me the best of luck."

GLÉMOT PROMISED he would find a seamstress for me, and would send someone over to the *Coloratura* later that day to pick up the uniforms and deliver them to her and tell me where to go for my fittings.

&

THAT NIGHT when I went to La Potinière Christine wasn't wearing an evening gown, but just a pair of long pants and a heavy sweater. She said she wanted me to come with her and visit her girlfriend Vera, who worked at Jimmy's Bar on the Rue d'Antibes and had just bought a brand-new Simca "Vedette" after having saved up for it for more than two years. Vera was terribly excited and made both of us ride around with her for about half an hour, which was fairly dangerous because she drove like a madwoman, half the time with only her dim lights turned on, which, actually, seemed to be the usual practice in France, and made me think over and over that what this country needed was some good old Miami cops to straighten them out, because you were really taking your life in your hands whenever you tried to cross a street like the Boulevard de la Croisette with all the maniacs in sport cars and on Vespas hurtling back and forth.

After that we visited another girlfriend of Christine's, Tanya, who worked at the Brasserie Alsacienne, down near Les Allées de la Liberté. And then we took a walk up the Croisette to the Blue Bar, where we got a table outside and sat and drank Cinzano and looked at all the top-of-the-line business girls with their dates for the evening.

These girls were very different from the sad, tired-looking, older girls who frequented the Rue d'Antibes. They were all young and wore expensive clothes. In fact, some of them didn't look a day over fifteen.

"They're really beautiful," Christine said. "You'd think they could be movie stars or something, instead of having to do this."

"I think they'd be movie stars if they could," I said. "But I have a feeling most of them probably can't act."

Christine smiled. "I don't know about that. I think they're very good actresses. Otherwise how could they put up with having to be around some of these awful-looking men?"

"Well, I guess you have a point there."

"I wonder if I could do it," she said. "Sell myself like that. Well, they say you can do anything if you have to. I imagine it only takes a little getting used to. I mean, the truth is, they want basically the same thing I do, don't they? They just go after it in a slightly more straightforward way."

"I don't think you could ever do it."

"Don't be so sure. You don't know me all that well, you know."

"I think I know you well enough."

"I still say don't be so sure."

I shrugged, and then, wanting to change the subject, said, "I had some good news today."

"Tell me what it is."

"I'm going to be promoted to second mate on the *Coloratura,* as of Monday morning."

"That sounds good. But what does it mean exactly?"

"Well, it means I'll be an officer on the yacht, for one thing, instead of just a common sailor. And the other thing is that I'll be making twice as much money as I do now."

"That's *marvelous.*"

"Yes, but I'm afraid the other news I have isn't so good. We're going on a cruise next week. And it sounds as if we'll probably be gone for quite a long time."

"I don't want you to go," Christine said.

"There's nothing that can be done about it."

"Well, how long is a long time?"

"Oh, it could be two or three weeks."

"That is a long time. Where are you going?"

"Monte Carlo, Portofino, Capri, Naples, and then probably down to Sicily."

"I wish I could go with you."

"I do, too."

"They don't allow girls to work on that yacht of yours, do they?"

"No, I'm afraid not."

"I'll really miss you."

"I'll miss you, too, Christine."

But then later, when we were back at La Potinière, I said, "Well, maybe my leaving will be a good thing for you, though. After all, you're never going to have your dream come true if you spend all your time with me."

She looked at me, and I could see that I had hurt her, which was what I had wanted to do.

"Yes, I think you're right," she said, and got right up and left me sitting alone at the table, and wouldn't come back for about twenty minutes.

Then she said, "What day are you leaving?"

"I'm not sure," I said. "I don't think Mr. Apollodorus has made up his mind about that yet."

"Well, you wouldn't leave without saying goodbye to me, would you?"

"No, I promise you I wouldn't do that, Christine."

Again, I stayed until closing time, and when Christine asked me if I was going to come back and see her tomorrow night, I said I couldn't because I was going to have to stand the night watch—for the last time.

She kissed me and said, "Well, in that case, I'll come and see *you*."

ॐ

THE NEXT MORNING I went for the fitting of my new uniforms to a charming woman who worked where she lived, in a small apartment overlooking a courtyard off the Rue Félix-Faure. She took all my measurements very quickly and cheerfully and said I could come back in two days and she would have everything ready for me.

On my way back to the ship I decided it was time to talk to Max Guyard, a young Frenchman who was a sailor on a yacht called the *Mistral*. My choice for the new sailor on the *Coloratura* was between him and Jim Manderson, an Australian, or, as he said it, a "Strine," who had been hanging around Cannes for several years making a marginal living by working on any yacht that would have him. Max and Jim were both very nice guys, but Jim had the reputation of being a little crazy, and also of drinking too much, so I was worried about recommending him to Captain Marryat. On the other hand, the thing against Max was that he was a Frenchman, and Captain Marryat really didn't have much use for Frenchmen.

When I came to the place where Max's yacht was moored on the Jetée I didn't see him around anywhere, so I asked a sailor named Roger if he was on board.

"He's down below," Roger said. "Want me to get him for you?"

"I'd appreciate it," I said.

Roger, who, as far as I was concerned, was one of the meanest and most objectionable people around the waterfront, came a little closer to me, smiling a very oily smile.

"There's a story going around that you're the new second mate on the *Coloratura.*"

"It's not a story," I said. "It's a fact. I am the new second mate on the *Coloratura.*"

"Please accept my heartfelt congratulations," he said.

"Thank you."

"But this means you've got to hire a new seaman to take your place, isn't that true?"

"Yes, that's true."

"Is that why you want to see Max?"

"Yes, he's one of the people I'm thinking about for the job."

"You know, I'd like to have that job myself."

"So would a lot of others."

"Yes, but how many of them could do something for *you* in return for giving it to them?"

"I don't know what you mean."

"*I* could do something for you in return. Want to hear about it?"

"I'm afraid I don't have time for it, Roger."

"Just listen to this," he said, coming even closer to me. "Not many people know this, but I have a brother-in-law who's a croupier at Palm Beach. All I'd have to do is say the right word and you could start having some very good luck at the roulette table, understand?"

"Roger, just get Max for me, will you?"

He shrugged. "You just don't know a good offer when one comes along," he said, and then went off to fetch Max for me.

When Max came out on the Jetée I asked him if he would like to have the deckhand's job on the *Coloratura.*

"I would kill for it, you know that," he said.

He was about medium height, about my age and had straw-blond hair and blue eyes. He had told me that he came from Brittany, and also that he had spent three years out in Indochina in the French Army, fighting against the Viet Minh. I thought he seemed serious and disciplined, and of course I had been impressed when he had told me once that he was working in his spare time on a book about his experiences in Indochina.

"Can you leave this job without any problems?" I said.

"Don't worry about that."

"Well, I want to speak to someone else before I make the decision."

"Jim?"

"Yes."

"All right. I just hope it goes my way."

"I'll let you know."

"Soon?"

"Yes. Soon."

I continued along the Jetée until I came to the *Red Pirate,* the yacht on which Jim Manderson was a combination deckhand and cook and part-time engineer. The *Red Pirate* was not in a class with most of the other yachts in Cannes. In fact she was a fairly sorry-looking spectacle, but at the same time had a rakish charm to her, as her name implied.

I knew that the owner, a wild and unpredictable gentleman who Jim always said was half French, half Italian, half Spanish and half crazy, was not in Cannes at the moment, so I went aboard and discovered Jim and the captain of the *Red Pirate,* Sampeyre, and the other deckhand, Jallez, down in the fo'c'sle, where they were sitting around the messtable unshaven and in their underwear, drinking wine, playing faro and smoking cigars that had totally fouled the air in the compartment.

The fact that they weren't up on deck working wasn't the least bit out of the ordinary, because they never did much of that even when the owner was on board. There was also a laissez-faire attitude about uniforms. In fact, they were pretty much free to wear anything they felt like. And they also mingled with the guests just like one big happy family.

"Welcome aboard, Your Excellency," Jim said, when I came down the ladder. "How would you like to sit in on this little game and redistribute some of your new-found wealth among the lower orders?"

Jim looked like a tough guy, and he was pretty tough, but he could also be a reliable friend, and he had done me a couple of important favors in the time I had known him.

He was about twenty-five and very handsome, and the fact that he drank much too much, got into too many fights, babbled in French with an Australian twang and had a tooth missing in front didn't bother the girls who hung around Les Allées a bit, because most of them were crazy about him.

"Sorry, I don't have time," I said. "Actually, I've come to offer you the deckhand job that's open on the *Coloratura* now."

"Do you mean that, mate?" he said.

"Yes, I mean it. In fact, you're my first choice for the job. So if you want it just tell me and it's yours."

"Take it, for God's sake, Jim," Sampeyre said. "Think of all the beautiful American dollars you'll be making."

"How about me?" Jallez said. "Offer me the job and see how fast you get an answer."

"Who else do you have in mind for it?" Jim said.

"Max."

"He's the only one?"

"Yes."

"Well, can I have a little time to think it over?"

Sampeyre groaned.

Jallez groaned, too.

"Yes, but you'll have to let me know by early this afternoon," I said.

"Okay," Jim said.

He accompanied me when I went back up on deck.

"You know, I never thought you'd consider me for that job," he said.

"Why not?"

"You know damn well why not. Because of the bloody awful reputation I have around here."

"Captain Marryat doesn't know anything about that."

"And it doesn't bother you either?"

"I don't think you'd let me down."

"It's nice of you to say that," he said.

"You know we pay two hundred and twenty-five dollars a month American, don't you?"

"Yes, I know," he said. "And that sounds like millions to someone who has never made more than twenty thousand francs a month in the entire time I've been in this town. How much is two hundred and twenty-five dollars in francs?"

"Close to a hundred thousand," I said.

He shook his head. "My God, a bloody *fortune.*"

"Jim," I said, "frankly, the main reason why I want you to be the one to get this job is that I keep thinking of how it would be for me if I were in your situation, a damn foreigner here in Cannes, trying to survive on what you can make from an occasional job on a yacht. What I want to do is give you the chance to save up some money so you can get a little ahead of the game, and won't be completely at the mercy of these boat owners."

"Okay," he said, "just let me think about it for a little while, and then I'll come over to the *Coloratura* and tell you what I've decided, one way or the other."

"All right, I'll be waiting for you," I said.

ABOUT TWO O'CLOCK one of the deckhands on the *Coloratura*, Tommy Lindquist, came down to the fo'c'sle, where I was talking to the chef. Lindquist was around forty years old, and apparently for that reason alone felt that he should have been the one who was selected to be the new second mate. We had never gotten along particularly well, but now our relationship was worse than ever. He was the only one of the sailors on the yacht who resented my promotion. All the others had wished me well and said they thought I deserved it.

"That fucking Australian Manderson is out there on the quai," he said. "Says he wants to talk to you."

"Well, go tell him to come on down here," I said.

"Go tell him yourself," he said. "You ain't an officer yet, you know. And even when you are, don't give me any orders because I ain't taking any orders from you."

"Yes, you will, Tommy," I said.

"Don't fucking well count on it, that's all I've got to say."

"This is what I've got to say," I said. "I'll either count on it, or I'll put you on the beach so fast it will make your head swim."

"Try it," he said bitterly. "Just try it."

"Are you drunk?" I said.

"What if I am?" he snarled.

It seemed that the longer Lindquist stayed in Cannes the more he drank, and the more he drank the more surly and belligerent he became. I knew for a fact that Captain Marryat was waiting for him to make the final mistake that would justify his firing Lindquist and sending him back home. Being drunk on duty was the worst thing you could do, in the captain's estimation, and could certainly be the excuse he was looking for.

"Take my advice, Tommy," I said. "Stay out of Bill Wimmer's sight. If he sees you like this he'll tell the skipper and you're finished."

"Mind your own goddam business," he said, and climbed back up the ladder, missing his footing a couple of times and damn near killing himself in the process.

I went out to the quai and found Jim sitting at the foot of the gangway.
"Don't think I'm ungrateful, but I'm turning down your offer," he said.
"I knew you would," I said.

He grinned. "That's what I figured. You knew I could never shave every day and wear a uniform, right?"

"Right."

"Even for a hundred thousand francs a month, I just couldn't do it, mate."

He stood up and we strolled down to the end of the Jetée together.

"See, the freedom is the thing that I've always liked about my life here. If I didn't have that, if I couldn't tell these bloody yachtsmen to go to hell any time I felt like it, that would take all the fun out of being here, and I would just clear out and go back home."

"I understand," I said.

"And another thing, when I'm on the beach there's always some girl who will look after me."

"I realize that," I said.

"So you'll give the job to Max?"

"Yes."

"That's good. He deserves it, and he'll do a good job for you."

We walked back along the quai, and parted at the *Red Pirate*'s gangway, where he shook my hand.

"It was nice of you to give me the chance," he said. "I'll remember it."

I said it was nothing, and went on down the quai to the *Mistral* and told Max the good news.

THAT NIGHT Christine came out on the Jetée and said she was going to keep me company for a while, and since Mr. Apollodorus and his guests had gone ashore by then, I took her on a tour of the yacht that included the very luxurious staterooms aft, and she was impressed.

"You're lucky," she said. "I would love to work on a yacht like this, where everything is so clean and well-kept, and you're always going to wonderful places like Monte Carlo and Capri."

"But there's a lot of hard work involved in it, too," I said.

"Oh, I wouldn't care about that," she said. "Hard work doesn't bother me. Listen, are you positive, now that you're an officer, that you can't get the captain to hire me?"

"I'm afraid not, Christine," I said.

"I'd love to go with you, and be with you all the time."

"And I'd love to have you go with me. It just isn't possible, that's all."

She stayed with me about two hours, and then kissed me and said good night. She started to go, but paused and said, "I really will miss you very much when you're gone," and then hurried off down the Jetée.

æ

ON SATURDAY NIGHT the crew of the *Coloratura* gave a farewell party for Fred Appel at Les Allées. He had made some good friends around the waterfront, and they were all sorry to see him go, and there were many drunken speeches made and drunken songs sung, and then very early the next morning a taxi came out on the Jetée and took him to the railway station for his trip to Paris, where he would make connections with the boat train to Le Havre.

That afternoon I moved my gear from my locker in the fo'c'sle into Fred's stateroom, and the next morning I put on my officer's uniform for the first time. Around ten o'clock one of the deckhands told me the captain wanted to see me up on the bridge, and that was when he told me we would be leaving Cannes the next morning to begin our cruise, and that he thought we would be gone about three weeks.

When I went to La Potinière that night and told Christine the news, she said, "All right, this is what I want you to do. Go to the Splendid-Hotel and reserve a room for us, right now. I'll come along and wait downstairs until it's all taken care of, and then I'll come up. But listen to me. The room must be one of those in front that have the balconies, because that's what I told Tanya, how romantic I thought it would be to make love in one of those rooms in the front, with the balconies, and with the music from the orchestra on the terrace of the Alsacienne filling the room."

"You'll stay all night with me, Christine?"

"Of course."

"What will Hélène say?"

"Don't worry about that. You know how much she likes you, and I've told her you're going away tomorrow."

She went and talked to Hélène for a minute, and then Hélène came over alone to the table where I was sitting.

"I would never approve of this," she said, "if I didn't know Christine truly cares a great deal about you. Do you understand that?"

"Yes, I understand," I said.

"Now I just have one question. Do you have any sort of protection?"

"On the ship. On the ship I have some protection."

"Well, promise me you'll go and get it, and use it."

"I promise," I said.

She leaned down and kissed me. "All right, then go, and be happy."

Christine and I hurried off along the Croisette to the Splendid-Hotel, which stood on the Rue Félix-Faure, near the harbor. It was only a small hotel, nothing like the Majestic or the Carlton or the Martinez, but I had always thought myself that it looked very charming, with its front rooms with French doors that opened onto balconies that looked out toward the harbor and the Jetée Albert-Edouard. And down below was the Brasserie Alsacienne, where Christine's girlfriend Tanya worked, and where a small orchestra played every night.

Christine took a table on the terrace, and I entered the hotel through the entrance on the Rue Félix-Faure.

The desk clerk looked at me suspiciously when he saw I wasn't carrying any luggage, and asked to see my passport. I said I didn't carry a passport, but instead produced a slip of paper on which the Director of the Port of Cannes "attested" that I was part of the "equipage" of the American yacht Coloratura, which was now in port and moored on the Jetée Albert-Edouard.

The desk clerk studied the slip of paper for about a minute and a half, glancing up at me twice in that space of time.

Then he said, in a very bored way, "Well, I suppose this will have to do."

"There's just one thing," I said. "It's very important to me that I have one of the rooms in the front, with the balconies."

"They're three thousand francs."

"That's all right."

"Sign the register," he said, handing me a pen, and I signed and then paid him the three thousand francs, which was the equivalent of $7.50, and he presented me with the key to Room 23.

I went out on the terrace of the Alsacienne and told Christine to wait for me while I went back to the ship, but she said no, that she wanted to go up to the room right away, and would wait for me there. I ran to the Coloratura, got the protection, and then, on an impulse, went through the main salon and took a bottle of Mr. Apollodorus's very best cognac and two glasses, all of which I jammed into the front of my windbreaker. I hurried past the night watch, clinking a little in my haste, but he didn't seem to notice anything.

As I approached the Splendid I saw Christine standing on a balcony on the second floor smiling down at me.

I went up the stairs, not bothering to take the lift, and down the hall Christine opened the door to Room 23.

"It's just as I hoped it would be," she said delightedly.

I took the bottle of cognac and the two glasses out of my windbreaker. "Look what I've got," I said.

"Oh, I *knew* you were romantic," she said, and then took my hand and said, "Come with me, I want to show you something," and led me to the bathroom. "Isn't this beautiful?" she said. "Have you ever seen anything as beautiful as this before in your whole life?"

I had to admit the bathroom was very beautiful. It was large and had marvelously fluffy towels that were warmed by a system of steam pipes, and then there was even a white terry bathrobe thrown in, plus a plumbing fixture I had never seen before in my life, but which Christine, very amused, told me was a bidet, and I said all right, but I still couldn't really imagine what the damn thing was good for.

Anyway, the bathroom alone was worth every sou of the three thousand francs I had paid, but the rest of the place was very nice, too. There was a vast double bed, an armoire that looked at least three hundred years old, a great thick rug on the floor, armchairs, bureaus, an escritoire, and, of course, the best thing of all, the balcony.

We stood out there on the balcony for a long time, leaning over the railing to wave at Tanya down below us and hugging each other and drinking the cognac to stay warm.

Then Christine told me to stay there and went back into the room, and a few minutes later I heard her say something and looked around and saw her standing in the doorway wearing nothing but the terry-cloth bathrobe.

It was just as she had said it would be. We made love with the music from the little orchestra on the terrace of the Alsacienne filling the room. It was very poignant music, mostly gypsy airs, and some of those tunes I can remember to this day.

ೞ

ALWAYS IN THE PAST I had enjoyed going on our cruises, and had never really given much of a damn how long we would be away from Cannes. In fact, usually, as far as I was concerned the longer we were gone and the more new places we visited the happier I was.

But not this time. This time I was fretful and impatient, partly because the cruise was taking me away from Christine, and partly because I was afraid she would meet someone new while I was away and would have forgotten all about me by the time I returned.

Of course there were some very nice features to this cruise too. For the first time I was giving orders instead of taking them, and there were no more all-night deck watches to stand. Also, the owner and his guests treated me with a good deal more respect than when I had been a plain deckhand. And there was the very pleasant thought that as of now I was making a second mate's pay.

I didn't go ashore in Monte Carlo, even though we were there for two days. Mostly that was because it was such a dead town anyway, except in the vicinity of the grand hotels and the Casino. When you went ashore there you usually found yourself wandering through absolutely empty, silent streets, seeming to go from the pool of light at the base of one lamppost to the pool of light at the next, and if you ascended the hill that overlooked the harbor all you came to when you got to the top was a one-room, blindingly lighted bar with a very high ceiling and a faded photograph of Prince Rainier looking down at you, and not one other customer in the whole place except you and whomever you were with, if you were with anyone, which really made you wonder what on earth they were staying open for. The only other living thing in the place was the pretty girl behind the bar, who stared at you as if she couldn't imagine for the life of her where you might have come from, but was very nice anyway, and gave you a beautiful smile, and your bottle of beer, but not one word except for good evening and what would you like and goodbye. Then you went across the street and leaned on the parapet and smoked a cigaret, gazing at the lights on the hills in the distance, and at the *Coloratura* where she lay all lighted up in the middle of the pitch-black harbor, and finally went back down the hill to the harbor and stood on the quai and yelled across the darkness for the launch, and stood there shivering, watching for the little red and green bow lights to come for you.

Portofino was more fun, but after five days I was bored with that too, and ready for Capri, which had always been one of my favorite places in the Mediterranean. In the evenings I went up the narrow dirt road that zigzagged between vineyards to the town square and sat at a table outside one of the cafés, in the midst of some of the most sophisticated people in the world. There, contessas got into knock-down drag-out fist-fights with marquessas, transvestites got into screeching hair-pulling matches with their rivals, homosexuals from all over Europe made eye contact, lesbians smooched, and when peasants led whole flocks of sheep and goats right through the middle of the square, nobody paid the least big of attention to all the baaaaaaaaaa-ing.

Mr. Apollodorus and his guests usually spent most of their mornings and afternoons waterskiing, and their evenings having galas on the afterdeck, to which large numbers of friends they had run into ashore were always invited, and so, since only a couple of sailors were required to pull them around behind the speedboat and the galas were entirely in the hands of the stewards, I had plenty of time to climb the hills in the afternoons and lie on the warm grassy hillsides listening to giant firecrackers booming back and forth in the valleys, and gaze at blue Vesuvius way off across the Bay of Naples.

A couple of times I rented a Vespa and rode over to the other side of the island to a small restaurant beside a serene inlet I had been to before, where you had dinner out on a pier under a cupola in the midst of whole big happy families who gorged themselves on mountains of fettucini and mussels and clams and squid served in immense bowls set down in the centers of their tables and into which they all joyously dove fork-first, and where everyone drank new wine straight from slender green unlabeled bottles, and where as darkness closed in and everyone began singing, and urged me to join in, too, I couldn't help thinking what a really marvelous life I had, and how amazingly lucky I was.

After a week in Capri we sailed across the Bay of Naples to Castellammare di Stabia, where we lay for three days while the party went on their excursions to Pompeii and Herculaneum. Then we set sail for Sicily. In the late afternoon, as we were about to enter the Strait of Messina, we passed close by the British aircraft carrier *Centaur,* and when we saluted them by dipping our colors, they returned the gesture by dipping their own huge white ensign, and sent us the message by blinker:

"Welcome to the Mediterranean Sea." In the gathering darkness we plunged into the narrow and dangerous strait, which Captain Marryat said had the heaviest volume of shipping anywhere in the Mediterranean except the Strait of Gibraltar, while back on the afterdeck they were having another gala. Under the paper lanterns the stewards had strung up for them they were hysterically laughing as they tried to dance on the heaving deck to the music of a portable phonograph.

We dropped our anchors off Taormina around two o'clock in the morning, and by the time we got the ship all squared away it was close to four o'clock. When we came back up on deck again at seven we found ourselves in a peaceful harbor looking at sheer cliffs that rose straight up out of the water to an altitude of about two hundred feet.

There was a tiny village at the foot of the cliffs and after breakfast the captain told me to go ashore in the port launch and negotiate to have some taxis sent down from Taormina that afternoon to take our party up to the town.

When I landed on the beach a good crowd turned out to look at me, and I could see that they were very impressed with my uniform, the likes of which they probably hadn't seen since they took down their pictures of Mussolini. It was a very genial gathering of fishermen and their wives and their cats and dogs and kids, and I could tell by their big smiles that they wanted me to feel right at home. Fortunately, I was able to make myself understood with my limited Italian vocabulary, and a man who was dressed all in black and looked like a Mafia don, and probably really was one, told me not to worry about anything, that he was taking my case into his own hands.

"If you want taxis I'll see that you get the very best," he said. "You will have the very finest taxis in all of Taormina at your disposal, my friend. Just don't worry about anything. It will all go smoothly."

Then he led me off to a bar where he put in a call up to Taormina requesting that a taxi be sent down right away.

I thanked him and asked him if there was anything I could do for him. He said not to worry myself about it, he liked Americans, that was all. He asked me where I came from, and when I told him Miami, he said he didn't know anything about that, but he had relatives in New York. I took out my cigarets, and when he saw that they were Pall Malls, he said that was one thing I could do for him, get him some American cigarets. I asked him what brand he liked and he said, "Camels," and I said, "Okay, I'll get you a carton."

I went down to the beach and told the sailor who was standing by with the launch to go back to the *Coloratura* and tell the captain that I had a deal cooking, and then to get a carton of Camels from Mike O'Conner, the second steward, and bring them back with him.

A few minutes later a marvelous old relic of a car that looked as if it had been left over from a Harold Lloyd comedy appeared at the top of the very steep and narrow cobblestone road that led to the top of the cliffs, and with an enormous amount of backfiring came tearing down at breakneck speed. My friend in the black suit went over to the driver and had a word with him, and then he came back to me and told me the driver said I would have to go up to Taormina with him and talk to his employer about my "situation." I said all right and started to get in beside the driver, but he told me I would have to ride in the back, it was a regulation.

Then we began an agonizingly slow ascent of the road that had my heart stopping every few minutes as the car would lose momentum and gradually come to a stop and begin to fall back, only to suddenly regain power, give off a couple of terrific backfires and then chug on valiantly upward.

Taormina was a beautiful town with breathtaking views. To the east it overlooked the dark blue wind-swept waters of the Ionian Sea and to the west, startlingly, eleven-thousand-foot snow-capped Etna. But I didn't have time to admire either the sea or the volcano. I talked to the owner of the taxi and made arrangements for him to send several taxis down to the beach when I called him later on, and then took another perilous ride back down the cobblestone road, got the carton of Camels for the don from the launch, presented them to him with what I hoped was a flourish, and then returned to the yacht and reported to Captain Marryat, who seemed to think I had done very well.

After Mr. Apollodorus and his guests, of whom there were sixteen, had had their lunch I took them over to the beach in the starboard launch. They were all buzzing about the Greek temples and the Greco-Roman amphitheater, and the Roman ruins and the Palazzo Corvala and the Convent of San Domenico, but they shut right up when I put in the call for the taxis and they caught sight of the three old cars that came backfiring down the cobblestone road.

Mr. Apollodorus took me aside. "Is this the best there was in all of Taormina?" he asked, looking worried.

"That's what I was told," I said.

I noticed that although a fairly large crowd had gathered to stare at the exotic creatures from the yacht, the don was nowhere to be seen now.

"I don't trust these cars," Mr. Apollodorus said. "I don't believe they're really safe."

"Let me go and speak to the drivers," I said.

I went over to where the drivers were gathered and asked them if they honestly thought their taxis could make it up to Taormina with this many passengers.

They had a good laugh at that, and assured me that their cars could make it to Taormina with twice as many people as they saw there, and I went back and told Mr. Apollodorus what they had said.

"Well, all right," he said, but without much enthusiasm, and he and his guests began piling into the three taxis, and I stood there thinking that perhaps I was about to go into the record book as having been responsible for the mass wiping out of some of the biggest names in international society.

One of the taxis couldn't move at all once it was loaded with passengers, so a bunch of the fishermen had to get together and give it a good long run along the road before its engine took hold and it followed the other two taxis, which were now about halfway to the top the incline and breathing very hard. Standing there I could hear a strange sound over all the backfiring, and it took me a moment to comprehend that it was cheers coming from Mr. Apollodorus and his guests as they urged the taxis on. When the first taxi got to the top I heard a joyous whoop go up, and when the second made it, too, another great shout went up. Of course the third taxi was the big question mark, and when it arrived at the top the cheer was the longest and loudest of them all.

Once the cars had disappeared the don came out of the bar and strolled over to me and smiled.

"It all went very smoothly, didn't it?" he said.

"Oh, yes, very smoothly," I said.

"What did I tell you?"

He offered me a Camel, and I accepted it.

"If there's anything else I can do for you, just let me know," he said.

"Of course," I said.

He smiled again and took a Camel for himself from the pack, and I lit it for him. I could see that he truly appreciated that display of civility.

"You know where to find me?"

"Absolutely."

"May God be with you."

He went back to the bar, and I returned to the dock where the starboard launch was tied up and settled down to wait for the party to return, and killed the time watching some old guys who were sitting there in the sun fishing for sardines with the littlest hooks I had ever seen in my life.

෧

WHEN WE GOT BACK to Cannes, I found that Christine had neither forgotten all about me nor met someone new whom she liked much better than me.

The first night we were in Cannes I went to La Potinière and she was so happy to see me that she threw her arms around me and kept kissing me passionately in front of all the customers. Then she took me off to a corner where we could be alone.

"I felt lost while you were away, Dooglas."

"I felt that way, too."

She shook her head. "I don't believe you. I think you were probably having all sorts of fun in those exciting places you went to, while I was just sitting here night after night missing you."

"No, the truth is, I couldn't wait to come back to Cannes."

"You swear?"

"I swear."

"All right, I believe you. But tell me, will you have to go away again any time soon?"

"Oh, Christine, that's one thing you can never predict in this business."

"Well, I hope not."

"So do I."

"By the way, I wrote to my parents and told them all about you. And I also told them I'm not coming back to Clichy in September as they keep telling me they want me to. I've told them that I'm going to stay right here so I can be with you."

"And what will they say to that?"

"What can they say? I'm eighteen. I can do whatever I want."

She paused and smiled. "And do you know what I want now?"

"Tell me."

"I want you to go to the Splendid-Hotel and reserve a room for us again. Will you do that?"

"Now?"

"Yes, now. I'll go with you. Just let me go and tell Hélène where we're going."

Again, she waited for me on the terrace of the Brasserie Alsacienne, and before I went to the reception desk, she said, "Will you try to engage that same room? You know, it has such very fond memories."

Fortunately, Room 23 was available, and we stood out on the balcony in the cold hugging each other for a while as before, and then made love with the music from the Alsacienne filling the room again, and later, when she had fallen asleep and I was lying there in the darkness holding her, I thought, as I had in Capri, what a wonderful life I had, and how lucky I was—an officer on one of the best yachts in the Mediterranean (and to make things perfect my new uniforms had arrived from Harry Cohen while we were gone, so I didn't have to wear Fred Appel's hand-me-downs any longer), making lots of money, and adored by the most beautiful girl in Cannes, if not on the entire French Riviera.

But then, in the middle of the night I woke up, and the first thought that came into my mind was how crazy it was for me to feel so safe and secure when the fact was that there was nothing safe or secure about my situation. After all, I was totally dependent on the whims of one man, who could change his mind about everything tomorrow without any warning and lay us all off, or send us back to Miami, or whatever he felt like doing.

I got out of bed and put on my pants and lit a cigaret and looked at my watch in the flame. It was four-thirty. I went out on the balcony. Cannes was sound asleep. The terrace of the Brasserie Alsacienne was dark and deserted, and so was Les Allées de la Liberté. Nothing moved except a stray piece of newspaper that sailed in the wind through the light under a lamppost toward the Place du General de Gaulle. I stayed awake until dawn, when I began to feel a little better, and fell asleep for about an hour. Then I got up and put on my clothes, and woke Christine gently and kissed her goodbye, and then hurried out on the Jetée Albert-Edouard to the *Coloratura* in the cold gray light, and went below and just stayed there lying on my bunk until the chef rapped on my door and asked me if I wanted a cup of nice fresh coffee.

THE WORLD CAME to an end for me one beautiful morning in early August, when the second steward, Mike O'Conner, came running up the ladder to the boatdeck, where I was supervising the refinishing of the bright work on the starboard launch, and shouted to me that something terrible had happened to Mr. Apollodorus.

Mike had turned white. "I think it's a stroke," he said. "He can't talk. And he can't move his left arm at all."

I couldn't believe it. I had seen Mr. Apollodorus just a little while before having coffee on the afterdeck with several of his guests, and he had seemed in marvelous spirits. I knew that he was planning on driving up to Paris that day in his Jaguar, and that his reservations had been made at the Plaza Athenée, as always, and his bags had been packed and stowed in the Jaguar.

I was the only deck officer on board. Captain Marryat had gone to Nice for the day on ship's business, and Bill Wimmers had gone to Glémot's office to conclude negotiations for a deal on some diesel fuel.

I told one of the deckhands to get his ass over to Glémot's as fast as he could and tell Bill Wimmers what had happened, and then I went with Mike down to the main salon, where they had laid Mr. Apollodorus out on a sofa. His friends had gathered around him, all looking as if they were in shock, and were murmuring softly in their various languages. I made my way through them and stood over Mr. Apollodorus and looked at him. His face was a strange color, almost silver, and his eyes were wide open and staring up at me, and there was spit all over his mouth and his chin.

"Sir," I said, "I'm going to get Dr. Ferren right now. Don't worry. He'll come immediately."

He raised his right hand and touched my arm, and I could see that he was trying to speak, but only one side of his mouth worked and all he could do was make a chuffing sound.

My heart was pounding, and I realized that I was soaked with sweat.

"I'll be right back, sir," I said, and hurried out of the main salon and across the afterdeck and down the gangway to the Jetée, and just then, for a moment, I had the strange illusion that the sky had suddenly turned black, although of course when I looked up it was the same brilliant blue as always.

The Jetée was very crowded. Ever since the last week of July it had seemed as if the total populations of all the major cities of northern Europe had come flooding down to the Riviera. I made my way through the throng as quickly as I could.

Dr. Ferren's office was in a very old, very dark, always very damp and cold building on the Rue d'Antibes only a few blocks away from the Jetée. The place always reverberated with the echoes of banging doors and disembodied voices that seemed to come at you from every direction.

Dr. Ferren was about thirty-five, and small and thin, and almost pretty with his curly black hair and large eyes and very girlish, delicate hands, and it was obvious that his receptionist and his three young nurses were all crazy about him.

He loved to talk about women. Particularly American women. And it seemed that no matter what you went to see him about, sooner or later he would find a way to bring the conversation around to American women and how much he admired their legs and their breasts.

"French women have neither legs nor breasts," he said. "But of course you've seen that for yourself. You know, when a French girl sees an American girl she has paroxysms of envy. It happens every time. You've noticed this, too, of course?"

Once, when I had gone to see him about a bad case of catarrh I had picked up in Malaga, I had actually come upon him on top of his receptionist on the couch in the reception room, him with his pants down and her with her legs locked around his waist. It was around ten o'clock in the morning and I guess all the other girls were out on a coffee break or something. Anyway, I babbled stupidly about being so very sorry for having intruded and started to go, when he looked around at me and very calmly said that if I would be good enough to go and wait in the hallway for a few minutes he would be right with me. And would I just close the door after me on my way out? In about fifteen minutes the receptionist, a very pretty girl, but, *malheureusement,* without either breasts or legs, had come out of the reception room with two bobby pins between her teeth, both her lipstick and mascara smudged slightly and her skirt hanging all wrong, and as she stood there twisting her hair up in back had told me that Dr. Ferren would see me now, and when I had gone into his office I had found him sitting behind his desk with his fingertips pressed together, smiling, and he had asked very cheerfully what he could do for me.

This time I raced right through the reception room and burst into Dr. Ferren's office, where an elderly man in his underwear was sitting on the examining table having his blood pressure taken.

Dr. Ferren looked much more upset than he had when I had burst in on him the other time.

"What's the meaning of this?" he said angrily.

I was out of breath. "It's Mr. Apollodorus," I said. "I think he's had a stroke."

"A stroke? Are you sure?"

"I don't know," I said. "But he can't talk. And he can't move his left arm."

Dr. Ferren grabbed his black bag and was on his way out the door instantly, only pausing to yell to the receptionist to have an ambulance sent right away to the yacht *Coloratura* on the Jetée Albert-Edouard. Then, with me right behind him, he ran out the front door and jumped into his Citroen "Deux Chevaux," and while I was still squeezing myself in beside him he slammed the car into gear and roared off along the Rue d'Antibes at breakneck speed with his left palm pressed firmly down on the horn. We swerved around the traffic circle in the Place du General de Gaulle on two wheels, narrowly missing a couple of cars and a pedestrian, and bringing shrill whistles from the flic on duty in the middle of the circle. As we approached the Jetée Albert-Edouard Dr. Ferren could see that it would be useless and time-consuming to try to make our way through the crowd in the car, so we bailed out near the Winter Casino and ran the rest of the way to the *Coloratura,* where he told me to stay and watch for the ambulance, which I could already hear off in the distance, making the weird, threatening racket of French ambulances.

While I was standing there Bill Wimmers, who was usually the picture of imperturbability, came down the gangway looking very pale.

"I'll tell you I never expected anything like this," he said. "He seemed in marvelous health to me."

"I thought so, too," I said.

"Of course he's a lot older than he looks. You know that, don't you?"

"How old is he?" I said. "I've never really known."

"Sixty-eight."

"I wouldn't have believed it."

"No, most people wouldn't have either. As active as he was, he could have passed for ten years younger than that easy."

"Bill, what do you think this means?"

"What do I think what means?"

"Well, this."

The ambulance was getting closer. I could see it come into the Place du General de Gaulle.

"It's hard to say," Bill said. "I guess it all depends on how serious this thing is. If it's as bad as it looks right now, well, I think this game is all over."

"I don't want this game to be over, Bill," I said.

"For God's sake, man, neither do I."

I looked behind me and saw that some of Mr. Apollodorus's guests had gathered on the afterdeck and were all just sitting there close together in silence looking anguished.

People were scattering out of the way of the ambulance as it came along the Jetée. I went to the top of the gangway and signaled to the driver, directing him to the *Coloratura.* The minute the ambulance stopped two men in white coats jumped out and ran up the gangway and asked where the "victim" was. I pointed to the main salon and they hurried in there, and then a moment later hurried back out, got a stretcher from the ambulance and then hurried back into the main salon again.

"This really looks bad," Bill said, and when he said it I had the strange illusion again of the sky suddenly turning black, and again had to look up to see that it was the same beautiful blue as always.

A minute or two later they brought Mr. Apollodorus out on the stretcher, and when I looked at his face I saw that it had lost its silver cast and was now just a frightening grayish-yellow.

I could see that his eyes were full of tears.

I said, "You're going to be all right. You're going to be all right."

Dr. Ferren said to me, "I'm having him taken to the Clinique Beausoleil for an evaluation. You'd better come along with me."

"How bad is it?" I said.

"Oh, I think it's very bad," he said. "But I could be wrong. I have been before, many times and, besides, I'm not a specialist."

Bill came over to me and said, "What did the doctor say?" and when I told him he said, "All right, then this game is over."

Out on the Jetée a throng had gathered near the stern of the *Coloratura,* and they stood there gawking as the stretcher-bearers put Mr. Apollodorus into the back of the ambulance, and when the ambulance tried to turn around they wouldn't get out of the way until two men got out and chased after them like cattle to make them disperse.

Dr. Ferren and I hurried back to where we had left his car, and we followed the ambulance to the Clinique Beausoleil, a small hospital staffed by nuns.

I waited about half an hour in the hallway outside Mr. Apollodorus's room, and then Dr. Ferren came out and said, "Can you make it back to the harbor? There's a specialist coming by helicopter from Nice. I'll come by the yacht and tell you what he says."

DR. FERREN came aboard the *Coloratura* several hours later and told me that the specialist had ordered Mr. Apollodorus to be taken by ambulance to his hospital in Nice, where the facilities for treatment were better than at the Beausoleil. "You know," he said, "Mr. Apollodorus's condition has deteriorated rapidly just in the past couple of hours. I think he's in danger of total paralysis of at least all of his left side."

When I told that to Bill Wimmers, he said, "A man who is totally paralyzed on his left side has no use for a yacht."

"So what do you think will happen?"

"What do I think will happen? I *know* what will happen. Any day now some guy from the line will come up the gangway and tell us we're going home, and that when we get there we're all going to be laid off because they'll be selling this bucket."

First, I went and told Mr. Apollodorus's guests the bad news. They seemed to have recovered their composure, and were mostly talking about where to go next.

Then I gathered the crew in the fo'c'sle and told them what Dr. Ferren had said, and of course they wanted to know what I thought was going to happen to us now.

"I don't know," I said. "We'll just have to wait and see."

"I'll bet they pay us off and send us back to Miami," the chief engineer said.

"No, I don't think they'd want to leave the ship here in Cannes without a crew to look after her," the boatswain said.

"That's right," the chef said. "They'll probably have us sail her back to Miami."

"We could always mutiny," the second engineer said. "Tell them we refuse to sail her anywhere, and then see what happens."

"I don't think that would be a very good idea," Mike O'Conner said.

"Why not?"

"Because if we did they'd send the French police in here and slap us in a French jail, and I don't think you'd want to spend any time in a French jail. You see, in France it isn't like in the U.S.A. Here, you're presumed guilty until proven innocent. They keep you in cages, and they never turn the lights off. I know all about it. I heard it from a sailor off the *FDR,* who got thrown into jail in Toulon and hasn't recovered from it yet."

"Don't waste your time worrying about it," Bill Wimmers said. "What's going to happen will happen and there's not a damn thing we can do about it because whatever it is we won't have any say in the matter."

Max came over to me and asked what would happen to him if the ship was ordered back to Miami. Could he come along?

I said that would be up to the captain.

"This is incredible," he said. "Here I've finally gotten what I wanted for such a long time, and now it's suddenly all over."

"How do you think I feel?" I said.

I left them, and went up to the bridge, where I could be alone. I stood up there looking at my beloved Cannes and feeling bitter and betrayed that something like this could have happened to me. For one thing, I was positive that this had been the high point of my life, and that nothing any good would ever happen to me again.

❧

THAT NIGHT when I went to La Potinière and told Christine the news, she said, "What does it mean?"

"I'm not sure yet."

"Well, what do you think it means?"

"It may mean that we'll have to go back home."

"Back to *Miami?*"

"Yes, back to Miami."

"I don't want you to do that."

"I don't want to do it, believe me, but I will have to go if they tell me to, that's all there is to it."

"Well, what if I won't *let* you go?"

"I will have to go, anyway."

"Why couldn't you stay here in Cannes?"

"Because I would starve to death."

"In other words, you're saying that you're going home if the *Coloratura* goes, and that's that?"

"I'm saying that I simply will have no choice in the matter."

"I think this is terrible," she said. "Couldn't you get a job on one of these other yachts here in Cannes?"

"Christine, wild horses couldn't make me be a sailor on one of those boats," I said. "I really would much sooner starve to death than do that, because the owners work their crews like slaves and pay them almost nothing at all for it."

"You really mean it then, don't you?" she said. "You really are going to leave."

"Yes, if I have to."

Hélène came over to where we were sitting and asked what was wrong. I told her what had happened to Mr. Apollodorus, and she looked very worried and said, "Well, what will become of you now?"

"He's going back to *Miami*," Christine said, bitterly.

"Hélène, I'm not sure about that," I said. "We haven't been told anything definite yet about what's going to happen."

"Well, all I have to say is this," Christine said. "You can just go on back to *Miami* for all I care."

Then she stood up and hurried away from us.

Hélène looked after her and shook her head. "She's really very much in love with you, you know. Perhaps even more than you realize."

"I'm in love with her, too, Hélène, so how do you think I'll feel if we have to leave Cannes?"

She smiled and touched my arm. "Yes, I know you're in love with her, and I know it will be hard on you, too."

Then she paused and said, "But of course it will be worse for her."

"Why do you say that?"

"Because it's always much worse for the one who has to stay behind. You know that."

"Oh, yes, of course, I know," I said.

"I didn't tell you this before," she said, "but all the time you were gone she talked about you constantly, to anyone who would listen. You know, you're a hero to her, because she thinks of you as an artist first of all, and not just a sailor on a boat."

"But I'm in an impossible position," I said. "I cannot stay here. I've already explained to her that I could not possibly survive in Cannes without my job on the *Coloratura.*"

"Yes, I know that," Helene said. "And, in her heart, Christine does, too. And that is what is making all this so much more difficult for her."

"But, listen," I said, "all this worrying may be for nothing. You know, it's entirely possible that Mr. Apollodorus's stroke wasn't nearly as serious as the doctors thought at first, and that when they get him to Nice and have a chance to get a really good look at him, they'll say he'll be perfectly all right with a little rest and send him right back here to the *Coloratura,* and he'll keep her in Cannes forever, as he's always saying he wants to."

"Oh, yes, of course, there's always that possibility," Hélène said. "Miracles have happened before, haven't they? Why not this time? Listen, you stay here and I'll tell Christine to come back and talk to you."

But she came back a minute later and said that Christine had told her to tell me that she didn't ever want to see me again as long as she lived.

"Come back tomorrow night," Hélène said. "I know she'll be feeling much better then."

So I went on down to Les Allées, where Louisette had seen the ambulance go out on the Jetée that morning and asked the same question everyone around the waterfront was asking, "What does it mean?"

"I just don't know," I told her. "We're all just going to have to wait and see."

&

BUT, ACTUALLY, IT all turned out exactly as Bill Wimmers had predicted it would. Four days after Mr. Apollodorus had his stroke a very tall gentleman with an impressive dark brown mustache, wearing a bowler hat, a Savile Row suit, gleaming handmade shoes, a silk shirt, a necktie that had to be that of Eton or Harrow, or at least the Brigade of Guads, and carrying a very battered but nonetheless very beautiful attaché case and a tightly furled umbrella, marched up the gangway, announced that he was from the London office of the line, and informed Captain Marryat that inasmuch as Mr. Apollodorus would not be requiring the use of the *Coloratura* again for a long time—and probably for a very, very long time—he was herewith ordered to sail her back to Miami immediately, and await further instructions there.

The captain broke the news to me and Bill Wimmers and the first engineer and the first steward up in his stateroom, after having poured us each a glass of cognac from the bottle on the table before us.

"Mr. Collingsworth also told me," he said, "that they're flying the boss from Nice to Paris this afternoon, and that they'll probably fly him on to New York from there. He said the doctors are saying now that there's a chance he may be paralyzed on his entire left side for the rest of his life."

"What a hell of a thing to happen to a prince of a man like that," Bill Wimmers said.

"Amen to that," the first steward said, and then we all said it, then the first engineer cleared his throat and said, "Skipper, I have to ask this. When that fella says he wants us to sail immediately, what does he mean by that?"

"He means he wants us to get out of here at dawn the day after tomorrow," the captain said.

"Well, my God, we've really got to get cracking then," the first engineer said.

"Don't worry, I'm turning all hands to the minute this meeting breaks up," the captain said.

"Skipper, what about these guests who are still on board?" the first steward said. "They keep promising me they're going to leave any time now, but they just keep on hanging around drinking up all the boss's booze and stuffing themselves like there's no tomorrow."

"Let me handle them," the captain said. "Frankly, it will give me a great deal of personal satisfaction to send all those damn leeches packing."

ॐ

WE WORKED like maniacs the rest of the day and straight on through into the night getting the *Coloratura* ready to cross the Atlantic, and it was close to ten o'clock before I had a chance to go to La Potinière and tell Christine the latest news.

She had barely been speaking to me the past four days. Every time I had gone to La Potinière she had pretended to be very busy, and had done everything she could to avoid coming anywhere near me.

But this time I told her she would have to listen to me, and she saw that this time I really meant it, and I led her outside, into the Rue des Serbes, and there, in the quiet street, I told her that we were going to be leaving the day after next, at dawn.

She wouldn't look at me. "All right, then, what is there for me to say?" she said.

"There's nothing I can do about it, you understand that, don't you?"

She just shrugged, and she still wouldn't look at me.

"Can we go for a walk?" she said.

"Yes, I'd like to."

We began strolling slowly down toward the Croisette, and she took my hand.

"You know something?" she said.

"What?"

"I've finally begun to realize something about you. Do you want to know what it is?"

"Of course."

"You have absolutely no confidence in yourself, do you?"

It was completely unexpected. I stopped and stared at her, and then she finally looked at me.

"It's true, isn't it?" she said.

I felt my cheeks burning.

"Isn't it true?"

"I don't know," I said. "I really hadn't thought about it."

"It is true."

"Well, what if it is?"

"Nothing," she said. "I would just like to know why, that's all."

"But I don't know why myself," I said.

"Oh, I think you do."

"No, I don't, Christine. I mean, it may be true, but I honestly don't know why."

"I just think it's so strange, that's all," she said, "because I envy you so much. I mean, if I could paint as well as you do, I'd be so happy, and have all the self-confidence in the world."

"But let me tell you something about that, Christine," I said. "There are millions and millions of people in the world who have the same little bit of talent I do. The fact is, I don't have a really first-class talent, and in order to succeed as an artist you have to have a first-class talent."

"There," she said. "That's just what I'm talking about."

"But it's simply the truth," I said. "You have to be realistic, you know. You can't wish things for yourself and expect them to come true."

"Do you know what I think?"

"What do you think?"

"I think the truth is you don't want to be an artist, because I believe that if you really wanted to be first-class badly enough you could be. I think it's just that you want to be something else."

I had to stop and look at her again.

"Is that true?" she said.

"Maybe it is."

"What do you want to be?"

"I *wanted* to be a novelist."

"Wanted to be?"

"Yes."

"Well, did you ever write a novel?"

"Yes, I did."

"And what became of it?"

"Nothing."

"What do you mean, nothing?"

"Well, I worked on it for a long time, but it just wasn't any good."

"Did you send it to publishers?"

"Oh, God, yes, lots of publishers."

"And what did they say about it?"

"They said it wasn't any good."

"So then you stopped trying?"

"Of course. There wasn't any point in going on with it. And, anyway, by then I had accepted the fact that I was never going to succeed as a novelist."

We had come to the Blue Bar, where we sat down at a table outside, and I ordered a couple of Pernods, after which there was a very awkward silence. Christine just gazed at the people around us, and I found that I couldn't think of one other thing to say.

Finally, I said, "You know, Christine, I believe that this was the high point of my whole life—being a sailor on a yacht here in Cannes, and having known you. I'm sure that nothing as wonderful as this will ever happen to me again. But I really don't care about that, because this will be enough for me. I will have this memory with me forever."

Christine didn't even seem to have heard. She just sat slumped way down in her chair, looking, I thought, very distant and mysterious, and I felt stupid because I knew what I had said was terribly sentimental, even though I had meant every word of it.

Also, by then, I could barely keep my eyes open because I was so beat from having worked at that frantic pace on the *Coloratura* all day.

She didn't touch her Pernod, but when she saw that I had finished mine she said, "I don't believe that."

"You don't believe what?"

"That nothing as wonderful as this will ever happen to you again in your whole life."

She stood up. "But, anyway, I want to go back to La Potinière now."

I didn't accompany her all the way back to La Potinière. We parted on the Croisette, and she was still distant and mysterious, and didn't even respond in the slightest degree when I kissed her, but just turned and hurried away.

⁊❧

THE NEXT DAY we continued working like maniacs getting the *Coloratura* ready to cross the ocean.

Late in the morning a couple of taxis made their way through the crowds on the Jetée to the gangway of the *Coloratura,* and the three stewards carried the luggage belonging to the last of Mr. Apollodorus's guests down the gangway and loaded it all into the taxis, and then hung around waiting for a tip, but not one of them got anything for their trouble but dirty looks.

"I don't understand how the boss, who was such a perfect gent himself, could have had anything to do with some of those people," Mike O'Conner said to me after they were gone. "Most of them were the most awful pigs, you know. Can you believe that after six weeks of being waited on hand and foot by us they couldn't even pass us a thousand-franc note? But not only didn't they do that, they also left their staterooms looking like a torpedo hit them, and they know very well that we're all breaking our balls now trying to get this bucket ready for the crossing."

It was almost nine o'clock before Captain Marryat finally said he thought the yacht was as ready as she would ever be, and we were allowed to knock off. I took a quick shower and wolfed down some chow, and then started to hurry off to La Potinière. But when I reached the Jetée, I saw Christine there waiting for me.

"I came looking for you," she said. "I was afraid you might not come to see me tonight."

"We only got off work about half an hour ago," I said. "But you really didn't have to worry. I would have come to see you tonight no matter what."

"Well, do you want to go to La Potinière now?"

"Of course."

"Hélène told me she would never forgive you if you didn't come to say goodbye to her."

"She should have known I would never have done that."

"Yes, but she worried about it anyway."

I could see that Christine was obviously trying to be cheerful, but it seemed to me that underneath it all she was just as distant and mysterious as she had been the night before.

When we got to La Potinière, Hélène came over and gave me a big kiss and told me how happy she was that I had come, and said she wanted me to stay until they closed up so that she could talk to me for a little while before they went home.

The band was still playing, and Christine asked me if I would like to dance. I really didn't want to, being dog-tired again, but we danced a few numbers, and then the band started packing up their instruments, and I was glad that I could go and sit down.

I had had some vague notion of asking Christine to go to Room 23 with me one last time, but now that was the last thing I wanted to do, and I sensed that she would have felt the very same way. In fact, all she seemed to want to do was stare into space, or talk absolutely inconsequential nonsense, or keep jumping up and running off to talk to Hélène and the other girls. Anyway, soon it was time to close up La Potinière, and I helped out, as usual, but very much aware that this time it was for the very last time.

Then Hélène brought out a bottle of her best cognac and poured glasses for me and Christine and herself.

"We three have to have one last drink together," she said.

"I won't ever forget you," I said.

"We won't ever forget you either," Hélène said.

Before we parted out in the Rue des Serbes, I said to Christine, "I know this is a lot to ask, but I really do wish you'd come out to the Jetée tomorrow morning and say goodbye."

Without any hesitation, she said, "I'll be there."

"We're supposed to leave around five o'clock," I said. "But of course there will be delays. There always are."

"I'll be there," she said.

I couldn't help feeling that there was something eerie about the way she looked at me, because her eyes seemed to glitter, almost defiantly. We walked together up to the end of the block, where I kissed Hélène goodbye.

Then I said to Christine, "And I'll see you in the morning."

"Don't worry," she said. "I promise you I'll be there."

I went on down to Les Allées, which was also just closing, to say goodbye to Louisette, who had been such a good friend for a long time.

"I'll miss you," she said. "Do you think you might ever come back?"

"Oh, I don't think so," I said.

She laughed. "Well, if you do, you can count on it that I'll still be right here at Les Allées."

Then she paused, and said, "How about Christine? How is she taking this?"

"Frankly, much better than I had thought she would," I said.

Louisette shook her head. "She's just hiding her feelings, that's all."

"Do you really think so?"

"I'm sure of it. Listen, Christine is truly in love with you. I know that for an absolute fact."

That made me feel better. I kissed Louisette goodbye and then went back to the *Coloratura,* where I lingered on the afterdeck for a while talking to Charlie Murdock, the man on watch, who looked as if he was going to fall asleep right in front of me. But I thought, after all, what difference does it make now if he does fall asleep? The owner is gone, and the guests are all gone. Just leave the poor bastard alone.

I, myself, had a hard time falling asleep, lying there thinking of how much I would miss Christine, and how depressing and lonely it would be to be back in Miami, and then, when I finally did fall asleep it seemed as if it was only a moment later that the messboy was going along the hallway pounding on all the doors and yelling that it was time to hit the deck.

I sat up and looked through my porthole and saw the dawn breaking.

꙰

MY LAST DAWN in Cannes. As cold and gray as always. I was standing back on the stern drinking a cup of coffee while I waited for the signal from the bridge that I was to order the two sailors on the quai to haul in the gangway and then cast off the stern lines.

One of the sailors was Tommy Lindquist. The other was Max Guyard. Captain Marryat had told Max that he could come to Miami with us, although he couldn't make him any promises about what would happen after we got there, any more than he could the rest of us. But that didn't bother Max. He just wanted to go to America, where he was sure he was going to make his fortune.

I kept looking down the dark and deserted Jetée Albert-Edouard, hoping to see Christine. I couldn't understand why she had promised to come and say goodbye if she hadn't really meant it.

Maybe I went into a bit of a trance thinking about her. Anyway, all of a sudden I saw Max and Tommy yelling at me and pointing behind me, and afraid that I had missed the signal from the bridge I quickly looked behind me, and what I saw was Mike O'Conner running toward me, his face as white as the day he had come up on the boatdeck to tell me that Mr. Apollodorus had had his stroke.

Directly below me the big screws of the *Coloratura* were throwing a powerful wash back against the seawall, making it very difficult to hear anything, so when Mike stopped about halfway across the afterdeck and yelled at me, I couldn't make out a word he said.

"What?" I yelled back at him. "What did you say?"

He cupped his hands to his mouth and yelled again, but all I could make out was one word: "Christine."

I ran over to him and grabbed his arm and literally dragged him across the deck and through the door of the main salon, and in there I said to him, *"Christine?* What about *Christine?"*

"She's on board, man!"

"You're crazy!"

"The hell I am! You see *this?"* He held up his right hand and showed me the teeth marks on his thumb. "That's what she did to me!"

"Where is she?"

"In the owner's stateroom. I went in there just now to check one last time that the portholes were all dogged down, and I happened to catch sight of her scrunched down over in the corner behind the bureau. So I took hold of her hand and tried to make her come with me, and this is what I got for my trouble. And then she even tried to *hit* me! So I'm leaving it up to you to go down there and get her off the ship."

"You're sure it's Christine, Mike?"

"Of course I'm sure. I know what Christine looks like when I see her. Listen, will you just tell me this? You really didn't know she was down there?"

"I swear to God," I said. "She promised me she would be here this morning, so I've been standing out there watching for her on the Jetée. Now I see that wasn't what she meant."

Bill Wimmers came through the door of the main salon looking alarmed.

"The skipper wants to know what's going on down here," he said.

"His girlfriend, Christine, is in the owner's stateroom," Mike said.

"Sweet shit," Bill said. "How did she get on board?"

"How do I know?" Mike said. "She must have slipped past Charlie when he fell asleep or went below for a cup of coffee or some goddam thing. Anyway, believe me, she's down there."

"Well, you know what you have to do," Bill said to me.

"All right," I said, "but will you go back up to the bridge and tell the skipper to give me some time, Bill? I can't just pick her up and throw her out on the quai. I'll have to be a little bit gentle about it, do you understand?"

"Sure, I understand," he said. Then he paused, "Listen, can I assure the captain that you knew absolutely nothing about this?"

"I swear to God," I said.

He hesitated again. "She must really be crazy about you," he said. "So take it easy on her, okay? And don't worry, I'll tell the captain to give you all the time you need."

"Well, even though she bit me, I have to give her credit," Mike said. "She really must have had this thing *planned,* you know. She's got all this food with her—three or four big long loaves of bread, cheese, a couple of bottles of wine, sausages, and God knows what else, all stuffed into this knapsack. Do you get what I'm saying? I think she was planning on hiding down there until we got out in the middle of the Atlantic, and if I just hadn't happened to have seen her that last time I went down there, it would have *worked.*"

Bill put his hand on my shoulder and said, "Better go on down there now and get it over with."

I went down the steps, and then walked forward along the narrow hallway toward the owner's stateroom, which was the one that was farthest forward. It was very cold down there, and you could see your breath just the same as up on deck.

When I entered the stateroom I saw Christine sitting on the bed, clutching her knapsack to her chest. She was wearing a ski jacket and what looked like at least three sweaters underneath it, and a ski cap and ski pants.

The first thing I noticed was that her cheeks were bright red.

"I got caught," she said.

I sat down beside her and put my arm around her. Below us the deck was vibrating and the sound of wash being churned up by the screws was thunderous even with the portholes all dogged down.

We were both shivering. I got out a cigaret and stuck it in my mouth and lit it, trying to kill a little time while I thought of what to say to her.

"You've very brave, Christine," I said.

She shrugged.

"You don't have to worry," she said. "I'm not going to embarrass you. I'm going to leave now of my own free will."

She stood up and slung her knapsack over one shoulder, and then leaned down and kissed me on the cheek.

"Just, please, stay down here until I'm gone, will you?" she said.

"Yes, if that's what you want," I said.

She went out the door of the stateroom and then I heard her going up the stairs to the main salon. I let a few seconds go by and then followed her up the stairs. At the top of the stairs I could see her, through the screen door of the main salon, go across the afterdeck and down the gangway, past Bill Wimmers and Mike O'Conner and Max Guyard and Tommy Lindquist and some of the others, looking neither right nor left.

I went through the screen door and stood on the afterdeck and watched her go all the way down the Jetée Albert-Edouard, and she never looked back once, but like the gypsy tunes the little orchestra played on the terrace of the Brasserie Alsacienne that I have never forgotten, if I close my eyes even now, I can see Christine at the moment just before she disappeared around the corner of the Winter Casino.

Part Four

"A MAN OF THE WORLD"

IN THE SPRING of 1955 I was the mate on a boat called the *Gerda,* a Danish-built North Sea trawler that had originally been converted to a yacht by Brigadier General Robert Wood Johnson, of Johnson & Johnson, who had subsequently donated her, as a tax write-off, to the University of Miami Marine Biology Laboratory, to be converted once again, this time to be used as a floating laboratory in the university's marine research program. This second conversion was a long and tedious process, most of it carried out in a dirty, noisy shipyard up the Miami River, and rather than live on board through it all (in a fo'c'sle that had no portholes), I rented a small room in a very old house near the mouth of the Miami River, and one day soon after I did what I had promised myself long ago I would never do again. I rented a typewriter and took it back to my room and began writing a novel.

But this was very different from all of my other experiences with trying to write a novel. This time I just wrote, and didn't sit there being my own worst enemy by criticizing every single word as I put it down, and by then going back and either tearing up everything I had written or crossing out every word. In fact, I didn't reread one word of what I had written until I had about fifteen thousand words, which I considered to be roughly the first half of my book. And then I still only read it to correct spelling errors and obvious grammatical mistakes.

I called this novel "A Man of the World." The hero was George Fox, the messboy on a big American yacht in Cannes, who meets a French girl about his own age, named Christine, and falls in love with her and tries to save her from her wicked old aunt, who owns a bar called the The Sparrow, where Christine is forced to dress up in sexy costumes to lure American sailors from the Sixth Fleet to the bar.

I had finished the first half of the novel in late June, a few days before we were to sail the *Gerda* over to the Gulf of Mexico on the maiden cruise as a floating laboratory, where we were supposed to study the latest outbreak of the so-called Red Tide, a malevolent and mysterious fungus that killed enormous numbers of fish in the Gulf.

The day before we sailed for the Gulf I took the two carbon copies that I had made of my manuscript and put them into manila envelopes, and mailed one to Scribner's amd the other to Simon and Schuster. We were gone for about a month, and when I returned to my room I found that the copy of the manuscript that I had sent to Scribner's had been returned. But there was a *letter* from Simon and Schuster. I opened the manila envelope from Scribner's and inside there was a form letter saying exactly what I had known it would say, in other words all the usual stuff about them being very grateful for my having let them read my manuscript, but that, unfortunately, it was not the sort of thing they were looking for just now.

The one chair in my small room was a wicker rocker, and I sat there in the rocker staring at the letter from Simon and Schuster, and one thing struck me as hopeful. At least they hadn't returned the copy of the manuscript I had sent them. But then I thought, don't be ridiculous, the damned thing is on its way. In any case, I couldn't open the letter, because I simply didn't feel that I could have stood two rejections so close together.

I left the letter lying there on the table and took a shower. It was early in the morning, but I was dead tired from having been on the wheel of the *Gerda* for something like sixteen hours straight, coming back around from the Gulf. When I got out of the shower I sat down in my rocker and picked up the letter from Simon and Schuster and looked at it again, but I still didn't think I could face another rejection, and I got into bed and slept straight through until noon the next day.

Then I got up and walked across the Brickell Avenue bridge into Miami and got something to eat, and when I got back to my room I knew I couldn't put it off any longer and sat down in my rocker again and lit a cigaret, and then slit open the envelope, and read the letter like a poker hand, squeezing out one sentence at a time.

The first sentence said, "We would very much like to see the second part of 'A Man of the World.'"

My heart stopped.

The second sentence said, "We enjoyed part one and would like the chance to consider the novel as a whole."

It stopped again.

The third sentence said, "Please send it along."

And again.

The letter was signed, "Sandy Wilson (and by the way, that's *Miss* Sandy Wilson)."

I began walking around the room in circles, in a daze, going back again and again to look at the letter to make sure the three sentences hadn't disappeared from the page.

But when the euphoria faded away a little, it struck me how similar this letter was to the first one I had gotten from Jean Luft, so the first thing I did was to take my copy of the manuscript and stick it in a drawer and resolve never to look at it again until I had finished the whole book.

I wrote to *Miss* Sandy Wilson and told her how happy I was that she had liked my book, and she wrote back saying that she was not the only one at S&S who had liked it, and quoted me some very favorable editorial comments.

I finished the novel in five weeks, by working every night after I got off work on the *Gerda* and all day and every night on weekends. As soon as I had finished I sent part two to Simon and Schuster, and then wrote a letter to a literary agency, McIntosh-McKee, which had been the first name on the list of agencies Bob Townsend had recommended to me long ago. I told them what had happened to my book so far, and asked if they would like to see a copy. A letter came back right away saying that they would very much like to see my novel, and that they would be happy to represent me in my negotiations with Simon and Schuster.

Next a letter came from Simon and Schuster saying they had found my story "enchanting," and that they were going to talk to my agent about a contract. Then Mavis McIntosh wrote to me saying that S&S had offered to give me an advance of a thousand dollars, which didn't sound like much, she knew, but she advised me to take it because they were so enthusiastic about my book, "and that counts a lot in this business."

I took a week off from my job on the *Gerda* and went to New York to sign the contract. McIntosh-McKee was a two-room suite in a building on East Sixtieth Street that looked just as I had always imagined an agent's office would look. It was pleasantly cluttered, and there were manuscripts piled everywhere. The three women who worked there were all very nice to me, and seemed genuinely interested in me and my book.

The next morning I went to the offices of Simon and Schuster in Rockefeller Plaza, where I met a lot of other people, including Jack Goodman, the editor-in-chief, who told me how much he liked my book, and that he expected great things from me in the future.

That night I was taken to dinner by Elizabeth McKee, who said she wanted me to meet an editor from Heinemann's who was in New York shopping for new books for their list. Immediately, there came into my mind Alex Latta's famous dictum: "If I had my choice of British publishers, it would always be Heinemann's," and I was very excited. The editor excused himself right after dinner because he said he wanted to go back to his hotel and start reading the copy of "A Man of the World" that Elizabeth had given him. Before he left, he assured her that he would call her in the morning to let her know his decision. I told Elizabeth that I was going up to Cambridge first thing in the morning, but that she could leave a message for me at the Lampoon.

Of course, by then I didn't know anyone on the *Lampoon,* but as soon as I came into the building that day, someone asked me who I was, and when I told him, he said, "There's a telegram for you on the bulletin board." It was from Elizabeth, and said that Heinemann's had bought the British rights to "A Man of the World."

Then, of course, inevitably, I was drawn to the Great Hall, which looked just the same as always. I sat in the president's chair, at the head of the long table, and let all the memories come flooding back, good and bad. I stayed there a long time, and then ascended the winding stone stairs to the Ibis Room, which I found was also completely unchanged, and I stayed there a long time, too, sitting on the dusty couch. Then I went up to the Square and took a taxi to Logan Airport and caught a plane for Miami.

My novel was published by Simon and Schuster in April 1956. The title had to be changed at the last minute from "A Man of the World" to "A Man's World" when it was discovered that a novel by that same title was coming out from another publisher a couple of months in advance of mine. It was published by William Heinemann in England in October 1956. There were several translations. The television rights were sold to CBS, and the story was presented live on *Studio One* on October 1, 1956, with Joanne Woodward as Christine.